Environmental Science

ISBN 978-1-934920-73-2

For permission to use material from this text or for general questions about permissions, submit a request on line to http://www.wordsofwisdombooks.com/contact.asp

Publisher: Words of Wisdom, LLC — Schaumburg, IL
Book Title: Environmental Science
Author: Editorial Board
Rights: Words of Wisdom, LLC
Publication Date: 2013
Edition: 1

VS 1 1

Acknowledgments

We would like to thank the Editorial Board for their time
and dedication to the creation of this book.

James Taylor
Wentzel Briar
Sandra Flemming
Dr. William Falls

TABLE OF CONTENTS

What Is Environmental Science?

The Fukushima Daiichi nuclear plant

THE FUKUSHIMA EARTHQUAKE DISASTER

On March 11, 2011, a 9.0 magnitude earthquake struck off the coast of Japan. The quake resulted in a 30-foot-high tsunami, and according to *Scientific American*, "the ocean bed moved as much as 50 meters laterally and 16 meters vertically. The magnitude 9.0 quake occurred close to the nearby Japan Trench that runs north to south in the Pacific Ocean." The tsunami killed thousands of people when it flooded the mainland but also caused unprecedented damage to the Fukushima Daiichi nuclear plant. The crisis that resulted from damage to the nuclear plant prompted scientists and government to develop remediation strategies.

The nature of this crisis forced officials to choose between minimizing environmental damage and minimizing human casualties. To avert human disaster, officials made a number of important decisions aimed at protecting health. For instance, the day after the earthquake and tsunami, reactor rods, responsible for powering the nuclear reactor, reached temperatures over 1,200°C, causing explosions that released radioactive materials into the atmosphere. In an effort to ensure safe breathing air, engineers pumped large volumes of seawater from the Pacific Ocean into the reactors to cool the rods and limit the radioactive release. Although this action solved the immediate crisis involving the reactor rods, it caused serious complications. Seawater used to cool the reactors was released back into the ocean, possibly affecting aquatic and human ecosystems for years to come. What will be the ultimate outcome? How will radioactive water impact the surrounding aquatic ecosystem? If humans eat contaminated fish, will they get sick? Answering these questions is important, because scientists and government officials must make decisions that minimize harm to the environment.

The scientific method provides a structured framework for scientists to frame questions, make observations, conduct research, and evaluate results. When making critical decisions with significant impact, the scientific method provides the structure and rigor necessary to answer questions, make new discoveries, and improve decision making.

THE SCIENTIFIC METHOD

The **scientific method** (see Figure 1.1) is a multi-step process used in a logical and systematic manner to acquire new information, observe phenomena, and/or disprove or modify existing knowledge. The **scientific method** is defined by Merriam-Webster as the "principles and procedures for the systematic pursuit of knowledge involving the recognition and formulation of a problem, the collection of data through observation and experiment, and the formulation and testing of hypotheses." A **hypothesis** is a statement regarding cause and effect in specific situations, based on observations that can predict future observations. A hypothesis can never be proven—only disproven. After testing, a hypothesis is either accepted or rejected.

SCIENTIFIC METHOD A multi-step process used in a logical and systematic manner to acquire new information, observe phenomena, and/or disprove or modify existing knowledge.

HYPOTHESIS An educated guess proposing an explanation for the occurrence of a phenomenon.

The first step in the scientific method is to make an observation. The observable or measureable empirical evidence is gathered by examination or experimentation so as to accept or reject the hypothesis. Empirical evidence is based on observation and experience and can be verified through inspection or experimentation.

The following are the basic steps in the scientific method:

1. Make an observation
2. Define the problem
3. Research the problem
4. State the hypothesis
5. Make observations or conduct experiments to test the hypothesis
6. Collect and record data
7. Analyze data
8. Draw conclusions about the hypothesis
9. Determine limitations
10. Report results

If the evidence obtained supports the hypothesis, it is accepted. If the hypothesis is not supported by the data, it is considered nullified, or null. A new hypothesis may be stated if the hypothesis is found to be null. The process then begins again with the new hypothesis. Even if a hypothesis is supported by the gathered measurements and observations, it may be tested in different ways in the future, possibly providing results that disprove the hypothesis.

QUESTIONS

1. The earthquake that occurred in Japan caused a number of threats to environmental health. What specific environmental problems occurred as a result of this disaster?

2. How could the scientific method have helped address the crisis at the Fukushima Daiichi nuclear plant? What other natural disasters have posed challenges for the environment?

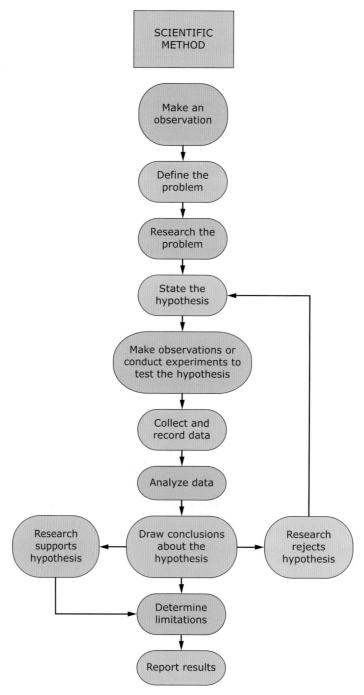

FIGURE 1.1 Scientific method flow chart

Scientists use the scientific method to ensure that research and inquiry are objective, that the experiments that lead to conclusions can be reproduced by other scientists, and that the effect of bias or prejudice in the experimenter when testing a hypothesis or a theory is minimized. Data gathered through the scientific method is recorded and shared with the scientific community in the spirit of full disclosure to allow other researchers to scrutinize and statistically verify the results.

Reproducible hypotheses put through rigorous examination over time can become theories. A **theory** is a framework from which scientific observations are defined and predictions are made. Scientific theories are only revised or discarded if new discoveries or experimental results contradict the theories.

THEORY A hypothesis that has been repeatedly supported through ongoing experimentation and review.

The first recorded use of a system to determine a scientific result may come from the 1600s BC under the guidance of doctors. The first recorded use of the scientific method to conduct an experiment occurred in about 587 BC when the people of Judah were incorporated into the Babylonian empire under King Nebuchadnezzar. The research was to determine if a vegetarian diet was as healthy as a diet of rich food. The research was primitive compared to today's standard, but it is still the first recorded use. The scientific method has been refined and more steps added throughout history.

In 1620, a lawyer named Francis Bacon described an approach to research that advocated the use of inductive reasoning as the foundation for solving problems. **Inductive reasoning** follows a general pattern in which observations are used as a means for creating general rules. Specifically, Bacon reviewed the work of Nicolaus Copernicus and Galileo Galilei, examining the steps taken by these researchers to make and test educated guesses about the Earth's rotation around the Sun.

Francis Bacon

Clearly, the scientific method is important for the study of all scientific issues. However, in reality, inductive reasoning is used in a broad range of disciplines and in everyday life. For instance, suppose you want to know how long it will take you to walk to work rather than drive. In order to solve this problem, you form an educated guess (hypothesis) about the time needed to walk, followed by an experiment—such as walking to work for several days and recording the time it took—to obtain results. Based on the results, you could draw a conclusion about the hypothesis and whether or not more (or less) time was needed to walk to work than you first estimated. The use of reasoning similar to the scientific method in everyday life indicates the usefulness of this approach to problem solving and decision-making.

While the scientific method has important utility for solving problems, the method also helps eliminate the effects of a researcher's bias. **Bias** is defined as prejudice for or against a particular view, and is discussed further in the following section. A researcher's biases may lead her to begin an experiment with a specific hypothesis that, if supported, would confirm that bias. However, if the scientific method is applied properly, using a structured approach to investigation that results in objective, definitive results, the researcher's bias should have no impact on the results. For example, if you do not use an accurate stopwatch or timepiece in the case above, your results may not be accurate. If you walk to work and estimate the time,

INDUCTIVE REASONING A pattern of thinking in which observations are used as a means for creating general rules.

BIAS Prejudice for or against a particular view.

you may introduce your personal bias into the problem resulting in incorrect results. The scientific method is self-correcting because the results are published with test methods. Other scientists may try the same experiments, potentially correcting for the original researcher's bias.

Specific Applications of the Scientific Method in Environmental Science

Although the scientific method can be applied in any number of disciplines, its use in environmental science is critical to helping scientists understand the world around them. An early application of the scientific method for solving an environmental issue occurred in Soho, located in Westminster and the West End of London in 1854. At this time, a cholera outbreak of unprecedented proportions broke out in the area. In an effort to combat the disease, a physician named John Snow began

ENVIRONMENTAL MISCONCEPTIONS: EXPERIMENTS ARE THE ONLY ROUTE TO SCIENTIFIC KNOWLEDGE

The scientific method provides researchers an unbiased method to collect data and draw conclusions about the world around them. While the scientific method provides a structured tool for demonstrating the reliability and validity of data, in reality, there are other routes to scientific knowledge. Given the emphasis placed on the scientific method as a foundation for experimentation, it is important to note that not all scientific discoveries or theories were generated using this particular approach to investigation.

In an effort to illustrate the role that non-scientific techniques have played in the development and understanding of science and the generation of knowledge, it is useful to consider the work of Charles Darwin. As an evolutionary biologist, Darwin did not engage in traditional experiments employing the scientific method. Rather, Darwin used the process of structured observation in an effort to review the development of various species. Based on his observations, Darwin was able to propose his theory of evolution by natural selection. Although Darwin did not use the process of controlled experimentation, he was able to make a compelling case for his theory based on how it explained the data in his observations.

Darwin is not the only scientist in history to use non-experimental techniques to establish a theory. Nicolaus Copernicus used his observations of the movement of celestial bodies to demonstrate that the Earth is not the center of the solar system. In this research, observation rather than experimentation was the foundation for the generation of a theory of how the Sun, planets, and comets moved in relation to one another. Johannes Kepler used similar techniques in his efforts to explain planetary motion. The work of these scientists demonstrates the role that other techniques can play in the development of scientific knowledge. Without this type of investigation, many concepts and ideas impacting human life would still be a mystery.

plotting the outbreak on a map and observing its development. Based on the data collected, Snow formulated a hypothesis about where the outbreaks occurred and what was causing them. He hypothesized that the cholera was present in the water pump well located on a specific street in the neighborhood.

To test his hypothesis, Snow had the identified water pump shut down by removing its handle (the experiment). Within several days, there were no new cases of cholera (results). Based on the data obtained through his experiment, Snow was able to identify the source of illness, preventing further harm to the residents of the neighborhood. The application of the scientific method in this case illustrates the way in which the method can be used to address environmental health issues and create a foundation for action that can change the way individuals behave. Snow's use of the scientific method to identify the source of the cholera outbreak was repeated in other cases, creating a clear foundation for applying the scientific method in practice.

MID-CHAPTER QUESTIONS

1. **What is the scientific method?**

2. **What are the steps of the scientific method?**

3. **What is a hypothesis?**

4. **What is inductive reasoning?**

FACTS (SEEING THROUGH BIAS AND SPIN)

The concept of bias was introduced earlier in this chapter as one reason for the use of the scientific method. Bias represents prejudice against a specific idea or subject. The scientific method reduces bias by creating an environment in which data serves as the foundation for decision making. Most researchers have personal opinions about the topics they investigate. In order to minimize bias, researchers use the scientific method to show a direct relationship between their experiment, the data collected, and the conclusions drawn. The scientific method ensures objectivity by requiring that hypotheses be reproducible by the same or other researchers and that the conclusions reached by one scientist be able to be replicated by others. Only then is the hypothesis accepted.

While bias represents prejudice that exists toward a specific subject, spin refers to the way information is conveyed. More specifically, **spin** refers to the decision to highlight specific aspects of research data to present a particular opinion, attitude, or belief. Policymakers frequently use spin to promote regulations and policies, which has implications for how the public views information and data. Spin is often seen in the media, especially in regard to the coverage of political issues. For instance, a public official whose district benefits from the operation of a factory might downplay a study that highlights health risks caused by the factory, or highlight anecdotes that appear to suggest that the factory is not harmful. On the other hand, activists looking to shut down the factory might use a study that suggests a moderate environmental risk, and portray it as a major risk.

One way to ensure that facts are presented without bias or spin is to use **sound science**. This is research conducted by qualified personnel that leads to verifiable

SPIN The portrayal of information in a way that conveys specific aspects of research and/or data to convey a particular opinion, attitude, or belief.

SOUND SCIENCE Research conducted by qualified persons that leads to verifiable results.

results. It presupposes that the scientific method was followed in reaching conclusions and that the data and results obtained are reliable. Sound science is promoted by the submission of scientific findings for consideration of publication in professional journals that are reviewed by peers. Advisory boards and committees of experts also are helpful in assuring that the scientific method results in sound science.

CASE STUDY: CLIMATE CHANGE, SCIENCE VS. POLICY

The issues of bias and sound science are especially relevant to the issue of climate change and policy decisions made based on scientific findings. Often, as evidence expands, a minority view turns out to be correct. Even though we continue to study our atmosphere and climate, we do not know enough about climate change (global warming) to enact government policy throughout the world. Technology continues to advance and assist in collecting climate data. Currently environmental scientists are researching the following climate change concepts: anthropogenic global warming, bio-thermostat, cloud formation and albedo, human forcing besides greenhouse gases, ocean currents, planetary motion, and solar variability. If we create policy to limit CO_2 without studying all forces that have a "cooling effect," we may end up doing more damage. Cooling effects include man-made gases, natural gases, solar activities, volcanos, la Niña and el Niño. CO_2 increases plant growth, increases food production, and has varied levels in the atmosphere throughout history. Depending on the severity, the causes, and if the climate is changing, governments will create international policy if required. For example, the Montréal Protocol has stopped the increasing size of the ozone hole over the Antarctic and it is estimated that the ozone hole will close during the twenty-first century.

Governments in some countries have pointed to data taken from ice cores, glaciers, sea levels, air temperatures, and other factors to conclude that the Earth is warming. They may use the scientific evidence to advocate action to reduce the burning of fossil fuels, for example. Others take a different view. They may argue that the science is not conclusive, and that the economic costs of new regulation outweigh the environmental benefits that they see as uncertain. By using specific types of data to support a political agenda, policymakers can defend positions and shape public opinion.

MID-CHAPTER QUESTIONS

1. **What is bias?**

2. **Who might be the "winners and losers" in global warming?**

3. **How can political considerations affect public opinion?**

THE ENVIRONMENTAL MOVEMENT

The **environmental movement** is a social movement aimed at increasing public awareness of the human impact on the natural world and formulating policy to mitigate this impact. Various environmental issues were recognized as early as the 1800s by ecologists and naturalists who brought these issues into the public forum. For example, George Perkins March, a diplomat, author, lawyer, and congressman, is credited with founding the science of ecology. Other early nineteenth- and twentieth-century American environmentalists include author Henry David Thoreau, naturalist and preservationist President Theodore Roosevelt, and environmentalist John Muir, among many others. This early advocacy made an impact, but political activism in the United States (US) in the 1960s accelerated these efforts.

The 1960s environmental movement was inspired by other social movements of the time and by the seminal book, *Silent Spring,* published by Rachel Carson in 1962. The book brought about a turning point in the public's environmental consciousness, particularly in regard to pesticide use. The public's attention again focused on environmental issues in 1969, when the Cuyahoga River in Cleveland, Ohio caught fire due to floating contaminants, generating widespread media attention. Although the river had caught fire many times since the late 1800s, the 1969 fire captured the public's attention about industrial pollution of US waterways, galvanizing the environmental movement.

In 1970, the environmental movement's profile increased again with the establishment of Earth Day. The movement began to acquire greater political and social legitimacy, most clearly demonstrated by the establishment of the US Environmental Protection Agency (EPA) under President Richard Nixon and the Council on Environmental Quality. In particular, wildlife conservation, wilderness preservation, and pollution control became important focal points for both political and social response. These efforts have resulted in new regulations, and in many cases have led to reductions in the human impact on the environment. For example, the level of sulfur dioxide released by coal power plants in the eastern US dropped by nearly half between 2005 and 2010. Sulfur dioxide is a gas that can contribute to acid rain and causes serious health problems.

In recent years, the environmental movement has expanded to encompass other environmental challenges, particularly those related to global climate change and reduced use of non-renewable energy resources. **Non-renewable energy resources** are energy sources that exist in limited supply and cannot be regenerated once consumed. Some examples of non-renewable energy sources are fossil fuels such as oil, natural gas, and coal.

Although the US currently derives most of its energy from fossil fuels, the environmental movement is concerned with two major drawbacks of these resources: their limited supply and their possible contribution to air pollution. Accordingly, the environmental movement seeks to replace fossil fuels with renewable energy sources that have a more limited impact on the environment. **Renewable energy resources** are sources of energy that are not depleted through use. Some renewable energy sources are listed in Figure 1.2 and the pros and cons of their development and use are also shown.

ENVIRONMENTAL MOVEMENT A grassroots social movement to increase awareness about issues impacting the natural environment.

NON-RENEWABLE ENERGY RESOURCES Energy sources that exist in limited supply and cannot be regenerated once consumed.

RENEWABLE ENERGY RESOURCES Energy resources that are not depleted through use.

RENEWABLE ENERGY SOURCE	PROS	CONS
Solar	• Abundant source • Low carbon emissions • Low maintenance • Low construction costs	• High equipment cost • No energy generated at night and less on cloudy days • Inefficient • Must be stored in a battery
Wind	• Abundant source • Low carbon emissions • Incentives for businesses and individuals • Potential for offshore locations	• High winds are necessary • Affect birds and bats • Not popular with some landowners • Low energy production • Noise pollution
Hydropower	• Abundant source • Low carbon emissions • Growth in industry would create jobs • Can create recreational facilities • Rapid recharge to power stations • Reliable • Low cost and maintenance • Small size • Long life	• Changes to ecosystem • Can have organized large scale public opposition
Geothermal	• Incentives for businesses and individuals • Inexpensive • Reliable • Predictable	• Creates toxic chemicals • Limited availability • Potential groundwater contamination • May be located in natural areas in need of protection from development • Plants can release carbon dioxide (CO_2) and hydrogen sulfide • Long build time • Regulations and financing difficult to obtain
Biomass Fuels	• Uses wood and agricultural urban waste • Moderate cost • Convertible to other fuels • Large supply • Efficient • Reduces methane (a greenhouse gas)	• Needs good management • Slow/resistant public acceptance

FIGURE 1.2 Renewable energy pros and cons

Although the environmental movement's focus on renewable energy resources, also known as "clean energy," provides an important foundation for protecting the environment, challenges in creating renewable energy alternatives remain. For instance, solar power is touted as a prominent resource that is both renewable and environmentally responsible. However, scientists have not yet found a way to convert sunlight to energy efficiently, and they struggle to develop efficient solar energy systems that work when the sun is not shining. As shown in Figure 1.2, other renewable energy sources also have barriers to widespread adoption. Overcoming these obstacles remains one of the most prominent challenges in establishing renewable energy resources as a principal means for power generation.

Challenges related to the depletion of non-renewable energy sources, coupled with the problems associated with establishing renewable alternatives, create a predicament for scientists and policymakers. Even though clean energy represents an improvement over the use of fossil fuels, the relatively high cost of clean energy necessitates the use of fossil fuels, at least in the near term. Non-renewable energy resources need to be used until technological progress provides a renewable energy resource that is inexpensive enough to compete with fossil fuels.

Nuclear power is often proposed as a solution to this dilemma. Questions about the environmental impact remain a pressing concern. In order to understand the controversy surrounding the use of nuclear power, it is helpful to take a closer look at this energy resource.

In general, a nuclear power plant generates electricity through the creation of steam that drives a turbine generator, producing electricity. To create this steam, nuclear fission heats water. **Nuclear fission** occurs when one atom splits into two, releasing energy. Nuclear reactors produce fission through the use of radioactive materials such as uranium. Since fission releases so much heat, nuclear reactors require a controlled process to capture the energy and ensure that the radioactive materials in the reactor do not overheat.

Overall, nuclear power has several benefits that make it a viable option in energy production. Specifically, the generation of nuclear power does not rely on the use of fossil fuels; instead it is produced with radioactive materials such as uranium. Nuclear power plants are more efficient than coal-powered plants and can produce as much as a million times more energy per unit than coal. Finally, nuclear power plants release minimal amounts of greenhouse gases, but spent nuclear fuel does pose serious disposal issues. Waste from nuclear power plants remains radioactive and a threat to the environment for thousands of years.

Despite all of the advantages of nuclear power, there are some important drawbacks to producing energy this way. In particular, the process of mining and purifying radioactive materials used in nuclear power plants is not a clean process. The storage of spent fuel rods, which are radioactive for thousands of years, and the costs of decommissioning plants are difficult issues. Radioactive waste from spent fuel used in nuclear power plants cannot be easily disposed and represents a deadly threat to human and environmental health. Human exposure to radioactivity can result in diseases such as cancer and birth defects in children. Water and soil contaminated by radioactive material is unusable. The "Not In My Backyard" (NIMBY) syndrome, which is the tendency for people to reject certain land uses near their residence or business, is common around nuclear power stations. These power plants are also considered targets for terrorist activity, strengthening the NIMBY syndrome for many people who live near such a facility. While nuclear power represents a source of energy that does not have high greenhouse gas emissions, the implications for the environment posed by radioactive waste cause many to oppose the expansion of this energy source.

The true impact and environmental devastation that can result from the use of nuclear power was seen in the case of the Chernobyl nuclear disaster. Located in Ukraine, Chernobyl had, for years, been an important resource for power generation in the community. In 1986, due in part to mismanagement at the

NUCLEAR FISSION The process that occurs when one atom splits into two, releasing energy.

plant, an explosion occurred in one of the reactors, releasing 50 tons of radioactive material into the surrounding area. In the immediate aftermath of the crisis, approximately 30,000 people were evacuated. The radioactive material contaminated millions of acres of forests and resulted in the deaths of thousands of people. Most of the deaths were the result of cancer and other diseases caused by the radiation. Even though the events at Chernobyl represent a cataclysmic event that does not typically occur with the use of nuclear power, the extent and degree of the devastation highlights the severity of the damage that can occur when these plants malfunction. Because one plant can cause such extreme harm to the environment, the construction and operation of nuclear power plants must be carefully scrutinized.

MID-CHAPTER QUESTIONS

1. What is the environmental movement?

2. What is the difference between renewable and non-renewable energy resources?

3. What is nuclear fission?

4. What are the benefits of nuclear power? What are the drawbacks?

HOW PEOPLE IMPACT THE ENVIRONMENT

Human impact on the environment is incredibly profound. Everything that individuals require for survival comes from the natural environment. Consider the clothes you wear. All of the basic materials needed to make clothing are extracted in some way from the environment. Cotton, for example, is produced by the cotton plant, which uses soil, water, sunlight, and nutrients. Large machines are used to harvest the cotton and these burn fossil fuels. Once harvested, cotton is processed to create fabric. This process requires energy resources (fossil fuels) that are drawn from the environment and, when burned, create greenhouse gases. Waste from these manufacturing plants also can impact the environment. Synthetic fibers, such as polyester, require chemicals synthesized from natural products found in the environment. Again, this process requires the use of energy. Manufacturing plants also create wastewater and air pollution that needs to be treated before being released, and every nation has its own environmental regulations. When framed in this context, it is evident that even basic human activity has broad implications for the environment.

Similar observations can be made about food. Humanity's continual efforts to acquire food have led to the extinction of some animal species, including the woolly mammoth and the dodo bird. The extinction of the dodo bird is believed by some scientists to have impacted the population of the Calvaria tree, as its seeds depended on ingestion and digestion by the bird. The interrelatedness of plant and animal species and their relationships illustrates the ecosystem damage that can occur from species destruction.

Today, the need to acquire food spurs the development of new farming and animal husbandry techniques that also have implications for the environment. **Factory farming** is a technique that allows for the mass production of food through the confinement of animals. Although factory farming produces large amounts of food very inexpensively, the practice can have a detrimental impact on the environment. Factory farms use large spaces of land to mass-produce animal products. Animals are in close contact with one another, sometimes resulting in the spread of disease that can decimate animal populations, a problem that is usually managed and avoided by feeding the animals antibiotics. Also, animal waste from factory farms can contaminate surrounding areas.

Colorado River aqueduct

Human impact on the environment is not limited to meeting our basic needs for survival. Over the course of history, the human race has consistently demonstrated an indifference to its physical surroundings, seeking to create livable environments in areas where life is not easily supported. This can be seen in the development of desert lands for human habitation. Prominent cities such as Las Vegas and Los Angeles were initially arid desert that did not support human habitation because of a lack of water. In order to overcome this obstacle, extensive water systems were developed. For instance, in Los Angeles a 223-mile aqueduct brings water to the city from the Owens River in the eastern Sierra Madre mountain range. The aqueduct was built in 1913 and serves as one of the principle sources of potable water for Los Angeles residents. The creation of these systems not only changes the physical landscape, but also impacts animal and plant ecosystems in the desert.

Human impact on the environment can also been seen in the context of our constructed environment. In order to support life in different areas of the globe, human beings create roads, construct factories, and build homes—all on a staggering scale. Developing new areas for human settlement often requires the destruction of ecosystems that support biodiversity. **Biodiversity** refers to the variety of living organisms inhabiting a particular area. Some modern biodiversity loss is attributed to the increase in the human population and the expansion of development as a result. Although new communities provide opportunities for human societies to grow and develop, such expansion often results in pollution of the natural environment, both in the form of toxins that may disrupt ecosystems and greenhouse gases that may contribute to air pollution.

It is clear that human beings have greatly impacted the environment. One goal of the environmental movement is to encourage the adoption of government policies and individual behaviors that limit damage to the environment. While some progress has been made in the areas of conservation and preservation, human beings continue to have a significant and sometimes devastating impact on the natural environment.

Modernization

One way human beings impact the environment is through modernization. **Modernization** refers to an evolutionary process in which society undergoes

FACTORY FARMING A farming technique that allows for the mass production of food through the confinement of animals.

BIODIVERSITY The variety of living organisms inhabiting a particular area.

MODERNIZATION An evolutionary process in which society changes to support the needs of its inhabitants.

specific changes to support the needs of its inhabitants. Examples of modernization can be seen through activities such as industrialization and technological advances. Various types of modernization have occurred throughout human history. Industrialization enabled the mass production of goods and the provided employment for millions of workers. Presently, society is undergoing technological modernization, a process fueled by the development of computer technology and the Internet. Information sharing and business transactions now occur more rapidly, enabling societies to modernize at a faster rate than at any previous time in history.

Modernization occurs as a result of the human need for change and improvement. In many instances, modernization is not orchestrated; rather, it develops as a consequence of social or economic needs. For example, the development of chemical fertilizers and pesticides has drastically increased crop yields over the last 40 years, enabling communities to successfully feed growing populations. However, scientists now understand that chemical run-off from agricultural areas in the Midwest flowed down the Mississippi River and contributed to a "dead zone" in the Gulf of Mexico that is too toxic to support the marine life that previously teemed there.

The modern highway system, a foundational part of modernizing societies, provides thousands of miles of roads that can be accessed by anyone with a vehicle. Roads created to connect cities and towns require the clearing of vast tracts of land. Clearing land to construct roads impacts the habitats of numerous plant and animal species. As a result of this process, some of the biodiversity of the North American continent has been lost. The availability of roads has prompted increased sales of automobiles, which in turn has increased the consumption of fossil fuels and the emission of greenhouse gases. Hence, even though modern transportation systems are viewed as essential to modernization, they do have a significant impact on the environment. In Los Angeles, for example, the large number of automobiles in the city contributes to smog. **Smog** occurs when nitrous oxide compounds (NOx) from automobile emissions, power plants, and industrial plants and volatile organic compounds (VOC) from gasoline pumps, chemical plants, paints, dry cleaners, and other sources become trapped in fog and then are exposed to sunlight. Photochemical smog (or just smog for short) is a term used to describe air pollution that is a result of the interaction of sunlight with certain chemicals in the atmosphere. One of the primary components of photochemical smog is ozone. While ozone in the stratosphere protects the Earth from harmful UV radiation, ozone on the ground is hazardous to human health. Ground-level ozone is formed when vehicle emissions containing nitrogen oxides (primarily from vehicle exhaust) and volatile organic compounds (from paints, solvents, and fuel evaporation) interact in the presence of sunlight. Therefore, some of the sunniest cities are also some of the most polluted.

While modernization is often viewed as an important part of human development and growth, the reality is that this process carries with it a host of implications for the environment. Recognition of these issues has prompted efforts to temper modernization with sustainable development. **Sustainable development** refers to the process of using current resources to meet needs without compromising the needs of future generations. Sustainable development brings together the recognition of the human need to modernize while taking into consideration the

SMOG Pollutant released when nitrous oxide compounds become trapped in fog and are exposed to sunlight.

SUSTAINABLE DEVELOPMENT The process of utilizing current resources to meet human and environmental needs without compromising the needs of future generations.

BUSINESSES GOING GREEN: THE AUTO INDUSTRY

As evidenced by the diverse selection of energy-saving vehicle designs at recent industry auto shows, almost every car manufacturer now has a hybrid vehicle, and many have introduced other fuel-efficient automobiles such as plug-in hybrids and electric vehicles, which are newer to the broad consumer market. A hybrid generally uses electricity stored in an onboard battery along with gasoline, thereby consuming much less fuel than traditional gasoline-only vehicles. Traditional hybrid vehicles such as the Toyota Prius can obtain mileages of over 50 miles per gallon.

Newer technology offers even better fuel mileage. For example, the Chevy Volt is a plug-in hybrid, using both gasoline and electricity to run the engine. This combination in the Volt allows drivers to travel 60 miles per gallon. The Nissan Leaf, an electric vehicle, comes in at even more-efficient 99 miles per gallon. (Since electricity is not measured in gallons, this determination by the US Department of Energy used a conversion factor to measure the gasoline equivalent of electricity use.) Consumer demand, lawmakers, regulators, and high gasoline costs have accelerated the development of such innovation. The US and other countries are producing these vehicles to meet social and regulatory pressures.

It is important for businesses to make environmentally friendly modifications to their products, and sometimes they not only to benefit the environment, but also improve their bottom line. Green is increasingly seen as being "good" for a company on many levels: social, political, and financial. Companies earn new customers and keep their existing customers through these efforts. New government regulations on fuel efficiency will require that the auto industry continue to innovate in this area to meet new standards.

impact of modernization on the environment. When undertaken successfully, sustainable development allows for modernization that has minimal impact on the environment, preserving resources for the future. One example of sustainable technology is artificial wood. Artificial timber prevents widespread deforestation, because it is a wood substitute that can be made available anywhere and costs much less than wood. Thus, by creating a brilliant replacement for a threatened resource, artificial wood has the potential to minimize or avert ecological disaster. The raw material for the artificial timber can be fly ash, silica, red mud, and other materials that are readily available anywhere in the world. Because artificial wood can be produced locally, no expensive procurement of raw materials is involved, which adds to its "sustainable" value.

Policy

Policy is another area in which human beings impact the environment. Many policies undertaken before environmental regulations allowed companies to operate in a way that caused significant harm to the environment. For instance, during the Industrial Revolution in the nineteenth century, there were few legal limits on what factories

could release from smokestacks. Accordingly, companies could release the by-products of industrial processes into the environment. The threats to the environment and public health were not known until the science advanced, linking pollutants to environmental degradation and health consequences. Later, as policymakers and the public became aware of the impact on industrial processes on the environment, regulations were developed to control pollution, issue permits, and monitor industrial activities in most developed nations.

Policymakers have made notable strides toward addressing environmental problems. One example is the Clean Water Act. Initially passed in 1948 as the Federal Water Pollution Control Act, the legislation was amended in 1972 and again in 1977, when it became more commonly known as the Clean Water Act. This legislation regulates the release of pollutants from point sources into the water system. With this legislation in place, the government can protect its citizens from harmful or contaminated drinking water. Under this legislation, individuals or companies responsible for contaminating the water systems are held accountable for their actions in the form of civil or criminal prosecution, resulting in monetary fines or even jail time.

Generally speaking, environmental policy has had a positive impact. However, there are instances in which policy creates some notable challenges for human development or corporations, who sometimes move operations to other countries to avoid making costly changes to meet government regulations. One example of a human challenge created by policy is the Endangered Species Act (ESA), passed into law in 1973. The legislation was designed to ensure that animals facing extinction would be protected. As a result of the ESA, hundreds of animals have been brought back from the brink of extinction, but the legislation has been a source of contention in public policy. In areas where endangered animals live, the government often prohibits land development. This occurs even in situations where development may be important for human survival. One example of this occurred in the state of Georgia in 2007. Facing extreme drought conditions, Georgia lobbied the US EPA to lift protections of endangered species living in the state's lakes. Lifting these sanctions was viewed as critical to providing needed water to drought-stricken areas. Although the provisions of the ESA were eventually eased, the process took months, impacting the ability of state lawmakers to provide water to residents.

The trade-offs involved with the enforcement of the ESA have created controversy. Proponents of the legislation believe that the ESA is necessary to protect animals threatened with extinction and ensure the nation's biodiversity. Opponents argue that human progress should be allowed even when it means that some degree of biodiversity may be lost. Overall, the ESA illustrates how policy can impact the environment. Policies such as the ESA prompt individuals and companies to consider their actions, their impact on the environment, and what steps can be taken to preserve the environment while still meeting the economic demands of American society.

Demographics

Demographic shifts in the population also have implications for the environment. In order to understand these impacts, it is important to consider global population patterns. Statistics provided by the Population Reference Bureau indicate that by 2050, the Earth's population is expected to increase to more than 9 billion. This represents an increase of more than 25 percent over the current population.

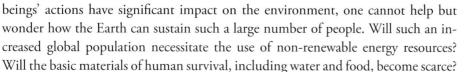

However, given the birth rate in developing countries, such predictions are hard to make with certainty. The term **carrying capacity** refers to the maximum number of individuals of a species that can survive over long periods of time. We do not know how many human beings can be adequately supported as the population increases, because technological innovations may allow for a greater carrying capacity. When considering that human beings' actions have significant impact on the environment, one cannot help but wonder how the Earth can sustain such a large number of people. Will such an increased global population necessitate the use of non-renewable energy resources? Will the basic materials of human survival, including water and food, become scarce?

The issue of water shortage has become important in recent years on a national and global scale. Increases in human population, coupled with changes in climate, have created water shortages in places such as California, the Middle East, and Africa. Because water is a basic element needed for human survival, competition over water resources has intensified in recent years, resulting in significant conflicts and even war. Efforts to address water shortages have resulted in the use of strategies such as **desalination**, the process of removing salt from ocean water to make it suitable for human consumption. Desalination is a very expensive and old technology, invented in 1869, but the process might prove useful for countries facing water shortages.

While growth in the global population is one demographic issue with broad implications for sustainable development, changes in the demographics of the population also have environmental impact. Many developed nations are witnessing the "graying" of their populations. For example, the baby boomer generation, which comprises approximately 78 million individuals in the US who were born between 1946 and 1964, is reaching retirement age. As populations in developed nations age, their longevity poses challenges for environmental sustainability. As people live longer, more resources are required to support them. However, populations can be self-regulating. The demographic transition model and theory illustrate how fertility and mortality rates change as a society develops. In developing societies death and birth rates are high. As they modernize, technology and socio-economic advances reduce the death rates. With further development, birth rates decrease, resulting in a stable population.

CARRYING CAPACITY The maximum number of individuals of a species that can survive over long periods of time.

DESALINATION The process of removing minerals and bacteria from saltwater to make it suitable for human consumption.

MID-CHAPTER QUESTIONS

1. What is biodiversity?

2. Name three ways in which man impacts the environment.

3. What is sustainable development?

THE STATE OF THE WORLD

Global environmental issues are integrally linked, impacting all countries, governments, and citizens. For instance, clean drinking water is a prominent environmental issue that has global implications for human development. Additionally, issues such as a decline in biodiversity and the consumption of non-renewable energy resources are also matters that impact society on a global scale.

Although governments and individuals across the globe impact the environment in a number of similar ways, the specific outcomes that occur in different parts of the world are dependent upon the social, economic, and political development of a particular nation or region. Development issues play a significant role in shaping how governments and citizens respond to the environment, the environmental policies created, the resources available for creating sustainable development, and the willingness of citizens to take an active role in environmental protection. With this in mind, it is worth considering the state of the environment in different areas of the globe.

The Developed World

Developed nations can be defined in several ways, but they often are identified as those countries with advanced industrial and technological capabilities as well as sustainable economic productivity. Examples of developed nations include the United States, Canada, Japan, and European nations such as Germany, Italy, and France. There are differences between the environmental issues facing the US and those facing Europe. As such, it is helpful to review these regions separately.

A major concern in the US is the issue of energy consumption. In 2008, 86 percent of the power used in the US came from non-renewable fossil fuels. Reliance on coal, natural gas, and petroleum not only serves to increase greenhouse gas emissions but also raises questions about the sustainability of US energy policy. In short, current rates of consumption of fossil fuels will leave fewer resources for the US and other countries to meet their energy needs in the future. Improving outcomes for energy consumption requires the development of renewable sources of energy. Conservation of energy resources, better energy efficiency, and development of new and renewable energy resources will affect energy consumption patterns in the US. Industries are conserving resources and making processes more efficient as cost-saving measures. The automobile industry is responding to increasing oil prices and new government requirements by increasing the fuel efficiency of cars.

Pollution and waste are also significant environmental issues worldwide. Through the mid- and late-twentieth century, the US government pursued environmental policies designed to reduce pollution and ensure safe disposal of waste. Even when policies are in place to mitigate the impact of waste and pollution on the environment, problems still occur. For example, the 2010 BP oil spill in the Gulf of Mexico poured millions of gallons of oil into the ocean and threatened numerous

marine ecosystems. BP, oil rig owner Trans Ocean, and subcontractor Halliburton were all accused of lax oversight and safety violations in the spill. Deep ocean drilling is highly technical and poses safety and environmental risks. Environmental and safety regulations attempt to mitigate these risks. The spill also raised concerns for human health as scientists sought to gauge the impact of petroleum contamination on the safety of seafood. Similar issues were noted in 1989 when the Exxon Valdez oil tanker spilled hundreds of thousands of barrels of oil off the coast of Alaska.

Air pollution is also a prominent issue in the US. As previously noted, 86 percent of the energy consumed in the country is from fossil fuels. The continued burning of fossil fuels has implications for air pollution and human health. Particulate matter in these emissions pollutes the air and makes it difficult for individuals with lung conditions (e.g., asthma, bronchitis) to breathe. Sulfur dioxide, released by the burning of sulfur-containing coal to generate electricity, contributes to acid deposition (or acid rain). Acid deposition is the acidifying of the air and water from atmospheric sulfur. Also, as discussed earlier, nitrogen oxides emitted from automobiles contribute to smog. Clean air legislation has reduced air pollution to the lowest rates in 10 years, although many US cities still do not meet air quality standards. The American Lung Association attributes air quality improvements to cleaner fuels and engines and restrictions on coal emissions.

The US faces some unique challenges with regard to the environment. In the past, the country used governmental policy as a central means of addressing many of the environmental issues. In recent years, political gridlock and budget issues have impacted both the ability and willingness of policymakers to take additional steps toward environmental protection. While some politicians have argued in favor of stricter regulation and a more cautious approach to development that could impact the environment, others have argued that regulations have gone too far, unnecessarily hampering businesses and stunting economic growth.

Europe

In Europe, changes in agriculture and land use, including urbanization, deforestation, and the growth of landfills, are important environmental issues. Climate change is a pressing issue of concern in Europe. One principle difference, however, lies in the way in which national governments in Europe have addressed the problem. In 2009, European Union (EU) countries participated in the Copenhagen Accord, designed to establish additional policies to reduce greenhouse gas emissions. While the specific targets established by each member county differ, the targets focus on a six to eight percent reduction in greenhouse gas emissions from their 1990 levels.

The EU's commitment to reduce greenhouse gases is connected to the efforts of the member countries to use alternative energy resources and other energy strategies. The European Commission's Energy 2020 Strategy focuses on energy efficiency, infrastructure, choice and security for consumers, energy technology, and the external dimension of the internal energy market. Their statement regarding alternative energy points to "essential" alternatives to fossil fuels in order to reduce reliance on fossil fuels, stimulate employment, create new technologies, and improve trade balances.

Leaders of the EU have established policies aimed at creating energy independent member states. This move is fueled by the recognition that fossil fuels cannot be renewed, and that excess consumption of these fuels has global implications. Alternative energy resources, including wind and solar power, are being developed. In addition, the EU is investing heavily in infrastructure to update its energy grid.

Protection of biodiversity is another significant environmental issue impacting EU member countries. In 2001, the EU established a policy to halt the loss of biodiversity by 2010. Unfortunately, this goal was not met. Although EU member states attempted to enact policies needed to protect biodiversity and ensure that no new species were lost to human development, the goal remains elusive. The EU continues to pursue initiatives to achieve the 2010 standard, demonstrating the commitment of member states to address this environmental issue.

A comparison of environmental issues and policy in the US and the EU reveals markedly different directions for development with regard to environmental issues. In the US, reducing CO_2 and other greenhouse gas pollution is required by the Clean Air Act. The EPA is reducing greenhouse gas emissions and promoting a clean energy economy through highly successful partnerships and common-sense regulatory initiatives. In Europe, reducing greenhouse gas emissions has become a focal point for public policy. The different directions pursued by policymakers will have implications for the outcomes achieved.

The Developing World

Developing nations' classifications and data reported for geographic regions are for low-income and middle-income economies only. Low-income and middle-income economies are sometimes referred to as developing economies. The use of the term is convenient; it is not intended to imply that all economies in the group are  experiencing similar development or that other economies have reached a preferred or final stage of development. Classification by income does not necessarily reflect development status. According to the World Bank, income groups for "economies are divided according to 2010 Gross National Income (GNI) per capita, calculated using the World Bank Atlas method. The groups are: low income, $1,005 or less; lower middle income, $1,006–$3,975; upper middle income, $3,976–$12,275; and high income, $12,276 or more."

In developing nations, population growth occurs at a rate faster than can be supported by the economy and infrastructure. As a result, basic health and survival needs are not met. Developing nations are primarily located in Africa, Asia, the Middle East, and Latin America. Because of their level of development, the environmental issues impacting developing nations are markedly different that those impacting developed nations.

In many parts of the developing world, a focus on economic development has given rise to lax environmental policies and the continued degradation of the environment. In some nations, industrialization continues to expand without environmental regulations to protect water and air resources. As a result, pollution often directly affects human health. Contaminated water is a persistent source of disease and death. Air pollution has also become a significant issue in recent years, as evidenced by the air quality problems in China before the 2008 Beijing Olympics. Due to air pollution in the city, the government ordered the shutdown of industrial plants within a 500 mile radius of Beijing for weeks prior to the games to allow the air to clear.

While US and EU leaders grapple with policies aimed at reducing greenhouse gas emissions, developing nations continue to contribute to greenhouse gas emissions without controls. Developing nations continue to use large amounts of fossil fuels in an effort to achieve a high level of economic development and prosperity. Because of a lack of economic infrastructure, not much alternative energy resource development occurs in these countries. These issues continue to make it difficult for developing nations to balance their need for economic development with the preservation and sustainability of the environment.

Environmental issues in developing nations are also impacted by population demographics. As noted earlier, the global population continues to expand at a significant pace. Most of the growth in the global population is occurring in developing nations. Issues such as a lack of health infrastructure and little access to contraception and education have created a situation in which women in these countries often give birth to many more children than women in developed countries. Many of these children die before their fifth birthday. High birthrates in developing nations mean these countries need a significant amount of resources to support the basic needs of the population.

Air, water, and soil pollution are another major challenge facing developing nations. In particular, developing nations are seeing an increase in acid rain. This is due to the fact that many of the groundwater resources in developing countries are contaminated with acidic substances. Imbalances in water ecosystems have also resulted in **eutrophication**, or the abnormal growth of algae. Destruction of rain forest habitat has also accelerated in recent years, indicating a general lack of protection of natural resources. While each of these issues has direct implications for environmental health in developing nations, these issues also have implications for the global environment. For example, acid rain produced in one country will eventually become an issue of concern for other nations.

Comparison of developing and developed nations with regard to environmental issues demonstrates how the political and economic climate in each of these regions impacts the response to environmental concerns. In developed nations, the availability of economic resources provides a foundation for citizens and policymakers to more carefully consider human impact on the environment and what steps to take to address the problems. As a result, environmental issues impacting developed nations are well defined and are primarily debated in the context of policy development. Differences exist between the US and the EU, with EU member states focusing more prominently on reducing greenhouse gas emissions and investing in alternative energy resources.

In some developing nations, however, the situation is clearly different. While issues such as air and water pollution are prominent concerns in some countries, few steps have been taken to effectively address the impact of humans on the environment because of the lack of sustainable economic and human development. Improving environmental outcomes in developing nations requires establishing basic social and economic infrastructure. Without fundamental changes in these areas, developing nations will continue to lack the resources and ability to address even the most pressing environmental issues.

EUTROPHICATION The abnormal growth of toxic algae.

Despite the challenges facing developing countries, some are beginning to address their environmental concerns. In 2008, Ecuador adopted a constitution that, among other things, recognized legally enforceable Rights of Nature, or ecosystem rights, becoming the first country to recognize these rights.

MID-CHAPTER QUESTIONS

1. What are some common global environmental issues that are important to all nations?

2. What differences exist between environmental policy in developing and developed nations? What is the primary reason for these differences?

PRESERVATION: THE ENDANGERED SPECIES ACT

Environmental issues and the policies created to address these issues have implications for all living organisms on the planet. In an effort to maintain the natural environment, policies and action taken by national and international governments focus on two general directions for policy: conservation and preservation. Generally speaking, conservation focuses on the management of existing natural resources to ensure they are used responsibly. Preservation focuses on the direct protection and maintenance of natural resources. One pertinent example of environmental policy focused on preservation is the Endangered Species Act (ESA), which seeks to limit human impact on certain animal species. In addition to making it illegal to hunt or capture certain animals, the ESA protects the habitats of endangered species.

Preservation is a vital component of sustainable environmental policy. However, it has been met with considerable criticism. Preservation efforts focus on larger issues related to social, animal, and human rights policies enacted to preserve the environment. Unfortunately, these efforts can create a conflict between human needs and the welfare of the natural world. For example, the ESA was established to protect vulnerable species from extinction. As such, the legislation often limits human development. These challenges have raised concern over the viability and need for environmental preservation.

Controversy over environmental preservation is a significant issue because it impacts the ability of policymakers to find effective solutions that balance the rights of all living things with our ideas of human and economic rights. Although significant challenges exist in creating policies that balance rights, preservation remains an important component of environmental policy.

CHAPTER SUMMARY

Environmental science encapsulates a host of important issues and concerns as well as the scientific tools needed to study the environment and human impact on the environment. The scientific method provides a structured framework to acquire empirical data. With this data, scientists, policymakers, and the general public can draw conclusions and make decisions regarding environmental issues. Even though the scientific method is an important component of understanding the environment, non-experimental approaches to research, such as observation, can also be useful for generating scientific knowledge. Bias and spin must be considered when evaluating various positions on environmental issues.

The environmental movement concentrates its efforts on influencing and shaping policy aimed at environmental conservation and preservation. In recent years, the environmental movement has focused increasingly on efforts to generate renewable energy resources. Debate over nuclear power as a safe energy alternative remains a pressing dilemma for policymakers and environmentalists. Although nuclear power does not produce extensive greenhouse gas emissions, some feel that nuclear waste from power plants, as well as the risks of catastrophic accidents or terrorism, pose significant environmental threats.

People impact the environment in a host of ways. The environmental issues faced by developed and developing nations vary, but the most pressing concern globally is the availability of adequate food and clean water for growing populations. Over 90 percent of developing countries still discharge untreated waste water into streams and rivers. And, according to the UN Committee on World Food Security 2005 report, over 852 million people do not have enough food to meet their basic nutritional needs, and as many as one third of the world's population does not achieve optimal physical and mental development due to the lack of vitamins and minerals in their food.

REFERENCES

Canning, K. (2009). The art of transformation. *Private Label Buyer, 23*(8), 20–26.

Climate tension. (2005, July 5). *PBS News*. Retrieved from http://www.pbs.org/newshour/bb/environment/july-dec05/climate_7-5.html

Dykstra, P. (2008, December 15). History of environmental movement full of twists, turns. *CNN*. Retrieved from http://articles.cnn.com/2008-12-10/tech/history.environmental.movement_1_fierce-green-fire-american-environmental-movement-philip-shabecoff/2?_s=PM:TECHEuropean Commission. (2010).

Energy 2020. Luxembourg: Publications Office of the European Union. Retrieved from http://ec.europa.eu/energy/publications/doc/2011_energy2020_en.pdf

European Environment Agency. (n.d.). About climate change. Retrieved from http://www.eea.europa.eu/themes/climate/about-climate-change

European Environment Agency. (n.d.). Biodiversity. Retrieved from http://www.eea.europa.eu/themes/biodiversity

European Environment Agency. (2012, March 26). Climate change policies. Retrieved from http://www.eea.europa.eu/themes/climate/policy-context

Environmental Protection Agency. (2010). Air pollution. Retrieved from http://epa.gov/airtrends/2010/report/airpollution.pdf

Fischetti, M. (2011, December 1). Fukushima earthquake moved seafloor half a football field. *Scientific American*. Retrieved from http://www.scientificamerican.com/article.cfm?id=japan-earthquake-moves-seafloor

Ghadar, F. (2005). Population: Shifting demographics. *Industrial Management, 47*(5), 8–13.

Law. (1979). In *Oxford English Dictionary*. Oxford University Press.

National Aeronautics and Space Administration. (2012). Global climate change: Key indicators. Retrieved from http://climate.nasa.gov/keyIndicators/

National Institute for Environmental Studies. (n.d.). Environmental issues in developing countries. Retrieved from http://www.nies.go.jp/gaiyo/panf2002/developing/developing-e.html

National Snow and Ice Data Center. (2012). Arctic sea ice news and analysis. Retrieved from http://nsidc.org/arcticseaicenews/

National Wildlife Federation. (n.d.). Global warming and polar bears. Retrieved from http://www.nwf.org/Global-Warming/Effects-on-Wildlife-and-Habitat/Polar-Bears.aspx

Pool, R. (2011). Fukushima: The facts. *Engineering & Technology*, 6(4), 32–36.

Schleibe, S. (n.d.). What has been happening to polar bears in recent decades? National Oceanic and Atmospheric Administration. Retrieved from http://www.arctic.noaa.gov/essay_schliebe.html

Scientific method. (2013). In *Merriam-Webster Online Dictionary*. Retrieved from http://www.merriam-webster.com/dictionary/scientific%20method

U.S. Census Bureau. (n.d.). International data base: World population summary. Retrieved from http://www.census.gov/population/international/data/idb/worldpopinfo.php

U.S. Department of Energy. (2012). Fuel economy guide: Model year 2012 (Report No. DOE/EE-0603). Retrieved from http://www.fueleconomy.gov/feg/pdfs/guides/FEG2012.pdf

U.S. Energy Information Administration. (2009). *Annual energy review.* Retrieved from http://www.eia.gov/totalenergy/data/annual/pdf/aer.pdf

U.S. Environmental Protection Agency. (2009, June 2). Smog/regional transport of ozone. Retrieved from http://www.epa.gov/airmarkt/envissues/smog.html

Vidal, J., & Adam, D. (2007, June 19). China overtakes US as world's biggest CO_2 emitter. *The Guardian* Retrieved from: http://www.guardian.co.uk/environment/2007/jun/19/china.usnews

The World Bank. (2013). World Bank atlas method. Retrieved from http://data.worldbank.org/about/country-classifications/world-bank-atlas-method

World Health Organization. (n.d.). Health statistics: Mortality. Retrieved from http://www.who.int/healthinfo/statistics/indunder5mortality/en/

Ecosystems

Mouth of the Cuyahoga River in Cleveland, Ohio

CUYAHOGA RIVER BURNED—A DISASTER AND SUCCESS

The Cuyahoga River runs through Cleveland, Ohio, and feeds into Lake Erie. At 100 miles long, it does not rank as a major US river; in fact, there are 13 rivers nationwide longer than 1,000 miles. The Cuyahoga provides a successful example of American environmental policies. The summer of 1969 is known as the year the river caught fire. It may sound impossible since water does not burn under normal conditions, but such an event was not unheard of at the time. The Cuyahoga River first burned in 1868 and burned over a half dozen additional times in subsequent decades, costing millions in damage. These fires were clear evidence that regulations were needed to protect human health and the environment. How was it possible for this river to catch fire?

For many years, Cleveland was a booming industrial town with factories lining the river's edge. Untreated hazardous waste poured into the river, such fats and grease from slaughterhouses and rendering plants, acids used in steelmaking, dyes from paint plants, and much of the raw or partially treated human sewage from the entire Cleveland-Akron area. The result was that a layer of thick and highly flammable waste called "sludge" formed on the river's surface. The accepted theories of what caused the Cuyahoga River fire of 1969 are that a train passing over one of the wooden trestles sent sparks into the water and ignited the surface or one of the steel plants released sparks that started the fire.

News coverage of the two-hour fight to put out the flames was relatively modest at first, because the national media was filled with reports that Lake Erie had been declared "dead" due to heavy pollution that had killed most organisms in the water. Before long "the river that caught fire" garnered national attention because it was identified as one of the sources of the pollution killing the organic life in Lake Erie. Eventually, the Cuyahoga River fire became a major catalyst for additional government action to deal with the nation's pollution problems. In response to this and other environmental disasters, President Richard Nixon and Congress established the US Environmental Protection Agency (EPA) in 1970, ushering in a new era of federal environmental regulations.

While cleanup of this and other waterways around the country began earlier in the twentieth century on the state and local level, the Cuyahoga River fire is credited with prompting changes to the Federal Water Pollution Control Act of 1948 (now known as the Clean Water Act of 1972). This legislation was expanded with major amendments in 1961, 1966, 1970, 1972, 1977, and 1987 that increased federal regulation of the release of chemical contaminants into US waterways through mandating registration and permits, as well as levying large fines and tough punishment for violators, including prison time for individuals who violate discharge permits and other environmental regulations. After the new regulations took effect, Lake Erie and the Cuyahoga River recovered and are now much cleaner, with over 60 species of aquatic life in abundance. In 2009, Cleveland celebrated "Year of the River"—the return of aquatic life and cleaner water.

WHAT IS AN ECOSYSTEM?

An **ecosystem** is a "complex of living organisms, their physical environment, and all their interrelationships in a particular unit of space. An ecosystem's abiotic (non-living) constituents include minerals, climate, soil, water, sunlight, and all other nonliving elements; its biotic constituents consist of all its living members." A biome, also called major life zone, is the largest geographic biotic unit, a major community of plants and animals with similar life forms and environmental conditions. It includes various communities and is named for the dominant type of vegetation, such as grassland or coniferous forest." There are four primary compartments in an ecosystem (see Figure 2.1): the **hydrosphere**, which includes rivers, streams, oceans, etc.; the **atmosphere** (specifically, the troposphere), which is the air surrounding the ecosystem; the **biosphere** (includes the area of the Earth where living organisms live), which encompasses all spheres; and the **lithosphere**, which refers to both the outermost layer of the Earth and the upper section of the mantle. The crust is

ECOSYSTEM The interaction between living organisms and non-living components such as air, soil, and water, within the different environmental parts of an area.

HYDROSPHERE The water on, underneath, and above the surface of the Earth, including atmospheric water.

ATMOSPHERE The gaseous medium surrounding the Earth.

BIOSPHERE The Earth's spheres, including surface, water, and atmosphere, which support all living organisms.

LITHOSPHERE The outermost layer of the Earth and the upper section of the mantle. The crust is only a small portion of the lithosphere.

1. What would happen if a river near you caught fire? Would it change the way you think about the importance of protecting the environment?

2. What other disasters covered by news media have caused people to think about environmental issues in a different light?

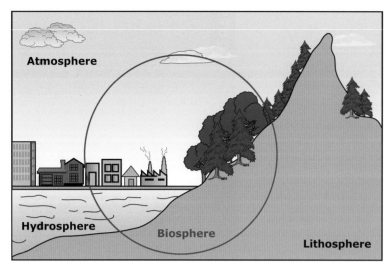

FIGURE 2.1 Components of the ecosystem

only a small portion of the lithosphere. These different parts interact with each other in similar ways regardless of the type of ecosystem. In a typical ecosystem, rivers provide water, bring nutrients, and transport wastes out of an area. The atmosphere provides oxygen and carbon dioxide (CO_2) for photosynthesis and respiration, as well as nutrients such as nitrogen, phosphorus, and potassium that plants can use to collect and hold water for transpiration events. Meanwhile, the biosphere uses water from the hydrosphere and gases from the atmosphere for photosynthesis and respiration; organisms in the biosphere also recycle water and nutrients into the hydrosphere and gases into the hydrosphere, lithosphere, and atmosphere. Even in extreme ecosystems these interactions can occur.

Desert ecosystems, for example, may not have an abundant water supply; however, aquifers, oasis watering holes, and plant and animal adaptations allow many organisms to survive the extreme climate. An example of a desert plant adaptation is found in plants called xerophytes. They grow close to the ground and have small leaves with a non-porous waxy coating, protecting them from harsh heat and sunlight.

Marine environments may seem, at first glance, to only interact with the atmosphere at their intersection. However, in actuality, the atmosphere constantly diffuses chemical compounds such as CO_2 into ocean water. The oceans have a carbonate buffer system that allows them to take on additional levels of dissolved CO_2. That system buffers the excess hydrogen ions and keeps the oceans from being more acidic; however, despite this buffer, the ocean pH levels have dropped fairly consistently over the years and the increased load of dissolved CO_2 in the water lowers the amount of carbonate ions in the seawater. This hinders the calcification of marine life (mainly coral). This entire process is called ocean acidification.

In a typical day, innumerable events occur in any given ecosystem. These events are either **abiotic** (without life) or **biotic** (with life). Abiotic events include changes in temperature, solar radiation, and rainfall, and chemical reactions. Abiotic events affect, and are affected by, biotic events. For example, rainfall recharges rivers and streams that provide drinking water for animals, and these animals breathe in oxygen and release CO_2 into the atmosphere. This gas and others react with each other abiotically in the environment and biotically with living organisms.

There is much discussion about the effects of pollution on the wildlife in an environment, but it is just as important to understand how the health of the environment impacts people and economies. While the benefits of physical health, fitness, and outdoor recreation may come immediately to mind when thinking about human uses of the environment, remember also that all our food supplies are grown, raised, or caught within ecosystems.

The health of the ecosystem, in some cases, dictates food quality. Plants, for instance, absorb their nutrients from the soil. If the soil is contaminated, these plants absorb the contaminants, which are then passed up the food chain. In fact, specific plants are sometimes used to clean contaminants in a method called **phytoremediation**.

ABIOTIC Related to events, reactions, or interactions that occur in the absence of living organisms (including with natural and man-made objects such as rocks, dams, or oxygen).

BIOTIC Related to events, reactions, or interaction involving living organisms.

PHYTOREMEDIATION The use of plants or algae to absorb and clean pollutants in the environment.

PRESERVATION: THE REPUBLIC OF CONGO'S FORESTRY PROGRAM

Every two years the environmental branch of the United Nations (UN), Habitat, honors groups that employ responsible environmental practices with its Dubai Award. In 2008, the Republic of Congo won the award for its forestry program.

The Congolese government began a program called the Tropical Forest Trust (TFT) in 2004, with the goal of

making the country's forests more sustainable. The project manages over 1.3 million hectares of forest in the attempt to provide a sustainable forestry industry for Congolese residents.

Instead of direct government mandates and oversight, the Congolese government worked with local officials, non-government officials, and the 9,000 indigenous people of the Congo forest to mandate these practices. Rarely before had indigenous people had a voice in the new practices that would affect them on a day-to-day basis.

Not only were the people of the forested area consulted on the program, but they were also made active participants in reaching the goal of sustainable forestry. For example, they were trained to use GPS mapping tools to guide them in their forestry practices. These mapping tools guide loggers to avoid areas that have already been harvested and help them develop new areas to harvest.

The Tropical Forest Conservation Act (TFCA), was created by the US to expand the Enterprise for the Americas Initiative (EAI) funds in 1991. To date, The US has signed treaties with 18 nations to protect rainforests throughout the world, including Argentina, Bangladesh, Belize, Bolivia, Botswana, Brazil, Chile, Colombia, Costa Rica, El Salvador, Guatemala, Indonesia, Jamaica, Panama, Paraguay, Peru, Philippines, and Uruguay. The goal of the treaties and programs is to ensure that rainforests around the world will be around for generations. By involving the people most affected by the different treaties and programs, they prevent feelings of disenfranchisement by the local population and reduce the likelihood of illegal logging and farming, which destroy rainforests.

Phytoremediation refers to a natural process in which plants or algae are used to treat soil contaminated with inorganic and organic waste. Hyperaccumulators are organisms that have the ability to take larger than normal amounts of contamination from the environment. Biomagnification refers to the increased concentration of a substance in the food chain because the environment does not have the ability remediate the substance—such as crude oil or mercury—faster than it is accumulated. Bioaccumulation is the accumulation of a substance, such as a toxic chemical, in various tissues of a living organism. Bioaccumulation takes place within an organism when the rate of intake of a substance is greater than the rate of excretion or metabolic transformation of that substance. For example, fish absorb chemicals from their environments and can pass them up the food chain. Consider the recent health warnings about mercury in tuna; these fish have accumulated unsafe amounts of mercury by

"Many modern medicines, while often now created synthetically, were originally plant derivatives, including aspirin, pseudoephedrine, ephedrine, and methyl morphine."

eating smaller fish with mercury in them. If an environment is not healthy, the food that organisms and humans eat from their environment will not be healthy either.

One benefit humans derive from ecosystems are healing compounds. Many modern medicines, while often now created synthetically, were originally plant derivatives, including aspirin, pseudoephedrine, ephedrine, and methyl morphine. Herbal and natural remedies such as aloe, St. John's wort, and ginkgo biloba (maidenhair tree) are used to help treat burns, soothe mild depression, and increase memory retention, respectively.

Another benefit is fitness and recreation. In 2006, camping attracted 48.6 million people to national, state, and private campgrounds. Activities often associated with camping include going on day hikes, backpacking, and rock climbing. While just getting out for a moderate hike, a man weighing 175 pounds can burn 472 calories. Besides the health benefits gained from exercise, there are also the aesthetic benefits to being immersed in the sights, sounds, and smells of nature. While such rewards are subjective, many people find that spending time in wilderness areas exposes them to a kind of beauty unmatched in any other setting. Natural settings are also used by hobbyists of all ages who enjoy bird watching, whale watching, and nature photography. According to a US Fish and Wildlife Service survey, bird watching is the nation's fastest-growing outdoor activity, with more than 51.3 million Americans participating each year.

Health benefits aside, a clean environment is also good for the economy. Outdoor adventure sports such as boating, water skiing, jet skiing, kayaking, and

others contribute $730 billion to the US economy through the travel, retail, food, and manufacturing industries. National wildlife refuges alone generated $1.7 billion in revenue and drew approximately 35 million visitors in 2006, according to the US Fish and Wildlife Service.

The US National Park System, started in 1872 with an act of Congress that created Yellowstone National Park, provides avenues for outdoor recreation and appreciation throughout the country while ensuring that these ecosystems remain pristine. Parks like the Bridger-Teton National Forest in western Wyoming, for example, allow for hunting, fishing, swimming, camping, biking, horseback riding, and nature watching, while maintaining nearly 1.2 million acres of forested areas in the greater Yellowstone ecosystem. Even the once-burning Cuyahoga River is now part of a national park, the Cuyahoga Valley National Park, which supports a number of outdoor activities that would have been impossible in 1969.

The Role of Climate

It is important to understand the effect that climate has on an ecosystem because it influences nearly every aspect of how an ecosystem functions. The climate maintains an ecosystem's temperature, fluid replenishment, and much more. Climate is an inclusive term that describes the collection of weather-related phenomena and should not be confused with the term "weather," which is time-specific. Average temperature, rainfall, atmospheric pressure, wind, humidity, and other meteorological factors shape an area's climate. Each of these characteristics plays a vital role in the shaping of an ecosystem.

Average temperature (often separated into average highs and lows) plays a defining role in the plants and animals that live in a region. For example, animals like reptiles and amphibians are **ectotherms** and require relatively high average temperatures in order to survive and thrive. Ectotherms use external stimuli such as the heat of the sun to maintain optimal body temperatures, a trait commonly known as being "cold-blooded." In contrast, birds and mammals are **endotherms**, which mean they maintain a constant body temperature through internal processes. Higher average temperatures mean that ectotherms need to exert less energy to maintain an ideal temperature and can therefore use more energy growing and reproducing. One result of this is their wide dispersion throughout the world. The areas with the highest biodiversity of reptiles and amphibians are those located near the equator, where average temperatures stay near 80°F year-round. Plants are responsive to temperatures as well, and many have special mechanisms for adapting to their environments. For example, forests in northern latitudes tend to be evergreen in nature to combat the cold winter temperatures and cool temperatures during the growing season.

Perhaps the most important limiting factor of climate, rainfall provides a crucial resource for all organisms. Areas with very **arid** climates are populated with specialized organisms that have adapted to these dry conditions. For example, a mossy relative of Juniper, the resurrection plant, can go dormant in time of drought, curling into a tiny ball. After rains, these plants "resurrect" into fully functioning and reproducing plants. Other desert plants, such as cacti, are **succulents** and store water in their large, fleshy leaves. These plants may grow very little from year to year. By contrast, rainforests may have annual rain averages of 100 inches or more, allowing plants such as kudzu (a vine) and bamboo to grow up to a foot a day, given the right conditions.

Other climate factors also affect ecosystems. The wind aids in the pollination of some species of plants and trees. For example, the wind disperses pollen released by pine trees. When the pollen reaches the cone of another pine tree, it fertilizes it. Humidity, which refers to the amount of water vapor in the air, can alter rates of evaporation, and, coupled with atmospheric pressure, plays a major role in the development of local storms. Storms develop when evaporated moisture in the atmosphere cools and is driven by the wind across a region until the atmosphere is overly saturated with water vapor, which then falls in the form of precipitation.

ECTOTHERM Organisms that regulate body temperature with external stimuli; also known as cold-blooded organisms.

ENDOTHERM Organisms that regulate own body temperature using internal bodily functions; also known as warm-blooded organisms.

ARID Dry, lacking water or moisture.

SUCCULENTS Group of plants often found in dry or arid climates, characterized by fleshy leaves and trunks specially adapted to store water.

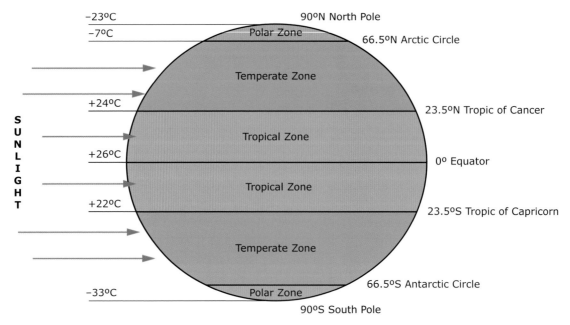

FIGURE 2.2 Earth's climates

Climates are divided into three main groups separated by latitude as in Figure 2.2. Low-latitude climates are located from 0°–25° north and south. These climates are warm year-round (average temperature of 80°F), and are controlled by equatorial and tropical air masses. Depending on their location, topography, and specific climate, they may have characteristics of a rainforest, such as the climate of Belize, or a desert, like that of Niger.

Mid-latitude climates range from 30°–65° north or south. These climates are much more temperate than the other two groups. They are dominated by both tropical air masses as they head to the poles, and polar air masses as they head toward the tropics. Coupled with their tilt in relation to the sun, these air masses give the mid-latitude climates their seasonal differences. This type of general climate includes the continental US and can be arid in nature or very wet.

The final group is the high-latitude climates, which extend beyond 65° north or south. These climates are often extremely cold and are dominated by polar air masses, have very low biodiversity compared to the other two, and only specialized plants and animals reside here year-round.

Microclimates are climates that are very **geo-specific** and can be confined to an area as small as a few square yards. Microclimates are the site-specific climates of an ecosystem. In some cases, geographical structures such as wetlands and mountains can be defining borders for these climates.

MICROCLIMATE A small area that has a different climate than neighboring areas; may be as small as a few square yards.

GEO-SPECIFIC Specific to a certain area or geographical location.

MID-CHAPTER QUESTIONS

1. What are the four component parts of an ecosystem? What is an abiotic interaction?

2. What benefits do human beings derive from ecosystems?

3. How can climate affect an ecosystem? Which type of climate supports the most species of ectotherms? In which geographic regions is this climate usually found?

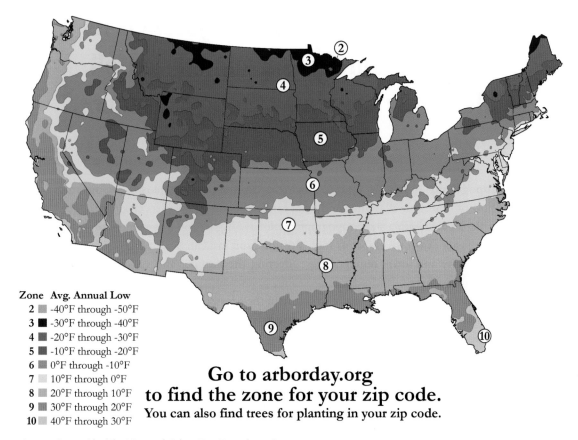

Zone	Avg. Annual Low
2	-40°F through -50°F
3	-30°F through -40°F
4	-20°F through -30°F
5	-10°F through -20°F
6	0°F through -10°F
7	10°F through 0°F
8	20°F through 10°F
9	30°F through 20°F
10	40°F through 30°F

**Go to arborday.org
to find the zone for your zip code.**
You can also find trees for planting in your zip code.

Source: © 2006 by The National Arbor Day Foundation®

FIGURE 2.3 Types of plants that grow per region and the best time to plant

HOW DO ECOSYSTEMS WORK?

A working ecosystem is a complex arrangement of interconnected parts. Ecosystems rely on an intricate food web, in which different organisms have very specific roles, as well as many different biotic and abiotic interactions. Because of its complexities, an ecosystem functions somewhat like the human body, with many different organs working together to support the activities of the body as a whole.

The lifeblood of most ecosystems is their water resources and annual rainfall, collectively known as the hydrosphere. The hydrologic cycle is the constant movement of water above, on, and below the Earth's surface. Water transports vital nutrients to the many different organisms that reside in an ecosystem. Waterways or wetlands are also vibrant ecosystems teeming with life. Many different microorganisms, both beneficial and pathogenic, reside in water. Beneficial microorganisms filter the water and provide food and energy for other small organisms, while pathogenic microorganisms, such as some amoebas and bacteria, can cause diseases in humans and other animals. Another vital function that water serves in ecosystems is waste removal. As wastes (which may include manmade chemicals as well as biotic wastes) are released, the water dilutes these wastes and carries them away from one ecosystem and into another. During heavy rain events, waterways also catch excess runoff water that may be carrying pollutants and excess nutrients from nearby farming, residential, or commercial areas, eventually flushing the contaminants into the runoff downstream.

"The lifeblood of an ecosystem is its water resources and annual rainfall, collectively known as the hydrosphere."

||||||||||||||||||||||||||||||||||||||||||||||||||||||||||||||||||||||||||||||||||||||||||||||||||||||||||||||||||||||||||

Topography and soil structure, sometimes referred to as the **geosphere**, dictates the flow of water as well as how and what kinds of plants grow in a certain area. For example, an area with a steep topography will have higher soil loss because of water moving faster down the slope. At high altitudes, soil loss can be caused by increased wind velocity and lower temperatures, affecting the number and variety of plants that can grow there.

Perhaps more important to the structure of the ecosystem is the soil composition. Soils are made up of a combination of three types of particles: sand, silt, and clay. Soil comes in thousands of combinations, and can range from the pure sand often found on beaches and in desert areas to clays found in swamps. Loamy soils contain all three particles. The mixture of the particles, coupled with **organic material**, helps determine how much water can be held by the soil and how fertile the soil will be. Soils low in clay and high in sand are highly **permeable** and do not hold water very well. As a consequence, these soils may not easily support life. Soils that are higher in clay hold water well and also have high **cation-exchange capacity** (CEC), which allows chemical reactions to occur in the soil. These chemical reactions help buffer the pH and hold valuable nutrients such as nitrogen and phosphorus, which plants need. The most fertile soil has a combination of all three soil particles and a lot of organic material to provide quality nutrients for plants.

Each group of organisms—plants, animals, fungi, and various microorganisms—has specialized roles to play in an ecosystem. **Autotrophs**, organisms that make their own food, and **heterotrophs**, which consume other organisms for food, fill different roles. Through photosynthesis, autotrophs convert CO_2, water, and light into glucose and emit O_2 as they respire. This conversion cycles the expelled CO_2 from animals into fresh O_2 for animals to breathe. Heterotrophs consume autotrophs and other heterotrophs, controlling their population and helping maintain the balance of growth in a habitat.

The specific role that an organism fills within an ecosystem is known as its **ecological niche**. Different species occupying their unique niches allows the ecosystem as a whole to function and support life. Microorganisms and some plants filter the water and soil of impurities and use them for nutrients. Plants collect nutrients from the soil and create energy via photosynthesis. Herbivores and some omnivores consume these plants, and this energy is used in the completion of the organism's tasks. These energy units are then passed on to predators, whose key role in an ecosystem is to control and maintain the population of these primary and secondary consumers. Finally, insects, fungi, and various microorganisms consume dead and decaying plants and animals and turn them back into nutrients that can be absorbed by plants and other microorganisms. This carefully balanced life cycle is the engine that drives an ecosystem. When this balance is upset—either by the removal of important parts of the system or the addition of foreign invasive species—the entire ecosystem may be disrupted.

TOPOGRAPHY The elevation and geographic layout of an area.

GEOSPHERE The area of the earth that includes the topography and geographical outcroppings and shapes.

ORGANIC MATERIAL Decomposed plant and other carbon-based material.

PERMEABLE The quality of a medium that refers to the ability of liquids or gases to pass through it.

CATION-EXCHANGE CAPACITY The quantity of positively charged ions that a soil can hold.

AUTOTROPH An organism capable of synthesizing its own food from inorganic substances, using light or chemical energy.

HETEROTROPH An organism that cannot synthesize its own food and is dependent on complex organic substances for nutrition.

ECOLOGICAL NICHE A specialized role or placement for an organism within an ecosystem.

MAJOR BIOMES

Ecosystems located above water are categorized as one of six different types of terrestrial **biomes** distributed around the globe (see Fig. 2.4). These biomes are **tropical rainforest, temperate deciduous forests, grassland, desert, taiga (also known as coniferous forest)**, and **tundra**. Each biome has several characteristics that make it habitable to different kinds of organisms. For example, reptiles that are commonly found in the warm, humid, tropical rainforest biome are not adapted to survive in the cold, frozen biome of the tundra.

The tropical rainforest biome is characterized by high humidity, high average temperatures (between 93°F and 68°F), and abundant rainfall (up to an average of 260 inches per year). Tropical rainforests are located between the Tropic of Cancer and the Tropic of Capricorn. Tropical rainforests are known for an abundant diversity of plants and animals. Perhaps the most well-known example of this biome is the Amazon Rainforest, which spans most of the continent of South America.

The temperate deciduous biome is characterized by moderate temperatures (yearly average of 50°F) and moderate rainfall (30–60 inches). These biomes surround the tropics, and have distinct yearly seasons of summer, fall, winter, and spring. Because of these seasons, the hardwood deciduous trees, from which the biome gets its name, drop their leaves and become dormant during the cold seasons. One notable example of a temperate deciduous biome is the eastern half of the US.

The grassland biome has a similar average temperature as the temperate deciduous. However, grasslands generally lack the average rainfall to support tree growth. This lack of rainfall also limits seasons to only a growing season and a dormant season. Low rainfall in the grassland biome also lends itself to a high risk of drought and wildfires, which can move quickly through dry, tall grass. The land itself is often very fertile, as in the prairie lands of the central US.

The desert biome is characterized by either very high or very low average temperatures and by very dry conditions, with low precipitation year-round. Because of the extremes of this climate, biodiversity is often very limited, and only animals adapted to such harsh environments—such as desert foxes and certain varieties of reptiles—are able to survive. The world's largest desert is the Sahara, which spans from the Atlantic coast of western Africa to the Red Sea in eastern Africa.

BIOME Large geographic area with a particular climate.

TROPICAL RAINFOREST Biome defined by high temperatures, high humidity, and heavy rainfall year around.

TEMPERATE DECIDUOUS FOREST Biome defined by moderate temperatures and weather and deciduous trees.

GRASSLAND Biome defined by moderate temperatures, open fields, and grasses.

DESERT Biome defined by high temperatures, little moisture, and little biodiversity.

TAIGA Biome defined by low temperatures, harsh winter, primarily evergreen trees, and low biodiversity.

TUNDRA Biome defined by very low temperature and very low biodiversity.

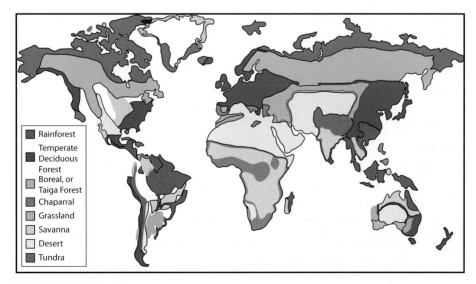

FIGURE 2.4 Major biomes

The taiga biome is characterized by very cold winters with temperatures falling to -65°F (although temperatures in the summer can reach 70°F) and often mountainous landscapes. Also known as the boreal forest, the taiga is the largest of all the biomes. While the largest in size, the taiga biome does not support much biodiversity. Only a few animals—such as moose, snow leopards, and weasels—live there year-round. The most notable boreal forest is the Siberian Taiga in Russia.

The tundra biome, like the desert biome, is known for its extreme climate. The tundra receives an annual average of 6–10 inches of precipitation (mostly snow) and features a biosphere with a layer of **permafrost** anywhere from ten inches to three feet thick. The tundra is found from 55°N to about 70°N and stays very cold even during the summer. Even with extremely low temperatures (yearly average is -18°F), several species of animals live there, including the musk ox, snowshoe hare, and polar bear.

AQUATIC SYSTEMS

Aquatic systems, ranging from freshwater to marine, are the lifeblood of terrestrial ecosystems. They provide water for plants and animals. However, aquatic systems often have their own rich ecosystems. Aquatic ecosystems have diverse microbiological populations, ranging from bacteria, phytoplankton, and zooplankton to amoebas and other protozoans. There are often healthy populations of algae and plants, including kelp, sea grass, and many others. Aquatic systems are also home to fish, shellfish, and specialized mammals such as dolphins and whales.

There are three main types of aquatic systems on earth: freshwater systems, **brackish** water systems, and saltwater, or marine, systems. Generally speaking, these systems are interconnected with one another, with the exception of a few landlocked lakes and swamps.

Freshwater aquatic systems are characterized by having only trace amounts of salt dissolved in the water, and they make up the largest variety of aquatic systems. These systems range from seasonal snow melt streams in the mountains, to wetlands, to creeks and large rivers such as the Mississippi, to small ponds and large lakes such as Lake Michigan. But there are other freshwater aquatic systems that are often overlooked, such as peat bogs in the northeast US and freshwater swamps in the South. Freshwater systems provide an abundant array of fish and shellfish that are harvested for human consumption. In addition, countless species of insects reside in and around these waters, and many support large recreation and fishing industries. Many freshwater systems, such as wetlands, not only provide food but also act as large filters for runoff and can absorb and remediate chemical pollutants.

A brackish water aquatic system is an area where freshwater and saltwater aquatic systems meet. The salt concentration generally runs between 0.5 and 17 parts per thousand. Found along the coasts of continents, these areas include estuaries, brackish marshes and swamps, and mangroves. They are often breeding and nursery grounds for fish, reptiles, and birds.

Saltwater or marine aquatic systems include seas, bays, oceans, and a few saltwater lakes, such as the Great Salt Lake in Utah. These aquatic systems are almost all tidal, and they have a high salt concentration (35 parts per thousand, on average). Marine systems cover nearly 70 percent of the Earth's surface and contain more biologically diverse habitats than the other aquatic systems—including reef life and deep sea life. Marine systems also support large recreation and commercial fishing industries.

MID-CHAPTER QUESTIONS

1. What are the three main aquatic systems on earth?

2. What types of organisms are supported in freshwater systems?

3. What is a brackish water system?

BIODIVERSITY

As discussed earlier, the vast array of organisms in an ecosystem can be compared to the organs in the human body, all performing specialized tasks and all working together to maintain the Earth. These tasks include abiotic and biotic events. Abiotic events are events that are not produced or caused by living organisms. Temperature, humidity, precipitation, and sunlight are examples of abiotic phenomena. Other abiotic phenomena include chemical reactions such as atmospheric acid deposition in soils through acid rain and other forms of precipitation, and carbon deposition from volcanic eruptions. These events, while not produced by living organisms, affect living organisms in a multitude of ways. Consistently extreme weather can kill animals that are not adapted to these conditions. Even less extreme events such as short periods of drought can kill plants. However, these abiotic conditions can also help living organisms thrive and multiply. For example, abundant sunshine helps plants grow; these plants use nitrogen by a process called nitrogen fixation, in which nitrogen is deposited into the soil through the atmosphere.

"Marine systems cover nearly 70 percent of the Earth's surface and contain more biologically diverse habitats than the other aquatic systems—including reef life and deep sea life. "

ENVIRONMENTAL MISCONCEPTIONS: EXTINCTION MEANS FAILURE

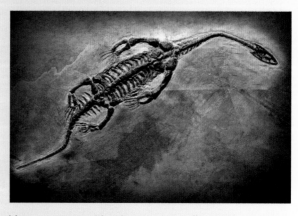

Great emphasis is put on the effects that man has on the environment and man's role in extinction. While humans share some responsibility for the extinction rate around the world, they are not wholly to blame. In fact, there is a natural extinction rate. This rate is a baseline, to gauge the rate of man-caused extinction. Some species have not adapted or been able to compete with other species well enough to survive and have therefore become extinct.

It is estimated that 80 percent of large animals in the Americas were extinct or were going extinct by the time of the first human. Even several **hominid** species, such as the Neanderthal, have come and gone. Some organisms become so highly specialized that a single event may wipe them out. Consider the **symbiotic** relationship between the yucca moth and the yucca plant (see page 39). If a bacteria or virus affected and killed off the moths, the yucca would not be able to pollinate and would in turn go extinct.

In some cases, rapid environmental changes can lead to extinction. One example may be dinosaurs. Some scientists believe a major climate change event occurred that the dinosaurs could not cope with. Other scientists suggest disease or new competition from mammals and birds changed the ecosystem in a way that the dinosaurs could not adapt to.

Finally, some human-caused extinction events may be seen as beneficial for the human race as a whole. The extinction event of **megafauna**, such as woolly mammoths, saber-toothed tigers, and giant ground sloths, are prime examples. These large animals were not only a threat for food but in some cases they were early man's predators. Some research has shown that humans caused the extinction of these large animals after their populations were weakened from an ice age event, giving rise to man's dominance on Earth.

HOMINID Human-like organisms.

SYMBIOTIC A relationship between organisms that benefits both parties.

MEGAFAUNA Large animals generally found on Earth up to the Ice Age.

HERBIVORE An organism that feeds only on plants.

CARNIVORE An organism that feeds only on other animals.

OMNIVORE An organism whose normal diet includes both plants and animals.

DETRITIVORE An organism that feeds mainly on dead and decaying material.

FOOD WEB A complex grouping of interrelated food chains in an ecological community.

When scientists make assessments as to the health of an ecosystem, they primarily consider biotic events. As explained above, there are two types of organisms that comprise biotic interactions: autotrophs (producers, such as plants, that use sunlight and CO_2 to synthesize their own food) and heterotrophs (animals, protozoans, fungi, and other consumers that feed on producers or other consumers). Heterotrophs can be further divided into three categories depending on what they consume. **Herbivores** forage on plants, **carnivores** feed on herbivores and other carnivores, and **detritivores** feed on the dead and decaying matter of herbivores, **omnivores**, and carnivores.

The interactions between autotrophs and heterotrophs make up a complex **food web** that is specific to each type of ecosystem. Food webs (such as the one shown in Figure 2.5) can be extremely complex in temperate and tropical ecosystems or very simple in areas with extreme climates, such as deserts and tundra biomes. These food webs often contain specialized organisms that fill a niche in their environment.

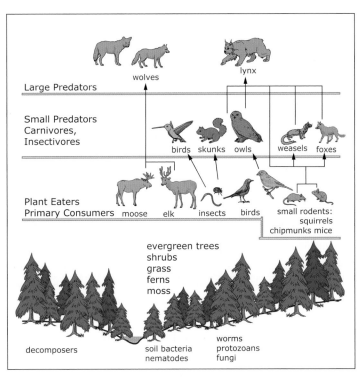

FIGURE 2.5 A food web in the coniferous forest biome

These niche organisms are important components in the food web and are vital to the health of their respective ecosystems. For example, the yucca plant, a common ornamental and wild plant, can only be pollinated by the yucca moth. If the yucca moths were to go extinct, this plant would also go extinct. This would affect not only these two organisms but all the other organisms that use the moth or plant for food or shelter. The loss of large predators can also create problems in an environment. For example, if the predator is the only organism feeding on another organism, that second organism's population may grow uninhibited, which, in turn, may stress the producers (or lower consumers) farther down the food chain. This occurs because as the population of the prey grows there is more predation on their food source. This producer or lower consumer's population is then greatly reduced.

Before the importance of biodiversity is discussed, it is important to understand exactly what is meant by this term. In the most basic definition, "biodiversity" is a variety of living organisms. However, the term usually encompasses much more than this. In fact, biodiversity actually includes three different aspects of **ecology: ecosystem diversity, species diversity**, and **genetic diversity**. All three are important to healthy environments and biomes, but each refers to a distinct concept.

Ecosystem diversity is the variety of ecosystems within a geographic area, such as a swamp, river, or forest. Just like individual species inside an environment have special jobs, different ecosystems have specialized roles. For example, wetlands help break down organic materials and act as filters for neighboring ecosystems. Forests provide large amounts of nutrients for an array of organisms, produce oxygen, and act as sinks for atmospheric CO_2.

Species diversity is the variety of organisms in a particular area. It is not limited to a representation of one species of one group (e.g., a population of song sparrows representing all birds) but includes the variety of each group of organisms (e.g., many species of birds). Biodiversity is often assessed by studying one group of organisms

ECOLOGY The study of ecosystems and habitats.

ECOSYSTEM DIVERSITY The variety of ecosystems in a region.

SPECIES DIVERSITY The variety of species in an ecosystem.

GENETIC DIVERSITY The range of genetic variations within a species or population.

PANDEMIC Widespread or global epidemic, often referring to a disease.

RAPTOR A bird of prey.

at a time and examining their role in an ecosystem and their impact on humans. Genetic diversity is the most specific evaluation of biodiversity that scientists undertake. This assessment not only attempts to calculate a population's size but also its genetic variation. Genetic variation is a key factor in the health of specific species, especially those that are threatened or endangered. Because of their small populations, threatened and endangered species usually have less of the genetic variance that prevents hereditary diseases from passing through all members of subsequent generations and enables resistance to diseases to be built up and passed on to subsequent generations. Populations with a diverse genetic make-up are better suited to survive a pandemic.

A **pandemic** event such as the H1N1 virus of 2009, which affected thousands of people worldwide, could have been devastating to a human population due to immune response and possible cytokine storms. Some populations are more susceptible to one disease than others, and are thus more prone to death. The smaller the genetic variance within a population, the greater the chance that a disease could kill a large percentage of the population. An example of this dynamic can be seen in the American chestnut and the chestnut blight fungus (discussed in greater detail later in the chapter). Large stands of American chestnuts were lost to this fungus from 1904 to 1940. However, some stands were resistant to the fungus and were naturally protected from it. If not for this genetic variance, the American chestnut may have been completely lost.

While this small, non-diverse genetic pool is an example of an artificially created genetic bottleneck, similar events can play out in nature as well. The aquatic microorganisms known as rotifers are one example. Some species of these microorganisms reproduce almost exclusively via cloning. A harmful mutation of their genetic code will be passed down to all subsequent generations. Genetic mutations or birth defects could easily pass through a small population, rapidly decreasing that population's ability to compete with other species.

MID-CHAPTER QUESTIONS

1. What is a food web?

2. What does the term biodiversity mean?

Importance of Biodiversity

Of the three different aspects of diversity, the most crucial to the health of an ecosystem is its species diversity. Biodiversity refers to the diversity of species in an ecosystem and the diversity of individuals within a population of a species. Even animals within the same order, such as the order *Aves* (birds), fill different roles in an ecosystem. For example, the diets of different birds may represent specific roles within an ecosystem. Some birds are insectivores and can eat a large percentage of their body weight each day in insects. These birds control the insect population, allowing plants to grow and easing stress on other animals from biting flies and midges. Birds that eat berries, seeds, and nuts also play a vital role, but in a different manner. Some plants, such as cherry trees, require the seed to be digested or damaged before it can germinate. By feeding on the berries, these birds aid in the life cycle of the tree. **Raptors**, such as hawks and eagles, feed on small birds, fish, reptiles, and small mammals. These birds help regulate the population of primary

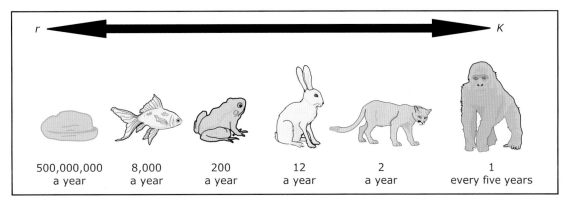

| 500,000,000 a year | 8,000 a year | 200 a year | 12 a year | 2 a year | 1 every five years |

FIGURE 2.6 The r-K scale of reproductive strategy: Balancing egg output versus parental care

consumers. Finally, carrion birds such as vultures feed on carcasses of dead animals. By filling this role, carrion birds reduce the amount of decaying material in a habitat and remove possible sources of pathogens. These roles, like departments within a single business enterprise, are staffed by members of the same company, though each department performs a job that another department cannot fulfill.

The populations of these groups often reflect a form of predator-prey interaction. Those species lower down on the food web (autotrophs and primary consumers) have a high-fecundity reproduction model, or **r-type reproduction**. These organisms produce a high number of offspring and have little or no involvement in raising them. For example, a female salmon may lay several thousand unfertilized eggs at the bottom of a river. These eggs are then fertilized by a male. Of the few thousand eggs released, less than 10 percent reach full maturity and reproduce. Since salmon die after spawning and are unable to care for the young, this r-type reproduction is beneficial to the species. Other r-type organisms (such as plants) may not be able to tend to the young, or the level of predation may be high on both adults and young. R-type reproduction plays the odds in a strategy that ensures that even if the adults die and predation is high, some percentage of the offspring will survive.

Higher-level consumers and predators often have **K-type reproduction**. This reproduction strategy involves low fecundity and a high amount of energy spent on offspring. These offspring are generally unable to take care of themselves for a period of time, months or sometimes years, after birth. Modern humans are an extreme example of K-type reproducers, with 2.10 average children produced per female in the US. Parents may spend 18 years or more raising their offspring before they are deemed mature. Other large animals have similar, yet not as prolonged, reproduction cycles; the female brown bear, for example, produces two cubs every three years on average. This style of reproduction requires more energy on the part of the parent but ensures a high survival rate among offspring.

Regardless of an organism's ecological niche, its place in the food web, or its reproduction type, it must compete to survive. There are two kinds of competition to which every species is subject: **interspecies competition** and **intraspecies competition**. Interspecies competition

r-TYPE REPRODUCTION
Style of reproduction characterized by high births, low energy in, and low survivability.

K-TYPE REPRODUCTION
Style of reproduction characterized by low births, high energy in, and high survivability.

INTERSPECIES COMPETITION
The interactions between two different species.

INTRASPECIES COMPETITION
The interactions between two members of the same species.

involves two individuals from two different species. A typical example of this type of competition includes a lion stalking a gazelle, or a fox and coyote both chasing the same rabbit. There are also unseen interspecies interactions occurring constantly. Different species of plants can compete for space or nutrients; different types of fungi can attempt to establish colonies on the same rotting log.

Parasitism is a special kind of interspecies competition. Some parasites are microscopic, like *Giaradia duodenalis,* a parasitic bacterium that resides in the intestines of small animals and is responsible for causing giardiasis, commonly known as "beaver fever," an intestinal illness often experienced by hikers. Parasites can also be seen with the naked eye, as is the case with the common holiday decoration mistletoe. Mistletoe is a parasitic plant that attaches itself to the branches of trees and shrubs and draws nutrients from the infected hosts. Parasites compete with their hosts for nutrients that the host would otherwise use for growth and reproduction.

Intraspecies competition occurs when two members of the same species compete against one another. This type of competition often occurs during the mating seasons of birds and mammals. The iconic image of two bighorn sheep ramming each other is an example of this competition. These sheep fight each other for territory and mating privileges. The winner gets his pick of land to feed on and is seen as the stronger male by females looking to mate. Members of the same species often compete with each other for resources, shelter, control of territory, or dominance in a community. These forms of competition occur in the daily lives of humans as well; whether competing for a job or a mate, humans challenge each other often. Within ecosystems, this intraspecies competition is crucial for ensuring the fittest members of the species survive and pass on their genetic traits.

Sometimes species are lost through **total extinction** or **geographical extinction**. In the case of total extinction, an organism is lost forever, as was the case of the dodo bird. It is estimated that 99.9 percent of all species that have ever existed are now extinct. Geographical extinctions occur when a species is lost in a certain area. In the case of a geographical extinction, the organism may eventually be reintroduced by human beings or migrate back into the region when conditions improve. Events like these, which leave ecological niches unfilled, can change the health and function of an ecosystem.

Consequences of Biodiversity Loss

The loss of biodiversity can have major repercussions throughout an ecosystem. These effects depend on the scope and roles of the organisms that are lost. In some cases, other organisms fill the niche that the lost organism held. However, some roles cannot be filled properly and the entire ecosystem suffers. Consider an analogy to a corporation. Certain departments are linked closely enough that one could perform dual duties to fill a void caused by the departure of the other, such as human resources and training/continuing education. In a large corporation these may be two different departments, but if the training/continuing education department were lost, the human resources department could fill the role and preform both tasks. A similar ecological example could be seen between butterflies and bees. Both do similar work, and in the event that one population is lost, the other may

PARASITISM Form of interaction where one organism survives by feeding on another organism without initially killing it.

TOTAL EXTINCTION The complete loss of a species from Earth.

GEOGRAPHICAL EXTINCTION The loss of a species from a specific area.

be able to pick up the extra pollination for most plants. However, in some cases there is no replacement available. Consider the role of shipping and receiving in a company that sells paper. This task, while crucial for operations, is unique enough that other departments would not be able to readily fill the void. This is analogous with some species inside of ecosystems, such as **apex predators**. These highly specialized animals are at the top of their food chain, often with little interspecies competition. Because of their vital role in managing the population of their prey and a lack of organisms available to fill this void, the loss of an apex predator often means a surge in the population of the organisms directly below in the food web. This surge can have ripple effects in an ecosystem. These effects can include over-predation of a lower prey, overconsumption of vegetative species, or an increase in digestive waste due to the increase in organisms entering the environment.

While not all loss of biodiversity is a result of human activity, the Ecological Society of America suggests that there are six main ways humans damage biodiversity:

1. Habitat loss and destruction
2. Alterations to the ecosystem composition
3. Overexploitation of a species
4. Pollution and contamination
5. Global climate change
6. Invasive species

Habitat loss and destruction—depending on the scale—can result in a total loss of biodiversity, or it could wipe out key species. In some cases, we may never know what is lost. For example, the Amazon rainforest has millions of acres of dense jungles, many of which are unexplored. Unexplored areas like these have a twofold reason to protect biodiversity. Because of their high annual average temperature and abundant rainfall, rainforests as a whole have a larger biodiversity index than other biomes. Second, because some of the areas are still not explored, there could be hundreds if not thousands of species in Amazon rainforests still undiscovered. It is also important to protect these areas because many modern-day drugs are synthesized from plants. The destruction of unexplored areas may cost humans potential lifesaving medicines.

Alterations to the composition of an ecosystem can result in an event called **trophic cascade**. If a species' population declines or disappears, it can have a drastic effect on the members of the food web above and below its trophic level. The loss of gray wolves due to overexploitation in Yellowstone National Park illustrates this example. After the geographical extinction of gray wolves, the elk and mule deer populations in Yellowstone grew uncontrolled. This drastic increase resulted in the slower growth of many trees and plants, including cottonwoods. Other animals such as the coyote, which competed against the wolf for smaller game, also increased. The coyote increase led to a decrease in small animal populations like the beaver. However, after the reintroduction of the gray wolf, elk, mule deer, and coyote population levels began to return to more healthy levels. This decrease in their populations also translated to an increase in beaver populations and more growth in the affected plant populations.

Overexploitation can come in the form of overhunting, overfishing, or overcollection of a species. The above-mentioned gray wolf is an example of overhunting. Overfishing in is another prime example. Overexploitation of high commodity organisms such as blue crabs, blue fin tuna, and striped bass often result in drastic decreases in their populations. Presently, federal guidelines set limits to ensure that only sexually mature members of the population are taken. Examples of over-collection include collection of coral that damage reefs or collection of exotic animals for use as pets. The effects of overexploitation can occur even if a species is not lost completely. As these populations decrease, they are no longer able to compete as well with other species. If continued, overcompetition can also occur and a species may become endangered or extinct.

Pollution and contamination can also affect ecosystems, as discussed earlier in the chapter about the Cuyahoga River and Lake Erie. As filters and catch basins for surrounding areas, waterways, such as rivers, streams, and lakes, collect runoff and are collection point for aquifers. As water flows toward these waterways, it picks up contaminants from factories, homes, or farms. These contaminants can include chemical waste, nutrients such as nitrogen from fertilizers, animal waste from farming or from overpopulation, and even runoff soils from new construction and freshly tilled farm fields.

Common pollutants, the components of pollution, can be either foreign substances/energies or naturally occurring contaminants that can affect biodiversity. These pollutants, which are often beneficial to humans for a number of reasons, can infiltrate the environment. One such pollutant is the toxic pesticide p,p´-Dichlorodiphenyltrichloroethane, or DDT. The mosquito-killing pesticide saved countless people from diseases like malaria and typhoid. Unfortunately, DDT also had a negative ecological effect. Because of its overuse, DDT-laden runoff entered neighboring waterways. While this pesticide has little effect on basic life forms, like algae, DDT was absorbed and stored in these life forms. As algae and other life forms are at the bottom of their food webs, the stored DDT was passed up the food chain via trophic cascade. Fish can be affected by DDT, altering their rate of reproduction and size. However, the most well-known effect that DDT and trophic cascade have on these environments occurs in raptors, the apex predator of these ecosystems. This effect is not directly seen in adult raptors, but in their eggs, which are made weak and brittle by DDT. As the adult incubates the egg, it may be crushed, resulting in a major decline of these birds. DDT was eventually banned in the US.

Finally, invasive species—such as zebra mussels, kudzu, and daisies—which will be discussed in greater detail later, also greatly affect biodiversity. Invasive species are introduced organisms that can outcompete native flora and fauna because of a lack of natural predation or disease. If an invasive population is able to establish itself in a new habitat and thrive, it can outcompete native species that occupy the same niche. This is primarily due to the lack of predatory species preying on the invasive species. The native species still has its own predators preying on it and now must compete against a new organism for resources. If the invasive species can continue to survive unchecked, it can kill off the native species.

OVEREXPLOITATION
Stressing of a species due to overhunting, overfishing, or overcollection.

"There are over 20,000 different plants known to be edible to humans. Of these 20,000 plants, 20 plants (including corn, rice, and wheat) produce 90 percent of the world's food supply."

There is a financial impact to biodiversity loss. A 2010 UN report estimated that severe loss of biodiversity could cost global economies trillions of dollars and has the potential to affect every aspect of daily life. Overfishing limits the food supply and increases the market price of fish. Polluted soils could decrease agricultural production, again driving up the price of food. Resources like lumber, materials made from plants, and plant-derived pharmaceuticals could be greatly limited by biodiversity loss.

Finally, there is a nutritional value lost from a decrease of biodiversity. There are over 20,000 different plants known to be edible to humans. Of these 20,000 plants, 20 plants (including corn, rice, and wheat) produce 90 percent of the world's food supply. Such a non-diverse food supply creates a nutritional void that requires humans to supplement or enrich other foods in order to receive the proper nutrients missing from their diet.

MID-CHAPTER QUESTIONS

1. What is trophic cascade?

2. What are some examples of intraspecies and interspecies competition?

Restoration

Biodiversity loss can be dangerous to humans and ecosystems, and costly in an economic sense. However, it can be reversible most of the time. For example, the Cuyahoga River and Lake Erie are now healthier and more vibrant waterways teeming with fish and other aquatic organisms. This does not happen by accident. Numerous projects and initiatives, private and public, are ongoing to restore biodiversity and ecosystems. In 1988, the Ohio EPA founded the Cuyahoga River **Remedial Action Plan** (RAP). This action plan was developed to delist the Cuyahoga River from the EPA's definition of a river-at-risk. A "river at risk" can vary from one river to another depending on the environmental impact that the river faces. The EPA breaks these risk factors into units called "beneficial use impairments." In the case of the Cuyahoga River these beneficial use impairments included degraded fish populations, loss of fish habitats, and fish tumors and deformities. Actions to clean the Cuyahoga River have included skimming and cleaning all fuel and oil deposits from the river's surface as well as trash removal,

REMEDIAL ACTION PLAN
A plan devised to restore a habitat or clean up a contaminant.

The Chesapeake Bay

the reduction of point source pollution, and the creation of **riparian areas** (transitional areas between developed or cleared areas and waterways). Other actions have included removal of toxic sediments and the installation of Cuyahoga Habitat Underwater Baskets (CHUBs) to create protected places for fish larvae to grow. Actions like these have made vast improvements in the Cuyahoga River. Fish have returned, and, in 2006, two nesting pairs of bald eagles were seen on the river. In 2009, the Cuyahoga River Community Planning Committee petitioned the EPA to delist the above-mentioned risk factors.

Interest groups, like the Chesapeake Bay Foundation (CBF) and Ducks Unlimited (DU), are active in restoring biodiversity and habitats. The Chesapeake Bay drains 64,000 square miles from New York to West Virginia to Delaware and includes over 100,000 streams and rivers. As important as this waterway is, the CBF reports that since the establishment of the American colonies, the bay has lost half of its forested shoreline, more than half of its underwater grasses, and nearly all (98 percent) of its oyster beds. A moratorium in the Chesapeake Bay was ordered in 1985 in response to the collapse of the fishery during the 1980s in Maryland, Delaware, and Virginia. The Potomac River Fisheries Commissions followed in

FIGURE 2.7 Chesapeake Bay watershed

1989 with a moratorium on striped bass fishing altogether. The moratorium, lifted in 1990, was a relative success. The striped bass stock has been rebuilt and is maintained by monitoring, quotas, and seasonal closings, yet is still plagued by ecosystem health concerns.

The CBF's vision is to completely clean and maintain the Chesapeake Bay and its tributaries, and to protect them from pollutants and low oxygen levels. Among other things, the CBF plants trees and underwater grass as well as develops oyster habitats (all of which filter the water). The CBF also has educational initiatives to help spread the importance of this incredible water system. These initiatives include taking students through field investigation to see how water quality is assessed, teacher development, and student leadership programs. The CBF also lobbies on the federal and local level to guide legislation and regulation to protect the Chesapeake Bay.

Some private companies and organizations have begun to embrace restoration and sustainable practices as a policy. Companies like Starbucks, North Face, LL Bean, Ford, and many others have started to alter their practices to decrease their impact on the environment. These practices range from establishing recycling programs to buying sustainable supplies to constructing green buildings. For example, LL Bean uses as much recycled material in packaging and paper as they can. In fact, their corporate office copy paper is made from 100 percent recycled material and their cardboard packaging contains 80 percent post-consumer waste. They also have a corporate recycling program and ensure that all wood furniture and supplies are certified sustainable, which means the lumber is harvested by a method that ensures that harvesting can continue without affecting the population of the tree. Actions like this reduce wastes that would take up landfill space and requires less intensive use of natural resources such as trees and petroleum. Furthermore, they have a line of apparel made with cotton raised without harmful pesticides and fertilizers.

Ford has several different policies that protect and restore ecosystems. Among their products are hybrid cars such as the Ford Escape and Focus; two fuel cell cars; and, in development, two methanol-fueled cars. They also have incorporated green building ideas at the River Rouge Plant in Dearborn, Michigan. This plant has porous pavement to ease runoff, uses plants to remediate soils, and boasts the world's largest green roof. The green roof is a vegetative roof of approximately 500,000 square feet that can absorb several inches of rain, which reduces runoff from the building.

MID-CHAPTER QUESTIONS

1. What is a good example of biodiversity restoration?

2. What are some best practices that companies engage in to use fewer natural resources?

International Efforts for Protection

Similar to domestic restoration programs, the international community has started to embrace the importance of biodiversity and ecosystem restoration. Along with the UN's many environmental departments, all developed nations and many developing nations have an environmental agency similiar to the US EPA to establish policy, implement policy, and monitor to ensure compliance with laws designed to protect the environment and human health. Some developing nations have environmental policies similar to those in the US. Unfortunately, while some developing nations that have laws established to protect the environment, they may lack the funds to enforce these policies. Others ignore environmental issues in favor of promoting industrial growth. In some developing countries safety and environmental standards (as well as hazard waste assessment and control), lag behind developed nations. The 1984 tragedy in Bhopal, India is an example. On December 2, 1984, a major release of methyl isocyanate, a highly toxic chemical, leaked from a Union Carbide pesticide plant and spread throughout the city. Within hours the streets were filled with the bodies of 3,000 people and countless animals and birds. Another 2,000 died over the next two years and 578,000 people were affected by the leak. In 1986 the Indian government passed their Environmental Protection Act and created the Ministry of Environment and Forests. Much like the EPA in the US, the Ministry of Environment and Forests monitors pollution, protects the environment, and sets standards and regulations to maintain environmental health. Most nations that have experienced an environmental disaster have created environmental agencies and established laws to hold accountable those who harm the environment.

Events like this have occurred on different scales in many nations, creating environmental protection legislation throughout the world. Because many countries lack specific organizations designed to protect the environment, the UN's environmental groups work tightly with local governments to protect ecosystems and natural resources. These groups include the United Nations Environmental Program (UNEP), the United Nations Educational, Scientific, and Cultural Organization (UNESCO), and the United Nations Framework Convention on Climate Change (UNFCCC). These groups have very different roles but overlap each other when dealing with environmental policy.

Biodiversity actually falls directly under the UNEP scope of work. UNEP works with governments and other partners to develop action plans for a number of environmental issues in nations ranging from developed countries like South Korea to developing countries like Kenya. A major task that UNEP handles is research on biodiversity; it uses that research to make recommendations to the general assembly and to individual countries.

The main goal of UNESCO is to catalog, create, and preserve World Heritage Sites. These include environmental sites like Yellowstone National Park in the US, The World Heritage Site as well as cultural sites like the Acropolis in Athens, Greece, and The Great Wall in China. By assisting local governments with preservation of these sites, UNESCO ensures that the history and/or biodiversity of these areas remain for generations.

Nonprofit organizations including faith-based organizations, advocate groups, leadership training groups, and others that have programs to restore the environment, help restore lost habitats, remediate contaminated sites, and ensure sanitary conditions, such as clean water and waste disposal. Examples of these groups are Samaritans, World Wildlife Fund, Save the Rainforest, Jaycees, and smaller organizations like the Falls Brook Centre in Canada. While many of these organizations' efforts are well known, the work of smaller groups like the Falls Brook Centre is less publicized.

The Falls Brook Centre is located in New Brunswick, Canada. It is a sustainable community and training center, and it specializes in educating about sustainable practices in agriculture and increasing biodiversity both in Canada and internationally. The organization recently began working with Cuban farmers to develop sustainable farming practices and grow **analog forests,** which are designed to mimic **sustainable forests,** for both increased biodiversity and economic growth.

Often local governments work with their people to develop plans to restore biodiversity. For example, the Republic of Congo worked closely with the local people to create a sustainable logging industry, which will be discussed later.

ANALOG FOREST A designed sustainable forest that mimics native forests and is used as an economic resource.

SUSTAINABLE FOREST A managed forest environment in which mature trees that are cut are replaced with seedlings.

INVASIVE SPECIES A non-native species introduced into an ecosystem that can disturb the balance when in competition with native species.

MID-CHAPTER QUESTIONS

1. **What are some international organizations currently working to restore biodiversity?**

2. **Where has biodiversity restoration been successful?**

INVASIVE SPECIES

As discussed previously, ecosystems often operate in a very precise balance. The addition of a foreign species, even an apparently trivial one, can damage the ecosystem, resulting in a loss of biodiversity. These **invasive species** often thrive in new environments and their populations can quickly grow to unmanageable levels. There is an extensive list of invasive organisms that have been introduced around the world, some intentionally and some by accident; many damaged the ecosystems to which they were introduced. Invasive species range from bacteria to protozoans and from plants to animals. These organisms, while generally from different continents, can be separated by geographical structures like mountain ranges or large rivers. These structures act as barriers to separate organisms that share similar roles.

In some cases these species were introduced intentionally. The European rabbit's release into Australia is a prime example. The first rabbits were introduced into Australia in 1788 and arrived with the First Fleet, the group of ships that left Great Britain carrying colonizers and inmates. In 1827, the first feral population of rabbits was reported on the island of Tasmania. Perhaps because of the geographical isolation of Australia, there was not a confirmed feral population of rabbit on the mainland until shortly after 1859. A farmer, Thomas Austin, released an estimated dozen rabbits on his farm, for sport hunting. However, there was no natural predator of the rabbit in Australia. Moreover, in good conditions, the European rabbit can breed five or more times a year, having four to five offspring in a single litter. It is not hard to understand that even with open hunting the rabbit population covered a majority of the country by 1910. Even the government's plan to build a 1,700 -kilometer (about 1,050 miles) fence in Western Australia (see Figure 2.8) unning the entire length of the country did not work. The project—started in 1901 and finished in

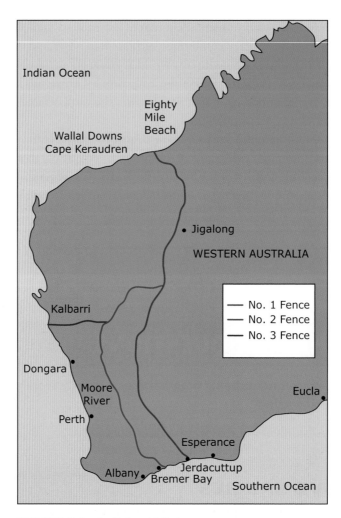

FIGURE 2.8 Australia's rabbit fence

1907—did little to stop the rabbit. The impact that the rabbit has had on Australia has been devastating. Several small mammals have gone extinct due to an inability to compete for food or habitat with the highly reproductive rabbit. Tree and plant populations have been devastated due to the voracious diet of the rabbit, and even some seabird colonies are stressed and at risk from the rabbit. In addition to open hunting of the rabbit and introduction of natural predators to Australia, the government has employed more modern methods of control. These methods include both chemical controls (the use of sodium fluoroacetate, a poisonous powder formed into bait for rabbits and wild dogs) and biological controls (the introduction of two different viruses that are specific to rabbits).

The Asian carp (a collective term for several species of carp originating from Asia) is another example of an invasive species that was initially introduced for a purpose. These fish were originally brought to the US as tank cleaners for large commercial **aquaculture** operations. At some point in the 1980s there was an accidental release or escape into the Mississippi River and Illinois River. By 1991 they were altering the ecosystem and outcompeting the native fish species. Like the rabbit, the Asian carp reproduces quickly and grows large (they can reach up to 110 pounds.) A study done from 1994 to 1997 found that the commercial fishing of these carp on the Illinois River increased from 5.5 tons to over 55 million tons. It is not uncommon for commercial fisherman to catch over 25,000 pounds per day on the Mississippi River alone. Asian carp threaten species in the rivers and possibly the entire Great Lakes

AQUACULTURE The industry of farming fish, seafood, and aquatic plants.

ecosystem not only because of their rapid growth, rapid reproduction, and lack of natural predators. They also have an incredible appetite. The Asian carp can eat up to 20 percent of its body weight a day and feeds on food sources native species also prefer. One of the more common species, the silver carp, has an added danger. A "nervous" fish, these carp can jump 10 feet out of the water when provoked by the sound of a boat motor. This leaping ability, made famous by numerous videos, can cause severe injury to boaters as well as damage to vessels. Officials employ a number of methods to control the Asian carp, however, none are very efficient. One method is a three-part electrical barrier, which keeps the fish from passing from the Illinois River into the Great Lakes. Officials also use the **piscicide** Rotenone, a natural substance made from tropical plants. Unfortunately, Rotenone affects any gilled animal and is only used in specific areas with large populations of the Asian carp.

Animals are not the only invasive organisms; plants can also be invasive. The Asian vine, Kudzu, and the Eucalyptus tree are prime examples. Brought to the US for ornamental purposes, livestock grazing, and most importantly erosion control, Kudzu soon began to get out of control. Aided by the long growing seasons found in the South, lack of native predators or diseases, and its ability to grow more than one foot per day, it soon began choking out native plants and blocking sunlight from trees. At this point eradication appears virtually impossible and officials merely try to control the growth and spread of Kudzu. They use several methods to do this, including cut-backs, controlled burning, advising livestock owners to let their herds graze on the vine, and herbicides.

Invasive species often are introduced accidentally from cargo or bilge water on boats from foreign countries. Two prominent examples include the zebra mussel and the chestnut blight fungus. The zebra mussel, a freshwater mussel naturally found in Europe and Asia, is a small (up to 2-inch) shellfish that was most likely introduced as free-swimming larvae into the Great Lakes via bilge water from freight-carrying ships. First discovered in 1990 in Lake Michigan, within a year they were found in the Mississippi. With little predation and fast reproduction, zebra mussels create colonies on nearly any submerged surface such as water intake pipes, the bottom of ships, and larger native mussels. Colonies that set up on these native mussels essentially starve the native mussels. An estimated $100 million to $400 million is spent annually preventing the spread of the zebra mussel. Unfortunately, there is no viable way to combat present colonies.

The chestnut blight fungus was another accidental introduction. First found in the Bronx Zoo in 1904, it is believed to have come from diseased trees from Japan. This belief arose because the blight was noticed after several chestnut trees were imported from Japan to the Bronx Zoo. Later it was discovered that Chinese and Japanese chestnuts had this fungus as well but were resistant to it. This only increased the suspicion that the blight came from Japan. The fungus quickly moved through the chestnut tree population, which at the time was the most dominant hardwood in the temperate deciduous forest of North America. The trees soon died off, stressing the animals that fed on the nuts and used the large chestnut trees for shelter. The blight fungus also affected some oak trees as well. Many people feared that the American chestnut would go extinct.

"Invasive species often are introduced accidentally from cargo or bilge water on boats from foreign countries."

However, a virus was discovered that occurred naturally in some chestnut groves. While not fatal to the tree, this virus kills the fungus and in some cases can be transmitted from tree to tree. In other cases, the tree can be inoculated with the virus to kill and prevent the fungus.

BUSINESSES GOING GREEN: STARBUCKS

Businesses like Starbucks working to go green do so not only to act responsibly but also to address the consumer appeal for green issues. Starbucks has instilled several measures to increase its "greenness" while decreasing its carbon footprint. Starbucks has attempted to tackle this venture by focusing on five points: water, recycling, energy efficiency, green buildings, and climate change.

Because of the nature of Starbucks' business, the company uses a large amount of water. However, it employs several methods to reduce water usage. For example, Starbucks uses high-power water pumps to clean blenders instead of open taps, which maximizes pressure and reduces the volume of water needed to clean blenders. The company also uses reprogrammed espresso machines that use less water to clean shot glasses, and in US stores, dishwashers that use less than one gallon of water.

Starbucks is making strides in its recycling program as well. Its cold drink cups are recyclable, as are their hot cup sleeves. They provide used coffee grounds to gardeners for use in compost, and offer a discount for customers using a reusable cup. In 2009, they held their first annual "Cup Summit" to discuss ways of producing hot beverage cups that can be recycled as well.

Energy efficiency is another critical area for most companies. Starbucks has initiated several steps to become more efficient. The company upgraded lighting to more energy efficient bulbs, installed HVAC equipment that runs more efficiently, and derives approximately 20 percent of its energy from renewable sources.

Starbucks is also building greener buildings. Their new buildings are LEED-certified (Leadership in Energy and Environmental Design). Some of Starbucks' steps to achieve certification include using low-flow valves, recycled tiles, cabinetry made from 90 percent post-industrial material, and paints with low volatile organic compounds (VOCs).

Finally, Starbucks is committed to working with its growers and Conservation International to conserve forested areas and reduce its carbon footprint.

The EPA lists other possible pathways for invasive species introduction, such as the release of domesticated animals that turn **feral**, like wild hogs in the South and Southeast, dumping of bait and aquaria into waterways, and disposal of dredged or **fill material** that may contain seeds. Some invasive species, such as the domestic cat, are benign in their effect on the environment. Others, like the zebra mussel, may eventually change the the country's aquatic resources forever.

FERAL Domesticated animals that have been released and turned wild.

FILL MATERIAL Earthen matter used to create mounds or fill holes in developments or industry. This material comes from many sources and can be contaminated by industrial, mining, or other waste.

MID-CHAPTER QUESTIONS

1. What is an invasive species?

2. Is there an invasive species in your geographical area?

CHAPTER SUMMARY

Ecosystems are a collection of the interactions between the atmosphere, hydrosphere, lithosphere, and biosphere. A tightly balanced organic conglomeration of autotrophs like plants and algae create food; these organisms are known as producers. Heterotrophs, which include herbivores, carnivores, and detritivores, are known as consumers. These organisms, from single-celled amoebas to apex predators such as the gray wolf, fill important roles known as niches. These organisms interact and compete in either interspecies competition or intraspecies competition daily. This competition is necessary for the health of an ecosystem and species in general. Loss of biodiversity, through a number of phenomena including overexploitation and pollution, can leave voids and disturb the balance.

Ecosystems vary from location-to-location and have specific climates, soil characteristics, and geographical structures. Climates of the Earth are generally divided into three regions: low latitude, mid-latitude, and high latitude. This positioning, coupled with associated climate characteristics including average temperatures, rainfall, and humidity, separates these ecosystems into different biomes, including tropical rainforests and temperate deciduous forests.

Humans interact with ecosystems in a number of ways. Humans use ecosystems for food, habitat, water, and recreation. Humans have not always been good stewards of their ecosystems. Events like the Cuyahoga River fire of 1969 in Ohio and the pollution of Love Canal in upstate New York are prime examples. However, from events like these, government agencies like the EPA, legislation like the Clean Water Act and the Comprehensive Environmental Response, Compensation, and Liability Act (commonly referred to as the Superfund) were established. Other organizations, like the Chesapeake Bay Foundation, assist to conserve and restore these precious resources. Private companies have also gotten in on the act and are moving to more sustainable business models. Examples include LL Bean, Ford, and Starbucks.

REFERENCES

American Recreation Coalition. (n.d.). Camping and hiking: Growth in recent years. Retrieved from http://www.funoutdoors.com/research

Arizona-Sonora Desert Museum. (n.d.). Genus yucca. Retrieved from http://www.desertmuseum.org/books/nhsd_yucca.php

Aronova-Tiuntseva, Y., & Herreid, C. F. (2003). Hemophilia: "The royal disease." Retrieved from http://sciencecases.lib.buffalo.edu/cs/files/hemo.pdf

Australian Department of Sustainability, Environment, Water, Populations and Communities. (2002). Rabbits are weeds too! [Invasive species fact sheet]. Retrieved from http://www.environment.gov.au/biodiversity/invasive/publications/too.html

Beck, E. (1979). The Love Canal tragedy. Retrieved from http://www.epa.gov/aboutepa/history/topics/lovecanal/01.html

Berens, D., Boudewyns, C., Chmielewski, S., Flehmer, K., Solin, S., Weber, K., & Wichlacz, A. (n.d.). Extinction, the death of everything: Causes of extinction. Retrieved from http://www.uwec.edu/jolhm/EH4/Extinction/CausesLink.html

Biome. (2013). In *Encyclopædia Britannica Online*. Retrieved from http://www.britannica.com/EBchecked/topic/66133/biome

Bird Houses 101. (n.d.). Bird watching interesting facts and statistics. Retrieved from http://www.birdhouses101.com/Bird-Watching-Interesting-Facts-Statistics.asp

Blue Planet Biomes. (n.d.). World biomes: Biome regions. Retrieved from http://www.blueplanetbiomes.org/world_biomes.htm

Broughton, E. (2004) The Bhopal disaster and its aftermath: A review. Retrieved from http://www.ncbi.nlm.nih.gov/pmc/articles/PMC1142333/

Chesapeake Bay Foundation. (n.d.). Our mission. Retrieved from http://www.cbf.org/page.aspx?pid=515

Cuyahoga River Community Planning Organization. (n.d.). Cuyahoga River Remedial Action Plan. Retrieved from http://www.cuyahogariverrap.org/

Day, K. (1996, December). Agriculture's links to biodiversity. *Agricultural Outlook, AO-236*, 32–37.

Ducks Unlimited. (n.d.). Leader in wetlands conservation. Retrieved from http://www.ducksunlimited.org/conservation

Ecological Society of America. (2007). Biodiversity. Retrieved from http://www.esa.org/education_diversity/pdfDocs/biodiversity.pdf

Earth Institute, Columbia University. (2010, January 22). *2000–2009: The Warmest Decade: Long Term Rise in Global Temperature Unabated*. Retrieved from http://www.earth.columbia.edu/articles/view/2620

Ecosystem. (2013). In *Merriam-Webster Online Dictionary*. Retrieved from http://www.merriam-webster.com/dictionary/ecosystem

Falls Brook Centre International Work: Cuba. (n.d.). Retrieved from http://www.fallsbrookcentre.ca/fbc/wp-content/uploads/2010/09/Cuba-Biodiversity-Restoration.pdf

Ford Motor Company. (2011). Sustainability report 2010/2011. Retrieved from http://corporate.ford.com/microsites/sustainability-report-2010-11/environment-operations-buildings

Greenberg, N. (2011, October 1). Deep ethology. Retrieved from https://notes.utk.edu/bio/greenberg.nsf/0/14f2db31736becfa852571fe004f3765?OpenDocument

Koel, T., Irons, K., & Ratcliff, E. (2000, November). *Asian carp invasion of the upper Mississippi River system* (U.S. Geological Survey Report No. PSR 2000-05). Retrieved from http://www.umesc.usgs.gov/reports_publications/psrs/psr_2000_05.html

Lateral Line, Inc. (2008). All about striped bass. Retrieved from http://www.laterallineco.com/fishing_journal/striped_bass/striped_bass_history_st ripedbass_migration_pattern.html

L.L. Bean. (n.d.). L.L. Bean and the environment. Retrieved from http://www.llbean.com/customerService/aboutLLBean/environment.html

National Oceanic and Atmospheric Administration, National Climatic Data Center. (2010, December). *State of the climate 2010*. National Oceanic and Atmospheric Administration. Retrieved from http://www.ncdc.noaa.gov/sotc/2010/13

National Oceanic and Atmospheric Administration. (n.d.).What is ocean acidification? Retrieved from http://www.pmel.noaa.gov/co2/story/What+is+Ocean+Acidification%3F

National Park Service. (n.d.) Welcome to Bridger-Teton National Park. Retrieved from http://www.fs.usda.gov/main/btnf/home

Parks Canada. (2013, February 22). Mountain pine beetle. Retrieved from http://www.pc.gc.ca/pn-np/ab/banff/natcul/natcul22.aspx

The Outdoor Industry Foundation. (2006, fall). *The active outdoor recreation economy.* Retrieved from http://www.outdoorindustry.org/images/researchfiles/RecEconomypublic.pdf?26

Pierzynski, Gary M., Sims, J. T., & Vance, G. F. (2005). *Soils and environmental quality* (3rd ed., pp. 73–83). Boca Raton, FL: Taylor & Francis.

Scott, M. (2009, June 22). Cuyahoga River fire 40 years ago ignited an ongoing cleanup campaign. *The Plain Dealer.* Retrieved from http://www.cleveland.com/science/index.ssf/2009/06/cuyahoga_river_fire_40_years_a.html

Scott, M. (2010, January 4). After the flames: The story behind the 1969 Cuyahoga River fire and its recovery. *The Plain Dealer.* Retrieved from http://blog.cleveland.com/metro/2009/01/after_the_flames_the_story_beh.html

Smith, D. W., & Bangs, E. E. (2009). Reintroduction of wolves to Yellowstone National Park: History, values and ecosystem restoration. In M. W. Hayward & M. J. Somers (Eds.), *Reintroduction of top-order predators* (pp. 92–125). Oxford, UK: Wiley-Blackwell. doi: 10.1002/9781444312034.ch5

Starbucks. (n.d.). Environmental stewardship. Retrieved from http://www.starbucks.com/responsibility/environment

United Nations Educational, Scientific, and Cultural Organization. (n.d.) World Heritage list. Retrieved from http://whc.unesco.org/en/list

United Nations Environmental Programme. (n.d.). Nagoya 2010: Hardwiring biodiversity and ecosystem services into finance. Retrieved from http://new.unep.org/ Documents.Multilingual/Default.asp?DocumentID=649&ArticleID=6801&l=en&t=long

United Nations Framework Convention on Climate Change. (n.d.). Panama Climate Change Conference—October 2011. Retrieved from http://unfccc.int/meetings/panama_oct_2011/meeting/6247.php

United Nations Habitat. (2008, November 13). Winners of Dubai Award named. Retrieved from http://www.unhabitat.org/content.asp?cid=4143&catid=5&typeid=6&subMenuId=0

USAID. (2011, May 3). Introduction to the Enterprise for the Americas Initiative (EAI) funds. Retrieved from http://transition.usaid.gov/our_work/environment/forestry/intro_eai.html

USAID. (2011, May 2). Introduction to the Tropical Forest Conservation Act (TFCA). Retrieved from http://transition.usaid.gov/our_work/environment/forestry/intro_tfca.html

U.S. Department of Agriculture. (2013, April 30). National Invasive Species Information Center (NISIC): Gateway to invasive species information; covering federal, state, local, and international sources. Retrieved from http://www.invasivespeciesinfo.gov/

U.S. Environmental Protection Agency. (n.d.). History of the Clean Water Act. Retrieved from http://www.epa.gov/lawsregs/laws/cwahistory.html

U.S. Environmental Protection Agency. (2011, August 9). Superfund's 30th anniversary: 30 years of protecting communities and the environment. Retrieved from http://www.epa.gov/superfund/30years/

U.S. Environmental Protection Agency. (2012, May 9). DDT: A brief history and status [Fact sheet]. Retrieved from http://www.epa.gov/opp00001/factsheets/chemicals/ddt-brief-history-status.htm

Waldman, A. (2002). Bhopal seethes, pained and poor 18 years later. Retrieved from http://www.nytimes.com/2002/09/21/world/bhopal-seethes-pained-and-poor-18-years-later.html

Population, Demographics, and Development

Modern buildings surround Namdaemun, Sungnyemun Gate, in Seoul, South Korea

COMPARING THE DEVELOPMENT OF SOUTH KOREA AND KENYA

Both the Republic of Korea (better known as South Korea) and the Republic of Kenya (better known as Kenya), located in eastern Africa, are members of the International Monetary Fund (IMF). The IMF has 188 member countries; it works to ensure global monetary cooperation, secure financial stability, facilitate international trade, promote high employment, create sustainable economic growth, and reduce poverty around the world. Both South Korea and Kenya underwent civil wars in the twentieth century that drew in foreign armies. Repeated artillery strikes and local plundering eventually destroyed the infrastructure of these nations. The Korean War left the country with a gross domestic product (GDP) equivalent to many smaller African nations. Both South Korea and Kenya have been classified as developing nations.

In recent years, however, South Korea has emerged as an economic powerhouse with a strong, sustainable economy. According to the IMF, individual annual income was expected to be $31,410.47 per person in 2011. By comparison, the European Union (EU) was expected to have average income levels of $31,197.21 per person for the same period. Meanwhile, the average income per person in Kenya was estimated to only be $1,800 in 2012.

According to the CIA World Fact Book:

"Kenya has been hampered by corruption and by reliance upon several primary goods whose prices have remained low. Low infrastructure investment threatens Kenya's long-term position as the largest East African economy. In the key December 2002 elections, Daniel Arap MOI's 24-year-old reign ended, and a new opposition government took on the formidable economic problems facing the nation. After some early progress in rooting out corruption and encouraging donor support, the KIBAKI government was rocked by high-level graft scandals in 2005 and 2006. In 2006, the World Bank and IMF delayed loans pending action by the government on corruption. The international financial institutions and donors have since resumed lending, despite little action on the government's part to deal with corruption. Unemployment is very high at 40 percent with 50 percent of all citizens living in poverty. The country has experienced chronic budget deficits, inflationary pressures, and sharp currency depreciation—as a result of high food and fuel import prices. The discovery of oil in March 2012 provides an opportunity for Kenya to balance its growing trade deficit if the deposits are found to be commercially viable and Kenya is able to develop a port and pipeline to export its oil."

Forbes magazine compared the countries of Kenya and South Korea:

"The difference between the two countries is mostly attributable to politics. Kenya's rulers are parasitic. They enter politics to get rich and care little about the little people. South Korean governments, though far from perfect, have consistently made economic growth their top priority. If you doubt that politics matters, consider the case of North Korea verses South Korea. Only half a century ago it was culturally identical to the South—and slightly richer. After two generations of homicidal Marxism, it is probably as poor as Kenya, although no one really knows because publishing honest statistics there can put you in a prison camp."

MEETING BASIC NEEDS

In order for a population to be interested in the care of the local environment, their basic needs of food, shelter, adequate medical care, and a sense of community have to be met first. When local residents are unable to meet these baseline needs for their families, government officials and business leaders have the opportunity to take advantage of potential employees, the community, and the local environment through the use of short term to long term practices. Organizations that implement strategies that increase profits by taking advantage of people and the environment usually weigh the options carefully when creating permanent change to the surrounding environment. Most developed nations and some developing nations have regulations and laws in place to protect all organisms that may be affected by human activities. Organizations that are found responsible for causing harm to the

1. What are some of the factors behind South Korea's economic rise?

2. What are some of the reasons that Kenya has fared so poorly?

3. What part has governmental policy played in both countries?

environment may be held responsible and be required to return the environment back to its original condition and pay large fines; leaders of these organizations may face jail time. All stakeholders should look for the balance between short-term and long-term objectives.

People started mining for various minerals and fuel resources many thousands of years ago. Their methods were much the same as those used today, including mining through manmade shafts and **strip mining**.

At Lion Cave in Swaziland, ancient miners cut a tunnel 25 feet wide, 30 feet deep, and 20 feet high. This tunnel was cut into a cliff face 500 feet tall. This is apparently the oldest known mining operation. The activity has been securely dated to go back at least 43,000 years by carbon 14 and probably goes back even further to 70-110,000 years ago. (Source: www.ancient-wisdom.co.uk/mining.htm)

The Romans used hydraulic mining methods (strip mining) on a large scale to prospect for veins of ore, especially a now obsolete form of mining known as hushing. It involved building numerous aqueducts to supply water to the mine head, where it was stored in large reservoirs and tanks. When a full tank was opened, the wave of water sluiced away the overburden to expose the bedrock underneath and any gold veins. The rock was then attacked by fire-setting to heat the rock, which would be quenched with a stream of water. The thermal shock cracked the rock, enabling it to be removed, aided by further streams of water from the overhead tanks. They used similar methods to work cassiterite deposits in Cornwall and lead ore in the Pennines. Surface mining methods are still used today throughout the world.

In most forms of surface mining, heavy equipment, such as backhoes, earthmovers, and bulldozers, first removes the overburden, which includes vegetation, topsoil, and other materials, to expose a wide variety of rare earth minerals (like gold, silver, or lithium) or fuel such as coal. Next, heavy equipment including dragline excavators, bucket wheel excavators, and sleuth boxes are used to extract the substance.

An example can be found in the Appalachian Mountain region of West Virginia, where the Environmental Protection Agency (EPA) and the US Army Corps of Engineers conducted a study on the lasting effects of surface mining, including strip mining. Open-pit mining and **mountaintop removal mining** are part of a broad category of mining in which soil and rocks overlying the mineral deposits (the overburden) are removed. It is the opposite of underground mining, in which the overlying rock is left in place and the mineral removed through shafts or tunnels.

Some of the environmental impacts identified by the study were:

- Heightened levels of minerals such as zinc, sodium, selenium, and sulfate in the water
- Streams that are filled in as a result of run-off or dumping
- Difficulties with reforesting due to compacted ground

In the United States, EPA regulations protect the population and the environment from the results of all methods of mining, including the Clean Air Act; the Clean Water Act; the Comprehensive Environmental Response; the Compensation and Liability Act; and the National Environmental Policy Act.

MOUNTAINTOP REMOVAL MINING
The practice of using heavy equipment and explosives to remove the top layer of material of a mountain in order to more easily reach the minerals or fuel.

STRIP MINING The removal of topsoil and other material to obtain natural resources.

The mining community had at first welcomed surface mining as a safer alternative to sending miners underground and thought it would result in more jobs for the local economy due to the increased volume of coal that could be excavated. The result has been the opposite because machines were able to complete most of the process. However, another consequence has been cheaper, cleaner-burning fuel for a much larger portion of the US population.

MID-CHAPTER QUESTIONS

1. **What basic needs must be met before people can begin to care about damage to the natural environment?**

2. **What impact does mountaintop mining have on the environment? Can the impact be reversed?**

HUMAN HEALTH AND THE ENVIRONMENT

The environment directly affects all living organisms, including human beings. History has many examples of how deleterious environments have had dire results. The Bubonic Plague in the fourteenth century spread rapidly, killing four million people, in part due to poor sanitary and waste disposal conditions. London experienced several outbreaks during several hundred years. Polio, a disease that affects the throat or intestines, spread through much of the world. Polio had existed for thousands of years quietly as an endemic pathogen until the 1880s, when major epidemics began to occur in Europe; soon after, widespread epidemics appeared in the United States. By 1910, much of the world experienced a dramatic increase in polio cases and epidemics became regular events, primarily in cities during the summer months. These epidemics, which left thousands of children and adults paralyzed, provided the impetus for a "Great Race" toward the development of a vaccine. Developed in the 1950s, polio vaccines have reduced the global number of polio cases per year from many hundreds of thousands to under a thousand. Enhanced vaccination efforts led by Rotary International, the World Health Organization (WHO), and UNICEF should result in global eradication of the disease. Both of these epidemics illustrate how the environment may impact human health.

An environment with positive attributes can have positive effects in the opposite direction. For example, Colorado is presently listed as a healthy region in which to live, with a lower amount of obesity than average. An abundance of hiking and biking trails, ski slopes, and other recreation areas promotes a general emphasis on outdoor activities that enable people to remain active. Colorado provides an environment that encourages people to care for a healthier environment and population.

The city of Celebration, Florida, is a planned community built by The Walt Disney Company with the intention of placing homes and businesses in close enough proximity to each other to encourage residents to walk to work or to run errands rather than drive automobiles. In 2004, Disney sold the 16-acre town center to Lexin Capital, a private real estate investment company. According to the 2010 census, 11,116 people call Celebration home. The surgeon general has

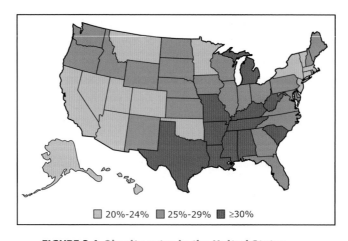

FIGURE 3.1 Obesity rates in the United States

Source: Centers for Disease Control and Prevention (CDC)

said that just 30 minutes or more of brisk walking per day is enough to reduce weight, ease depression, and strengthen bones, among other benefits. In addition to the reduction in emissions from automobiles, reducing the distance between destinations encourages residents to walk or bike. The architects of Celebration have created a place where it is easier for residents to achieve a healthy lifestyle in a healthier environment.

In recent years obesity has been identified as a rapidly growing problem in America, contributing to rising mortality rates and costing billions in increased health care expenditures. Many believe that the increase in consumption of fast food, increase in portion sizes, and lack of exercise has aided a rise in obesity since the 1980s.

Changes in the way food is produced and shipped have had a profound effect on human health. As late as the 1960s, American farmers grew what could be sold locally or at most several states away. Most consumers expected to find in their local grocery stores only seasonal fruit and vegetables from farms relatively close to their locale. Oranges in the Midwest were rare in the middle of February. Food had many natural boundaries. As a result, people used what they needed from the environment and left the rest of nature relatively untouched.

Families were also not as insulated from changing weather or animal intrusions and took it for granted that they would have to learn to live within certain ecological boundaries. Improvements in modern housing and the migration from city to suburb have resulted in a wider range of choices, but at times have also resulted in other consequences, such as longer commuting times. Whenever there is change, all of the consequences—both negative and positive—should be examined and weighed against one another.

Human beings' ability to manipulate their surroundings is only so effective. Times have changed, and with the advent of rapid transport, refrigeration, genetically modified crops, and animals bred for size or inoculated against disease, there are now more food choices available throughout the year. None of these advances is necessarily negative at face value, but consumers must consider how much, and just what, they eat.

As it became easier to ship food longer distances, manufacturers and grocery stores had to figure out how to deal with mold, fungus, and bacteria that could eat away at profits. Processing food into a product that was more stable and ready-to-eat by using preservatives and other additives became a viable solution. Technological advances in food production allowed the United States to feed more people at lower costs. Processed food—or "convenience food," as it is sometimes called because it is pre-cooked and packaged—has grown more popular over time.

According to the WHO obesity levels have more than doubled worldwide since the 1980s. In 2008, there were 1.5 billion overweight people worldwide, and 500 million of them were considered obese using the **Body Mass Index (BMI)**. In contrast, there were 925 million people in 2010 who were classified as starving throughout the world. Most low to middle-income earners and many nations are now facing a "double burden" of disease. People have high levels of infectious disease and under-nutrition. Low income earners do not have the funds to purchase quality, healthy food and experience a constant increase in communicable disease risk factors such as obesity. Most live in urban settings so they do not have the capability to grow food. It is common for low income families to suffer from under-nutrition and obesity at the same time within the same country, the same community and the same household.

Children in low- and middle-income families often experience inadequate pre-natal, infant, and child nutrition. Food scarcity is a world issue with those affected being exposed to high-fat, high-sugar, high-salt, energy-dense, low-nutrient foods that cost less. These dietary patterns, in conjunction with a lack of physical activity, result in sharp increases in childhood obesity.

Nations worldwide continue efforts to reduce hunger. On the other hand, many people are also facing the problem of obesity. Obese people have a higher level of chronic illness, including diabetes, heart disease, and cancer. While many people with limited income are becoming overweight due to high-fat and high-sugar diets, they are not necessarily better fed. Obesity often masks underlying medical conditions.

Pharmaceuticals improve the way of life for many who rely on these drugs for health and longevity but the disposal of these drugs through sewage, agricultural run-off, and poor disposal methods (flushing old drugs down the toilet, for example) often can have an impact on the local water supply. The U.S. EPA publishes guidelines for disposal that include removing all labels before sealing drugs in a plastic bag and throwing them in the trash. The guidelines for drug disposal come from the U.S. Food and Drug Administration. The EPA website (along with many other websites) reiterates the joint findings of the FDA and the White House Office of National Drug Control Policy. Furthermore, the FDA recommends not only removing the labels and placing the unused drugs in a plastic bag for disposal, but also to add an undesirable substance such as coffee grinds or cat litter.

In the developing world, poor environmental practices put populations already at risk in dire situations, such as when they lose access to clean drinking water, adequate food supplies, proper waste management, or air free of toxins. For this reason, the WHO and the United Nations Environmental Program (UNEP) joined together to create the Health and Environment Linkages Initiative (HELI). As

part of its mission, HELI states that, "Environmental hazards are responsible for an estimated 25 percent of the total burden of disease worldwide, and nearly 35 percent in regions such as sub-Saharan Africa." HELI works to address the interaction between the environment and human health in these areas in regards to clean air, access to clean water, transportation, food and energy sources, and healthy living and working conditions. One of the priorities of this organization is addressing the root causes of vector-borne disease. Currently, the disease in this category with the most impact globally is malaria, which kills 1.2 million people a year, mostly children in Africa who are less than five years old. The spread of malaria in these areas is tied to an environment with a lack of clean water, poor irrigation systems, poor waste disposal and treatment, and lack of adequate housing.

The issues are clearly different in the developing and developed world but the link to a healthy environment and its impact on the population is clear. To thrive, humans need at least clean water and air, adequate food supply, and proper shelter.

MID-CHAPTER QUESTIONS

1. What impact has portion size had on American obesity rates?

2. What are the environmental conditions that can cause the spread of diseases such as malaria?

THE CAPACITY OF EARTH

An ever-increasing human population requires more space, uses more of the earth's resources, and can pollute the air, land, and water. At what point does the number of people outstrip the planet's ability to provide for greater and greater human needs?

In 2011, the world population stood at just over 7 billion, according to the U.S. Census Bureau. This is double the number of people alive in 1967 and an additional 1 billion since 1999. Although the growth rate has slowed in this century, the pace may still be too much for the planet's finite resources. Even a slower birth rate of 2.0 children will result in another billion people added to the world's population in only 12 more years.

The question that faces all of us is not whether the planet will survive the increased population levels, but rather whether humanity will survive. Humanity must find methods to control birth rates (education, contraception), develop and produce greener technology, and recycle, reuse, and reduce waste at sufficient rates. If these changes are not made in time, many regions around the globe may be faced with increasing difficulty to survive. In other words, the Earth will still be here, but humans may find it difficult to live comfortably or even survive. The term used for reaching this critical mass is carrying capacity, defined in the first chapter as the maximum number of individuals of a species that can survive over long periods of time.

Diet, agricultural practices, and food production and processing are important in the Earth's carrying capacity. With development and industrialization, the human diet, agriculture, and food production tend to change. Advocates of a plant-based diet cite not only the purported health and ecological benefits of a vegetarian diet, but its implications for world hunger. Modern agriculture uses pesticides, fertilizers, and fossil fuels, resulting in greater food production and environmental impacts. Forests are cleared to create pastureland for animals that are consumed by humans. In the United States, over 50 percent of farmland is devoted to beef production. A vegetarian diet reduces the need for pastureland for animals and does not impact forests, which produce oxygen and can harbor medicinal plants. It is estimated that 100 million or more of the earth's people could be adequately fed if Americans reduced their meat intake by a mere 10 percent. The market has begun to respond to people's desire for a healthier menu by the creation of more natural, non-processed foods in supermarkets and restaurants.

The widespread removal of indigenous forests is a phenomenon that also affects the carrying capacity of the Earth. In addition to the role forests play in regulating global temperatures and producing oxygen from carbon dioxide (CO_2) in the atmosphere, forests help control weather patterns and supply fresh water and medicinal plants to the world.

Rainforests come in two varieties: tropical forests and temperate forests. Tropical forests are made up of moist broadleaf trees and are found close to the equator. The rainforest inside the Amazon River basin contains one fifth of the world's fresh water. There used to be 6 million square miles of tropical forests in the world, but that number has been reduced to 2.6 million square miles. Every day, more than 200,000 acres of rainforest are burned to create farmland for livestock and soy beans. After only a few short years, such land is no longer viable to farm, so farmers move on to complete the process again.

Temperate forests are made up of coniferous or broadleaf trees and are found mainly along the Pacific Coast of North America. At one time, almost every continent had a temperate rainforest, but now only about 75 million acres still exist.

The U.S. National Cancer Institute has said that 70 percent of the plants from the world's rainforests that have been identified are useful in the treatment of cancer. However, according to the Nature Conservancy, only 1 percent of the plants found in a tropical rainforest have been studied. As much as 90 percent of the world's 1.2 billion people living in extreme poverty rely on forests for their economic survival. Although the value of the rainforests is widely recognized, the immediate needs of an ever-growing human population have often superseded the longer-term benefits that rainforests provide.

The different factors affecting the environment are aggravated by the growing population and will take a concerted effort by everyone, worldwide, to find acceptable, effective, long-lasting solutions.

MID-CHAPTER QUESTIONS

1. Why are temperate and tropical forests important?

2. What are creative ways to reduce, reuse, and recycle?

3. What are some of the consequences of creating more than a population needs to live?

DEMOGRAPHIC TRANSITION

Although population growth can be difficult to control, there is plenty of evidence that certain related factors will naturally lead to lower birth and death rates. Demographic Transition is a model that describes population change over time. It is based on an interpretation that started in 1929 by American demographer Warren Thompson of the changes, or transitions, in birth and death rates in industrialized societies over the past 200 years or so. The Demographic Transition model provides an idealized, composite picture of population change. The model is a generalization that applies to nations as a group and may not accurately describe all individual cases. The model contains four transitions: stage one (pre-modern), stage two (urbanizing/industrializing), stage three (mature industrial), and stage four (postindustrial).

Stage one, preindustrial-society populations experience high death rates and birth rates that are close to the same level. Stage two, developing-country populations experience death rates that drop rapidly due to advancements with the food supply and sanitation. This increases average life spans and decreases the disease rate. Advancements to food supply usually include selective breeding, crop rotation, and improved farming techniques. Other improvements may include access to more technology, basic health care, and education. Because birth rates are higher and death rates are lower, the population experiences a large increase. Stage three populations experience a reduction in birth rates because the population has access to contraception, higher wages, urbanization, a reduced use of subsistence agriculture, an increase in the status and education of women, a reduction of child labor, and additional funding to invest in childhood education. Population growth starts to level off. Populations notice a decline in birth rates. Stage four populations experience low birth rates and low death rates. The reduction in birth rate may drop below replacement level and death rates remain low or rise due to increases in lifestyle diseases. This model is a generalization that applies to most countries as a group and may not accurately describe all individual cases.

According to the World Bank, in developing countries where economic conditions are improving, birth rates and death rates start to decline. Improved social services, such as widespread medical care and increased educational opportunities for women, lead to lower infant mortality rates. In turn, parents start to understand that they no longer need large families in order to offset the expected number of offspring who die before reaching maturity. Studies by the World Bank also show that as overall mortality rates fell due to advancements in antibiotics during the twentieth century, a natural decrease in the birth rate occurred to offset the human beings who were living longer.

As a local economy moves from mostly agricultural to include additional industrial or technological organizations, families with many members become a liability to a paycheck rather than an asset. Most nations that are developing do not have social security or advanced medical

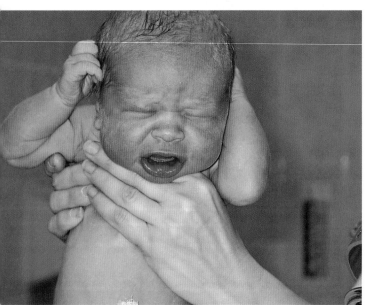

benefits. Parents in agricultural societies often have more children who can work with their family or obtain employment to help ensure family members have food and shelter. For example, when families sell their farm for development, the results is fewer family farms that are dependent on family members who can work in the fields. When people leave the farm and start to earn more money, they no longer have a need for larger families to work the fields.

As conditions improve, education begins to be seen as a necessity for the future of a developing country's economy and receives more resources. More children are educated, including girls, who then delay having a family. Higher education, access to contraceptives, and the benefits of family planning have an effect on the size of a family.

However, it can take time for the consequences of the past to be fully played out in a developing country. Although the childbearing adults in a country may be having fewer children, their numbers still increase for a period of time. In this scenario, a phenomenon known as **population momentum**, the overall number of children increases even though families and women individually have fewer children.

In more developed countries the birth rate begins to stabilize, average people live to an older age, and the death rate stabilizes due to an aging population. A few developed nations, including China and some European countries, have seen populations decrease. This is the opposite of population momentum and will result in a steadily decreasing populace over time.

However, in parts of Eastern Europe—such as Belarus, Romania, and the Ukraine—the mortality rate among men has increased, according to the World Bank. The reasons are believed to be an increase in cardiovascular disease due to diet among the older male population and an increase in murder or suicide among the young male population due to the stress from a poor economy. During uncertain economic times in developed countries, birth rates tend to decline due to worry over employment and the ability to sustain a family.

Although birth rates in developing nations have also been declining (though at a slower rate than in developed nations), worsening conditions could cause the birth rate to once again increase as families try to cope with infant mortality and the need to have more workers within a family unit. The increase in pregnancies as an attempt to build a stable family unit also leads to an increase in maternal mortality. In 2005, there were 536,000 maternal deaths worldwide. According to the WHO, 99 percent of all maternal deaths (deaths that can be directly attributed to pregnancy) occur in developing nations. Much of the work that needs to be done to stabilize population growth is in developing countries.

Although the world's population is increasing rapidly, the numbers are expected to stabilize at the end of the twenty-first century due to projected longer life spans and reduced fertility rates across the globe. However, most of the growth is expected to be in developing countries, which will pose unique challenges for the entire world. Crowding, poor medical conditions, lack of adequate food supplies, and high unemployment will push much of the population to migrate to other countries that offer better living conditions. Still others will choose to remain in their native country but will want reforms or change in order to create a more habitable situation, thereby causing political instability that can often draw in other, more developed nations.

POPULATION MOMENTUM When the population continues to grow larger, (beyond the need to replace population from mortality or emigration) even though average people are having fewer children. This may occur when children are born during an economic transition. Eventually, the number of childbearing adults decreases, resulting in a lower birth rate.

1. What government policies can contribute to lower birth rates? Do developing nations have a responsibility to adopt these policies?

2. Why are there people who have jobs in developed nations but lack the resources to purchase enough food to ensure their family will not go to bed hungry?

LARGE FAMILIES MAKE SHORT-TERM ECONOMIC SENSE

Levels of Urbanization

In 2008, the world population passed a milestone: more people lived in urban situations than rural areas. According to the UN Population Fund, by the year 2030 the number of human beings in towns and cities will have increased to 5 billion people, or 62.5 percent, with much of the growth centered on the continents of Africa and Asia. Recent decades have a seen unique migration coupled with accelerated growth in global population.

Most of the growth is occurring in the smaller cities and towns, which are less prepared to handle increasing population. However, the UN believes that it can be easier to dole out services such as education and health care in urban areas, where the population is condensed. In other words, there is an opportunity to create positive lasting change, but it will take assistance from more-developed countries and institutions that can share their wealth and knowledge.

The UN Millennium Declaration of 2000 set as a goal to cut in half the number of people living in extreme poverty by 2015 and to improve the lives of 100 million people living in slums by 2020. Currently, though, the picture is bleak, with one billion people living in urban slums or shanty towns on the edge of areas with better supplies of clean water and sanitation. The rate of infertility is lower in urban areas than in rural, but impoverished women within towns and cities have less access to family planning or contraceptives and a higher likelihood of larger families. Furthermore, the phenomenon of population momentum will again play a role because most of the migration is occurring among young adults of childbearing age. This means that the number of newborns will continue to rise in the most vulnerable places.

Infant Mortality

The UN Millennium Declaration also set the goal of reducing the worldwide infant mortality rate by 67 percent by the year 2015. In order to accomplish this goal, most of the changes will have to be made in developing countries.

Currently, 40 percent of all deaths of children fewer than 5 years of age occur during the neonatal

Bangkok, Thailand

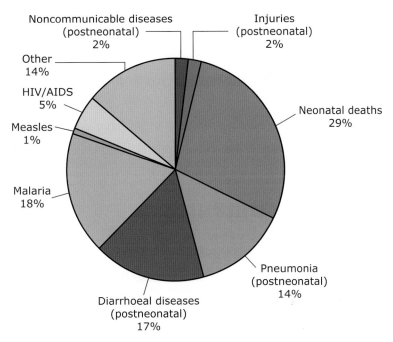

FIGURE 3.2 Major causes of death in neonates and children under five, African region, 2008

Source: WHO. The World Health Statistics 2011

stage, or first month of life, according to the WHO. That's almost 3.6 million newborn deaths, or the equivalent of the number of total births in the United States every year. Nearly all, 98 percent, happen in developing countries, with the majority in India, China, Pakistan, and Nigeria. According to the Global Health Council, almost half, or 49 percent, are in Sub-Saharan Africa. South Asia is second with 32 percent of infant deaths.

In regions where there is an effort by the WHO to change the mortality rate, positive trends, with fewer deaths among infants and young children, have been achieved. However, the trends are significantly less dramatic in Africa than in other regions. In many African countries, the WHO has documented a rate of mortality for children under five of more than 10 percent, with almost 37 percent of those occurring in the neonatal stage of life. Twenty nine percent of the deaths are attributed to low birth weights. Birth asphyxia, or suffocation during birth, and birth trauma account for 26 percent, and neonatal infections are responsible for 28 percent of neonatal deaths.

In Africa, malaria is the main cause of death in the post-neonatal stage (from the end of the first month of life to a year after birth), at 18 percent. Diarrhea is second at 17 percent, followed by pneumonia at 14 percent. Worldwide, diarrhea is the primary cause of death among children under 1 year old, causing 14 percent of deaths. Pneumonia is the second-place child killer at 13 percent, and malaria is third at 9 percent. Lower rates of malaria deaths outside of Africa can be attributed to international organizations' efforts to distribute inexpensive mosquito netting to prevent the spread of this insect-borne disease.

Another observed consequence of benevolent intervention that has been noted by the WHO is the drastic reduction in measles as a cause of mortality worldwide in all children under five years to only one percent. It is interesting to note that the US is consistently ranked seventh among developed nations in infant mortality.

CULTURE AND BIRTHRATE

Culture can play an important role in the level of birthrate and crosses borders between developing and developed countries. A study by the Drexel University College of Medicine and the University of Pittsburgh in 2009 found that US states whose residents identified themselves as more religiously conservative had higher rates of teens giving birth. Mississippi was identified as the leader in both lists. The religious factor was found to be prevalent even when income and abortion rates were taken into account.

Worldwide, cultural factors such as religion are taking a backseat to more pragmatic concerns, such as education or economics. For example, according to the Pew Forum on Religion and World Affairs, as late as the 1970s Western demographers were attributing higher birthrates in predominantly Muslim countries to religious norms in those cultures. But beginning in the 1980s, there was a decline in birthrates in these same countries, with the largest drop in South Asia, home to over 450 million Muslims. The Pew Forum discovered the declines were either due to socioeconomic reasons or an increase in education about family planning and access to contraceptives.

REPLACEMENT RATE The number of people that are needed in order to maintain a population; these can come from either births or migration.

In Western culture, birth rates have dropped even more dramatically in many nations for different reasons, including increased education, access to birth control, and more economic opportunities for both men and women. In colonial times, according to the Hoover Institute, the average American woman had eight children. Today, the **replacement rate**, which is the number of children needed to maintain the population, is 2.1. One consequence for developed countries that fall below the replacement rate will be a population that is increasingly more elderly. When the birth rate drops below the replacement rate, they may have to hire people from developing nations to maintain population, industry, and have a working society.

MID-CHAPTER QUESTIONS

1. What role does culture play in determining birth rates?

2. What consequences result when births and migration produce fewer people than the replacement rate?

DEMOGRAPHIC BREAKDOWN

In order to foster a developing country or to maintain the quality of life in a thriving developed country, it is necessary to be able to project **demographics** about future populations. Projections are based on assumptions made using collected data using the **cohort-component method**.

Demographics are the statistical data gathered from a specific population. In the US, the Census Bureau collects a multitude of data, such as age, education, ethnic background, and income, to determine future needs.

Population Profiles and What They Indicate: Pyramid Shapes

Population profiles can be broken down and displayed graphically as age structure diagrams to indicate the number of members in any given age group. These graphs are used to determine the number of economically dependent members in a population through age distribution. In the US, generally, the shapes of these population diagrams have a pyramid shape, with a wide base starting with children under five years of age and widening significantly for individuals in their childbearing years. This pyramid shape indicates population growth. In the US pyramid, the numbers start to decline for both men and women after age 34 and particularly after the age of 50. Factors such as migration, or immigration, and access to adequate health care play an important role in these patterns.

By the year 2050, the US Census Bureau projects that the diagram for the American population will no longer resemble a pyramid and the base, or people under 25, will grow to be the majority with a more gradual decline as the ages increase. This trend is expected to continue, with the most marked change being that by the year 2100 the elderly population, including those approaching 100 years of age, will decline more slowly as the population lives longer. Population profiles can help policy makers determine when an area may go over or under its capacity to sustain the projected population, which can affect the environment as well as the human population.

Traditional Pyramid: Young Population

The US population is expected to keep increasing in age over time. By the year 2050, the US Census Bureau estimates there will be 88.5 million people in the US over the age of 65, twice the estimated number for 2010. However, international migration is projected to offset some of this trend. As an example, the Asian-American segment of the population is projected to increase from a mean of 38 years in 2010 to 50.8 years by 2050, and would then be the oldest group in the US if there

DEMOGRAPHICS Data that describe the statistical characteristics of a specific population, including age, gender, race, education, and income.

COHORT-COMPONENT METHOD Demographic method that uses the components that cause population change, such as migration, fertility, and mortality, in combination with the cohorts, or people born in a given year, factored together with international migration rates to determine projected numbers of people in future years.

were no immigration. But with a high net international migration, the mean age of the Asian population in the US drops to 35.7 years in 2010 and only 43.1 years of age by 2050.

At present the two ethnic groups that are expected to experience the largest growth in population are Asian and Hispanic. The Hispanic population is projected to increase by 15 percentage points, from 16.3 percent in 2010 to 31.3 percent by the year 2050. This group is also experiencing higher levels of fertility than other racial or ethnic groups, which means that the relative median age of the group will increase more slowly, even if there were no migration. In other words, the dynamic growth in the Hispanic population has multiple factors and cannot be attributed to migration alone. The relative youth of the population and increased fertility rates in proportion to all other racial and ethnic groups are changing the face of the US population. At the same time, according to a Pew Report, more children of Hispanic origin who are living in the US, 6.2 million, are living below the poverty line, more than any other ethnic or racial group.

Rectangular: Maintained Population

The rise in migration to the US translates into a maintained population in terms of age, giving future projections more of a rectangular shape, in which all ages are fairly well represented. Most of the population growth is expected to be in the western region of the US. Eight of the fastest-growing states will be in the West, with California leading the way. The Northeast and Midwest will also grow, but at only half the projected national rate. Florida is projected to replace New York in 2015 as the most populous state, with Texas coming in at second place.

Inverted Pyramid: Declining Population

While the US population is becoming more balanced among age groups due to migration, some other countries' age projections are turning into an inverted population pyramid, according to the US Census Bureau. More of their population will be at the top of the pyramid, or elderly, than in the childbearing years or youth category.

China, Germany, Italy, and Japan are projected to be moving into the inverted pyramid category, and by 2025 those who are now in the 30- to 50-year-old category will start to move into retirement age and outnumber the portion of their population that can assist them financially or physically. In other words, without some creative ideas being put into motion now, there may not be enough caregivers when they are needed.

Another looming concern is the maintenance of a healthy economy. An inverted pyramid means the country will have to figure out how to maintain a heightened productivity with fewer workers. They will also have to export much of their goods in order to create enough of a financial flow to offset the liquidation of assets to pay for retirement benefits on the government, business, and individual levels. A large liquidation of assets can also lead to a devaluing of assets for everyone else and trigger a financial crisis.

At some point, a population will reverse the trend through natural mortality. However, if plans are not put into place early enough, poor living conditions can affect the quality of life for every age group.

1. What are some possible effects a declining population can have on a country's culture?

2. How does the growth of a population affect the local economy?

3. What is an inverted population pyramid?

POPULATION CONTROL

Cultures struggle with the complicated questions of population control. Some cultures wonder if it is really necessary or believe that any form of control goes against their religious beliefs. Others see dire circumstances ahead for the planet and for quality of life if the issue is not addressed soon.

But what are the right steps to take and where does necessity end and intrusion begin? It is a dilemma and an opportunity that keeps changing with the times and will have to be addressed over and over again with each passing generation. Factors such as current societal pressures, religions, cultural norms, economic health, and environmental concerns will have to be taken into consideration in order to create an ongoing environmental balance.

Effective Measures

Correlation of Education of Women and Drop in Fertility Rates

The UN Economic and Social Council, made up of representatives from both developing and developed countries all over the world, noted overwhelmingly the ties between the education of women and a drop in **fertility rates**.

FERTILITY RATE The ratio of live births in an area to the population of that area.

PRESERVATION: ECOTRUST'S CULTURAL PRESERVATION

Environmental preservation and cultural preservation are linked, especially in native cultures. Cultural preservation includes protection of history, language, art, religion, architecture, and customs. An organization headquartered in Portland, Oregon, Ecotrust, defines culture as:

> the highest expression of what it means to be human. It is a measure of our species' contribution to planetary biodiversity. Cultural preservation emphasizes the need to protect, restore, and honor all forms of cultural diversity. It is a cornerstone of community.

Ecotrust is currently working to preserve and restore the culture of native people in the Pacific Northwest through programs that encourage native languages to crafts, promote boat-building, and help manage fisheries. When people use traditional methods of working and living, cultural values are kept intact and passed on to future generations, and, in the case of fisheries management, economic resources are provided.

The vice-president of the council, Abulkalam Abdul Momen from Bangladesh, noted that when women are educated about opportunities and given the resources to take advantage of employment and schooling, they plan smaller families. This has the added consequence of providing more resources for the children in these families and improving the local society as a whole for generations that follow, setting a new standard of acceptable conditions.

BUSINESSES GOING GREEN: VILLAGE OF HOPE PROJECT

The Village of Hope Project in the village of Kigali, Rwanda, won the Dubai Best Practices Award in 2006 and is an example of how it is possible to create economic change and provide education in the most dire of situations.

The village is made up of 20 families with an average of six family members, or 120 people. They are all benefiting from the project, which is rebuilding homes destroyed in the 1994 national genocide. An additional center provided education and economic training to 1,200 women and children.

The focus of the project is the women who suffered through the massacre that is estimated to have killed 800,000 people, more than 75 percent of the male Tutsi population, in the East African nation of Rwanda. The genocide left many ill-equipped, traumatized women as the heads of households. That makes the education of the women who survived even more vital to the future health of the country.

However, another issue of epidemic proportions for Africa is the prevalence of HIV and AIDS, and the lack of access to adequate health care. Many of these women are HIV-positive and that had to be addressed through medication and counseling.

The project has proven to be not only sustainable, but replicable and has promoted peace among groups that needed to figure out how to live together and change their society for the better.

Ineffective Measures

Current projections suggest that India will surpass China as the most populated country by the year 2030. The rising numbers place a continuing strain on the Indian economy and the environment. The population growth has started to decline but the decline is thought to be too slow to ease overcrowding, poverty, and poor environmental conditions.

Some of the problems may be due to India's sterilization policies that began in the 1950s and were favored over family planning or access to contraceptives. Workers who consented were awarded with government loans or new televisions, while those who did not found their salaries withheld. The Indian government even declared a state of emergency in 1976 and tried to implement forced sterilization in the poorer neighborhoods, establishing the concept that the right to have a family is directly tied to wealth.

In more recent times, with aid from organizations such as the World Bank, India has made access to contraceptives and family planning education accessible even in the most remote areas and implemented a minimum age for marriage at 18.

One Child Policy

In 1975, leaders in China decided that, despite the policy of "later, longer, fewer" that was intended (along with local peer pressure) to discourage childbearing through education and access to contraception, birth rates were not dropping fast enough. Most of the surge in population had been since the end of imperial rule, which meant that half of the population was under 21 and approaching childbearing years.

By 1982 the population had reached 1 billion people, headed for 1.4 billion by the year 2000, and was already straining the economic resources. The "one child" policy was then implemented, with the goal of a population of 1.2 billion by the end of the century.

The policy has had mixed results. Chinese and Indian societies currently value male progeny over female. Sometimes there is a basis for this, such as on farms where males may be able to do more of the physical work, but more often it has been related to a sense of prestige. Daughters are often aborted, unrecorded, given away, or abandoned. This also creates an imbalance in population structure; more males than females will impact sustaining the population. The migration of rural workers to urban areas in search of work has also made it difficult to accurately count the population.

Future Population Predictions

Fertility rates and migration are subject to trends within countries that include economic health, political unrest, and environmental issues, both sudden and ongoing, such as a tsunami or a drought. The world population is expected to expand to over 9 billion by 2050, according to the UN, with the majority of the growth, 2.5 billion, in developing countries. The developed countries are expected to remain at nearly zero growth or 1.2 billion people. Most of the growth is expected in Africa and South Asia. Germany, Italy, Japan, and much of what used to make up the Soviet Union are expected to have lower populations.

MID-CHAPTER QUESTIONS

1. How much is the world's population expected to grow by 2050? Where is most of that growth expected to take place?

2. What factors cause an increase in population? What are some effective population control measures?

3. Why is China's one-child policy failing? Why have most stringent attempts by a country to control birth rates failed?

The Clayquot Sound Regional Aquatic Management Society is an organization of native and non-native people with similar interests brought together in partnership with Ecotrust. They protect areas for selective fishing of salmon where only traditional fishing methods are used. Here, fish are caught not by the gills but by the jawbone and the fish are bled and dressed while live. This provides higher quality and fresher fish for sale, benefiting the local fisheries economically. They also release any fish under a certain size to preserve future populations and focus on quality rather than volume.

ENVIRONMENTAL MISCONCEPTIONS: THE GREENHOUSE EFFECT IS A TRANSPORTATION PROBLEM

A large environmental misconception is the belief that the main culprits in the emission of greenhouse gasses in the environment are the vehicles we use for transportation, such as automobiles, trucks, and aircraft. The truth is that CO_2 is not the only compound trapping heat and raising global temperatures. Greenhouse gases (covered in detail in Chapters 7 and 10) also include:

- Water vapor
- Methane
- Nitrous oxide
- Ozone
- Substances that contain fluorine, chlorine, or bromine (often as a result of industrial activities).

According to the American Institute of Architects (AIA), buildings release man-made compounds that include 48 percent of greenhouse gases and emit 35 percent of CO_2, 49 percent of sulfur dioxide, and 25 percent of nitrogen oxide.

In recognition of the need to use energy more efficiently through the built environment, the US Green Building Council created the LEED rating system. This framework rates the design, construction, and operation of buildings based on a variety of sustainability measures. One of the measures is energy use and the effect on the atmosphere of the various greenhouse gasses produced by our homes, offices, retail buildings, schools, and hospitals. Each type of building has different standards, but this framework provides an objective way to compare the efficiency of the spaces where people work, live, and play.

One benefit from the downturn in the economy that began in 2008 was a momentary drop in total US greenhouse gas emissions by 6.1 percent, partly as the result of a decrease in overall energy consumption, including that expended constructing and operating buildings. Some scientists believe that greenhouse gas emission causes climate change; other scientists believe that the changes in climate are cyclic.

The Clayquot Sound Regional Aquatic Management Society is an organization of native and non-native people with similar interests brought together in partnership with Ecotrust. They protect areas for selective fishing of salmon where only traditional fishing methods are used. Here, fish are caught not by the gills but by the jawbone and the fish are bled and dressed while live. This provides higher quality and fresher fish for sale, benefiting the local fisheries economically. They also release any fish under a certain size to preserve future populations and focus on quality rather than volume.

CHAPTER SUMMARY

Demographic trends throughout the world play an important role in the ability of the planet to sustain human populations. Increasingly, public policy has become an important tool in educating local populations and creating change that leads to a better use of the surrounding environment. Public policy around population control has to take into consideration the general age (childbearing versus elderly), migration, and economic constraints in order to effectively provide for a nation's needs, as well as those of other countries.

It has been shown that developing countries will improve their environmental practices, such as population control or sanitation efforts, when targeted aid is provided that allows for economic opportunity and education. Efforts to achieve success and education about family planning are key aspects of creating better conditions for economic opportunity.

In order for human beings, plants, and animals to all thrive on a planet with limited space and resources, human beings, who have the greatest ability to manipulate their circumstances, will have to begin choosing balance over convenience and weighing the projected consequences for the worldwide population in order to keep the planet hospitable to human life.

REFERENCES

The American Institute of Architects. (n.d.). Why are architects and green buildings so important? Retrieved from http://info.aia.org/toolkit2030/advocacy/architects-green-building.html

The Appalachian Regional Commission. (n.d.). The Appalachian region. Retrieved from http://www.arc.gov/appalachian_region/TheAppalachianRegion.asp

Bryner, J. (2009, September 16). Teen birth rates higher in highly religious states. *Live Science.* Retrieved from http://www.livescience.com/5728-teen-birth-rates-higher-highly-religious-states.html

Cadman, M. (2007, March). *Consuming wild life: the illegal exploitation of wild animals in South Africa, Zimbabwe and Zambia: A preliminary report.* Animal Rights Africa and Xwe African Wild Life.

Centers for Disease Control and Prevention. (2012, August 13). Adult obesity facts [Fact sheet]. Retrieved from http://www.cdc.gov/obesity/data/trends.html

Central Intelligence Agency. (n.d.). The world factbook. Retrieved from https://www.cia.gov/library/publications/the-world-factbook/geos/ke.html

Cohen, J. E. (1995). *How many people can the earth support* (pp. 11–12). New York, NY: Norton Books. Retrieved from http://books.wwnorton.com/books/detail-inside.aspx?ID=13204&CTYPE=G

Dart and Beaumont, 1971, p. 10; Bednarik, 1992, p. 15; Dart and Beaumont, 1967; Vermeersch and Paulissen, 1989, p. 36.

Economy Watch. (2013, May 6). European Union GDP per capita (PPP), US dollars statistics. Retrieved from http://www.economywatch.com/economic-statistics/European-Union/GDP_Per_Capita_PPP_US_Dollars/

Economy Watch. (n.d.). Korea (South Korea) GDP per capita (PPP), US dollars statistics. Retrieved from http://www.economywatch.com/economic-statistics/Korea/GDP_Per_Capita_PPP_US_Dollars/U.S. Food and Drug Administration. (2013, April 24). How to dispose of unused drugs. Retrieved from http://www.fda.gov/ForConsumers/ConsumerUpdates/ucm101653.htm?utm_campaign=Google2&utm_source=fdaSearch&utm_medium=website&utm_term=pharmaceutical%20waste%20disposal&utm_content=7

Fengler, W. (2010, April 15). Can rapid population growth be good for economic development? [Web log post]. Retrieved from http://blogs.worldbank.org/africacan/can-rapid-population-growth-be-good-for-economic-development

Food and Agriculture Organization of the United Nations. (2002, January). The developing world's new burden: Obesity. Retrieved from http://www.fao.org/FOCUS/E/obesity/obes1.htm

Global Health Council. (2011). Causes of child death. Retrieved from http://www.globalhealth.org/child_health/child_mortality/causes_death/

Green Building Certification Institute. (n.d.). Credential maintenance program. Retrieved from http://www.gbci.org/main-nav/cmp/credential-maintenance-program.aspx

Greenpeace International. (2009, February 24). Where does e-waste end up? Retrieved from http://www.greenpeace.org/international/en/campaigns/toxics/electronics/the-e-waste-problem/where-does-e-waste-end-up/

Guest, R. (2005, July 6). Why has South Korea overtaken Kenya? Because its rulers can limit their greed. *The Telegraph*. Retrieved from http://www.telegraph.co.uk/news/uknews/1493489/Why-has-South-Korea-overtaken-Kenya-Because-its-rulers-can-limit-their-greed.html

Hansen, Z. (Ed.). (n.d.). Population control, India. Retrieved from http://www.colby.edu/personal/t/thtieten/Famplan.htm

International Institute for Applied Systems Analysis. (1996). IIASA population projection results. Retrieved from http://www.iiasa.ac.at/Research/POP/docs/Population_Projections_Results.html

International Monetary Fund. (2013). About the IMF. Retrieved from http://www.imf.org/external/about.htm

Jones, A. (2010, February 14). Case study: Genocide in Rwanda, 1994. *Gendercide Watch*. Retrieved from http://www.gendercide.org/case_rwanda.html

Kane, P., & Choi, C. Y. (1999). China's One Child Family Policy. *British Medical Journal, 319*(7215), 992–994. Retrieved from http://www.ncbi.nlm.nih.gov/pmc/articles/PMC1116810/

Kurtz, S. (2005). Demographics and the culture war. *Policy Review, 129*. Retrieved from http://www.hoover.org/publications/policy-review/article/7123

Labs, E. J. (1997, September). *The role of foreign aid in development: South Korea and the Philippines* (Congressional Budget Office Memorandum). Retrieved from http://www.cbo.gov/doc.cfm?index=4306&type=0

Montgomery, K. (n.d.). The demographic transition. Retrieved from http://www.marathon.uwc.edu/geography/demotrans/demtran.htm

Nash, J. (2010, December 7). Full ranking: America's healthiest and unhealthiest states. *Forbes.com*. Retrieved from http://www.forbes.com/2010/12/06/healthiest-unhealthiest-states-lifestyle-health-uhc-table.html

National Heart Lung and Blood Institute. (2012, July 13). What are overweight and obesity? Retrieved from http://www.nhlbi.nih.gov/health/health-topics/topics/obe/

Passel, J., Cohn, D, & Lopez, M. H. (2011, March 24). *Hispanics account for more than half of the nation's growth in past decade*. Pew Hispanic Center, Pew Research Center. Retrieved from http://www.pewhispanic.org/2011/03/24/hispanics-account-for-more-than-half-of-nations-growth-in-past-decade/

Ploiomyelitis. (n.d.). Retrieved from http://www.princeton.edu/~achaney/tmve/wiki100k/docs/Poliomyelitis.html

Schorr, A. (1965). Income maintenance and the birth rate. *Social Security Bulletin, 28*, 22–30. Retrieved from www.ssa.gov/policy/docs/ssb/v28n12/v28n12p22.pdf

U.S. Census Bureau. (n.d.). U.S. population projections. Retrieved from http://www.census.gov/population/www/projections/2009projections.html

U.S. Environmental Protection Agency. (2011). 2011 U.S. greenhouse gas inventory. Retrieved from http://www.epa.gov/climatechange/emissions/usinventoryreport.html

U.S. Environmental Protection Agency. (2012, November 14). Wastes—Resource conservation—Common wastes and materials: eCycling. Retrieved from http://www.epa.gov/osw/conserve/materials/ecycling/faq.htm#howmuch

U.S. Environmental Protection Agency. (2013, May 2). Mid-Atlantic mountaintop mining. Retrieved from http://www.epa.gov/region3/mtntop/

United Nations Economic and Social Council. (2011, April 14). Speakers link higher education among girls to declining fertility rates as Commission on Population and Development continues session [Press release]. Retrieved from http://www.un.org/News/Press/docs/2011/pop994.doc.htm

United Nations Population Fund. (2007). Peering into the dawn of an urban millennium. Introduction to *UNFPA state of the world population 2007*. Retrieved from http://www.unfpa.org/swp/2007/english/print/introduction.html

Vincent, G. K., & Velkoff, V. A. (2010, May). *The next four decades: The older population in the United States: 2010 to 2050: population estimates and projections* (Current Population Report No. 25-1138). Retrieved from http://www.census.gov/prod/2010pubs/p25-1138.pdf

The World Bank. (2011). Mortality rate, infant (per 1,000 live births). Retrieved from http://data.worldbank.org/indicator/SP.DYN.IMRT.IN

World Health Organization. (2011, June). Electronic fields and public health: Mobile phones [Fact sheet]. Retrieved from http://www.who.int/mediacentre/factsheets/fs193/en/

World Health Organization. (2013). Health and environment linkages initiative. Retrieved from http://www.who.int/heli/en/

World Health Organization. (2013, March). Obesity and overweight [Fact sheet]. Retrieved from http://www.who.int/mediacentre/factsheets/fs311/en/

World Health Organization. (2013). Pneumonia is the leading cause of death in children. Retrieved from http://www.who.int/maternal_child_adolescent/news_events/news/2011/pneumonia/en/

World Health Organization. (2013). Vector-borne disease. Retrieved from http://www.who.int/heli/risks/vectors/vector/en/index.html

Yellowstone National Park. (n.d.). Wildlife—wolves. Retrieved from http://www.yellowstonenationalpark.com/wolves.htm

Zuehlke, E. (2009, April). *Changes in fertility among Muslims in India, Pakistan and Bangladesh.* Population reference Bureau. Retrieved from http://www.prb.org/Articles/2009/karimpolicyseminar.aspx

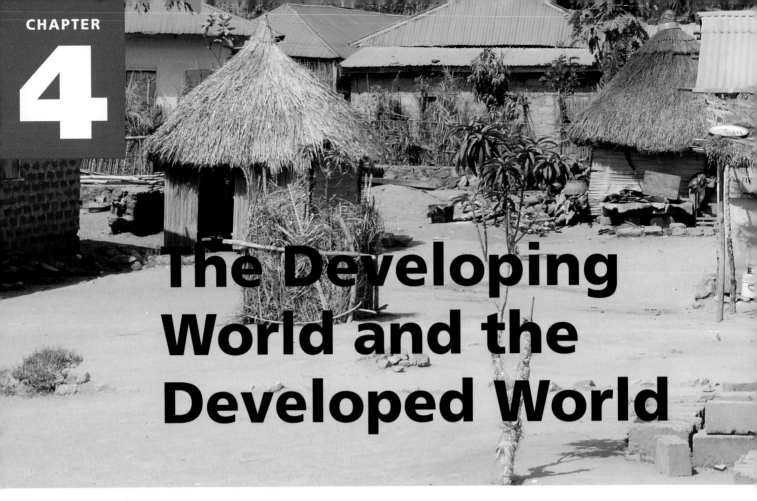

The Developing World and the Developed World

Street in Togo, Africa

THE WORLD BANK GROUP

There was a time when the economic policy of one country had a limited effect on neighboring countries' monetary decisions, particularly across most of Europe. Then, World War II cost millions of people their lives and destroyed most of the infrastructure of Europe.

The victors of World War II, particularly the United States (US) and Great Britain—saw the importance of nations working together to prevent the destruction and resulting stresses on the local populations from such conflicts. Those efforts led to the creation of the World Bank Group in 1944 to assist all of Europe in rebuilding. Since then, the World Bank's main mission has become long-term assistance to developing nations to overcome poverty and to assist older economies during an economic crisis. The World Bank is now a collection of agencies, each with a specific mission related to reconstruction, poverty reduction, and economic stability. The organization is committed to its mission through Eight Millennium Development Goals:

1. Eradicate extreme poverty and hunger.
2. Achieve universal primary education.
3. Promote gender equality and empower women.
4. Reduce child mortality.
5. Improve maternal health.
6. Combat HIV/AIDS, malaria, and other diseases.
7. Ensure environmental sustainability.
8. Develop a global partnership for development.

World leaders understand that in order to promote good stewardship of every resource—including the environment—financial concerns of the local populations must first be addressed.

Current concerns and barriers to achieving these goals in the world's poorest countries are rising food prices, disease, lack of infrastructure, and a cycle of conflict and poverty in many nations. These hinder economic sustainability in the same way that the initial crisis of WWII's aftermath resulted in the World Bank's creation.

WHAT ARE DEVELOPING AND DEVELOPED NATIONS?

The International Monetary Fund (IMF) classifies countries by economic strength into advanced, developed, and developing nations. There were 33 countries ranked in the advanced economy category in 2011, including the US, United Kingdom (UK), and Germany. Many more are described as developed countries, such as the nations that used to comprise the former Soviet Union, as well as Australia and Canada. The last IMF category, developing countries, is a broad spectrum of nations in transition that can include those struggling out of poverty to those with a more industrialized and improved standard of living. There are 126 nations, including Cambodia, Liberia, and Mexico, in the developing group, along with 46 other nations in a subgroup of least-developed economies in need of more assistance, such as Cuba and Greenland.

While many factors are used to identify countries as developed or developing, one simple and obvious measure is the varying levels of personal income. According to the Organization of Economic Cooperation and Development (OECD) Database on Income Distribution and Poverty, for example, the developing nation of Mexico's median income is $5,000 while the developed nations of the US and the UK have median incomes of $31,000 and $25,000, respectively.

The characteristics that define a nation's economic classification are not hard and fast, according to the IMF. These designations are employed when making policy decisions about who gives and who receives, which can lead to strenuous political debates. Membership in the OECD is used by some international organizations as a benchmark for being recognized as a developed country. In 2009, there were only 34 OECD members, which left 80 to 85 percent of the world in the developing category, skewing the bigger picture.

DEVELOPMENT TAXONOMY A ranking system of countries' development that takes into consideration multiple factors, such as personal income, life expectancy, and literacy; replaced the older classification systems of First, Second, Third, and Fourth World and developed or developing economy.

DEVELOPMENT THRESHOLD The minimum level of a criterion used in development taxonomy.

In 2011, the IMF suggested using a more universal classification system that would group countries based on a wide-ranging list of quality-of-life factors, such as personal income, life expectancy, and literacy. Such a classification is known as **development taxonomy**, and the minimum level of each criterion that a nation must reach to be considered developed is known as the **development threshold**.

This could potentially make the decisions surrounding foreign aid easier and faster to assess, and pinpoint what countries

1. What crisis led to the creation of the World Bank? What types of crises does the World Bank attempt to address today?

2. In the aftermath of WWII, what did world leaders recognize has to be addressed before there can be a discussion about a nation's environmental resources?

3. What forces do the leaders of the World Bank have working against them in their goal to eradicate poverty?

could benefit the most from directed economic relief. However, who is in the money and who is out is a constantly shifting picture that changes everything, including what countries carry the weight of global decisions about environmental concerns. In recent times, there have been major shifts in market growth among some developing nations, leading to speculation about which nations will be economic powerhouses in the decades to come.

The World Bank forecasts that by the year 2025, many nations that were seen as impoverished will join other Western nations in the developed category. These developing nations are expected to have a growth rate of 4.7 percent between 2011 and 2025, while advanced economies, and in particular older, established economies, are expected to grow at a slower pace of 2.3 percent.

China, Russia, Brazil, South Korea, India, and Indonesia are countries on track as of 2011 to make up half of all global growth. These nations' ability to begin lending money, rather than having to borrow, could change which nations receive aid, and will benefit lower-income countries that make cross-border financial and commercial agreements. Currently, there are several organizations and treaties in place that ensure cross-border transactions take place. We do not have any organization or treaties that govern cross-border trade worldwide. The General Agreement on Tariffs and Trade (GATT), a multilateral agreement among member countries, has reduced many barriers to trade. The World Trade Organization (WTO) has the power to enforce the rules of international trade between nations with agreements. The North American Free Trade Agreement (NAFTA) called for phasing out impediments to trade between Canada, Mexico, and the US over a 15-year period.

Countries that stay on top economically will be those with strong productivity gains and domestic spending, as well as an adaptable workforce and technological innovations. The six emerging economies have had rapidly expanding or even newly developed middle classes that have driven domestic spending and created a demand for new goods, lifting their economies in a positive cycle. The challenge for these nations will be finding ways to support and continue that growth without contaminating, destroying, or depleting their natural resources. The developed nations that have well-established middle classes will need to look for ways to shift their workforce from an industrial to a more service-oriented economy and continue with technological innovations.

When a nation lacks the financial resources to invest in its infrastructure and systems that can provide its people with education, quality medical care, or even plentiful food and drinking water, the average life expectancy declines in most cases.

Ouagadougou, Burkina Faso and Tokyo, Japan

The average citizen of Burkina Faso, with a national literacy rate of only 29 percent, will live to be 53 years old, while the average citizen of Japan will live to be 83 years old and will most likely be able to read.

A higher level of personal income is often tied to a better standard of health due to increased access to more consistent medical information and care, as well as better nutrition and living conditions. However, sometimes the reverse is true. A study in China in 1994 showed a significant rise in diabetes at the same time that there was a significant rise in personal income. Over 200,000 people ranging in age from 25 to 64 living in 19 different provinces (including cities and rural areas) were tested for diabetes, and two thirds (70.3 percent) were diagnosed for the first time. The findings were three times higher than in 1984. The study noted that the newly created middle class also had less education and less physical exercise than other residents of similar income, suggesting that education about how to incorporate healthy choices into a more affluent lifestyle is necessary as well. This is one of the reasons there is more to the definition of developed or developing than just individual income levels.

This also explains why a country like the United Arab Emirates (UAE) is still considered to be developing despite high average personal income. Individual income in the UAE is counterbalanced by a low literacy rate, restrictions on who can get an education, and the fact that social benefits are withheld from many people in the working class, the majority of whom are foreign nationals. A country's wealth alone is not enough to allow it to be considered a developed nation. Organizations such as the IMF use a wider range of criteria that reflect citizens' quality of life when classifying nations in economic terms.

Nonetheless, personal income is a major determinant of whether a nation is classified as developed. Cuba, for example, is a communist state and is one of the largest welfare states in the world. The existence of such welfare programs to improve living standards is often used as a reason to raise a country's development rankings. But because of its extremely low rate of personal income, Cuba is still considered a developing nation.

The History of Country Classification

The classification of countries based on their economic structure became widespread after the end of World War II. In this era, the world was often divided into communist, capitalist, and Third World countries, with sub-groups that divided nations from one end of the scale, economically expanding with some kind of working middle class, down to the other end of the scale, countries struggling to provide the basic needs for the local population. The terms First World (referring to Western industrialized democracies), Second World (referring to communist Soviet bloc countries), and Third World (referring to smaller, less economically viable countries that were not aligned with either of the first two groups) were often used to group nations into categories. The Fourth World, a term developed to better provide more useful information, refers to the most destitute populations residing in Third World countries. The Fourth World also includes nomadic tribes not bound to national borders, remote pastoral settlements, hunter-gatherer tribes, and highly impoverished areas, such as slums, in First World nations. These populations are essentially cut off from the industrialized and modern world.

When the Berlin Wall fell in 1989, marking the end of the Soviet Union, the method of dividing the world into capitalist or communist became much less relevant. The terms developing and developed were created to replace the terms capitalist and communist. The new definitions had less to do with politics or culture, and instead looked at how a

**GROSS NATIONAL PROD-
UCT (GNP)** The total value
of the goods and services produced by a country, measured
annually.

nation's citizens—as well as the business community—fare across a variety of categories, regardless of systems of government or economic ideology. The developing/developed system of classification takes into account a wide variety of criteria that measure economic activity and human welfare. As stated earlier, these measures include personal income, as well as access to health care and education, life expectancy, and **Gross National Product (GNP)**, which is the total value of all the goods and services a nation produces in a year.

MID-CHAPTER QUESTIONS

1. What are some of the consequences for a country's population when there are low personal income levels?

2. Why is the UAE listed as a developing nation even though it has a high rate of personal income?

HUMAN HEALTH AND THE ENVIRONMENT

Human beings have always been directly affected—for better or worse—by their immediate environment, which today includes the artificial and manufactured environment (where people live and work) and the surrounding natural landscape. The most basic needs start with protection from the elements—whether cold temperatures or a hot noon sun—and include concerns about ample sources of drinking water and food and safety from predators and pests, such as wolves or mosquitoes.

However, in modern times the interactions have become more complex, requiring government oversight to balance the variety of social and business interests. For example, new housing developments in the western portions of the US stress local water supplies, requiring limits on watering lawns and the rerouting of parts of the Colorado River. A 1944 treaty with Mexico that governs some portions of how the river is managed makes things even more complex as the river is pushed to its limits. An unforeseen drop in water levels along with a larger-than-expected population resulted in salinity issues. The irrigation return flow stirred up more of the river bottom and turned the water more brackish. This caused an international problem in the 1960s; as a result, the US agreed to deliver water to Mexico of the same quality as what was being diverted from the river for the benefit of US citizens. This resulted in the construction of a $250 million desalination plant in Yuma, Arizona that treats storm water runoff on its way to Mexico. So far, however, the plant has only been briefly used, in 1993, and has been on standby ever since, according to the US Geological Survey.

Both countries are looking for ways to preserve the Mexican Delta, comply with the treaty, and not put any group at risk of being short of water. Measures are under way to use the Yuma plant at partial capacity, but a solution that satisfies everyone has been difficult to find.

The Hoover Dam on the Colorado River

There are other concerns for the Colorado River, which has watersheds throughout seven US states and two states in Mexico. These include a rise in the level of salinity, which affects the quality of drinking water and the viability in agriculture, and threatens wildlife that rely on the river. Damage to US agriculture due to the increased salinity has cost $330 million per year, which, in turn increases the prices consumers pay for produce in grocery stores. As noted in the beginning of the chapter, economic fears such as rising food prices can make it easier to sway a population toward false promises and more difficult to draw attention to environmental concerns.

In 2005, Arizona Governor Janet Napolitano appointed a commission, the Clean Colorado River Alliance, to find solutions to the growing water-quality issues regarding the river, including increased bacteria and unwanted nutrients, metals, and other pollutants.

The EPA approved salinity standards for three locations of the river in Arizona, including below Parker Dam and at Imperial Dam, and the US and Mexican governments continue to work together on what will be an ongoing problem that can be helped or exacerbated by human migration, annual rainfall levels, and other factors.

Clean water for irrigation is an important health issue, as shown with recent *Escherichia coli (E. coli)* outbreaks. An *E. coli* infection results in diarrhea, and sometimes death, and is caused by eating food infected with the bacteria. An outbreak in 2011 was connected to clover sprouts consumed from Jimmy John's sandwich shops in 11 states, and a nine-state outbreak in 2012 was tied to Romaine lettuce. When a case of *E. coli* is found, public health inspectors work with the Centers for Disease Control (CDC) and with other state inspectors to find the cause of the illness, often linking it to a particular farm, distributor, or restaurant.

Another example of how the interaction between the human population and the environment can result in unexpected problems that need international intervention is the disease *onchocerciasis*, or "river blindness," as it is commonly known in West Africa. River blindness is a parasitic disease caused by a narrow worm that can live for up to 14 years in the human body, according to the World Health Organization (WHO), which has been working steadily to overcome the disease.

River blindness is transmitted from one human being to another through the bite of a blackfly. A blackfly will bite an infected person, ingest the worm larvae, move onto another human host and spread the disease. The worm larvae remain close to the surface of the skin as they mature into adult worms, often settling into joints. The symptoms manifest in a person one to three years after infection and include depigmentation of the skin, intense itching, and grotesque distortion of the genitals, as well as blindness. River blindness is the world's second-leading infectious cause of blindness and affects 18 million people worldwide, according to the WHO. This has serious social and economic consequences for the affected areas, because many potential wage earners and contributors to local society are sidelined by blindness and resources to handle such impairment don't exist.

However, since 1974 the WHO, along with the United Nations (UN) and a coalition of 20 countries and agencies, has been battling river blindness by spraying fast-moving rivers where the blackfly breeds and treating affected adults. By 2002, when the intervention program came to an end, river blindness numbers were vastly

reduced, and by 2007 disease transmission had stopped in Columbia and Ecuador. However, it still persists in some locations, and organizations like the Carter Center, in partnership with ministries of health, Lions Club International, and other agencies, are still at work in Brazil, Venezuela, and Africa, where it is still widespread, accounting for 99 percent of the current cases. The pharmaceutical company, Merck, has donated the drug Mectizan to agencies to treat the disease. This is another example of how a concerted effort among cooperating governments and organizations can work to solve a social issue and create a more favorable economic climate as well.

Sometimes, a natural disaster causes a direct, negative impact on the local human population. In January 1994, a sizeable earthquake in Northridge, California, led

MID-CHAPTER QUESTIONS

1. What was the US responsibility in the water treaty with Mexico?

2. What type of cooperation was required between agencies and governments faced with river blindness in their populations?

ENVIRONMENTAL MISCONCEPTIONS: RECYCLING OLD ELECTRONICS

While computers, cell phones, and video games have revolutionized the way people communicate, the question of what to do with these tools once they outlive their usefulness has become a global problem. Electronic devices are constantly improved with enhanced features, encouraging consumers to upgrade their gadgets at a faster and faster rate. The wider adoption of wireless technology has numerous economic and social advantages, but those devices contain metals, toxins, and chemicals that are dangerous to soil and water supplies if discarded inappropriately.

The Environmental Protection Agency (EPA) estimates that three quarters of the computers sold in the US are stored in garages, attics, and closets all over the country. "E-waste," as it is known, is becoming the fastest-growing type of waste. Heavy metals such as lead, cadmium, and mercury used in the production of electronics make it impossible to incinerate old computers or phones without polluting the air.

Developed countries, like those in the European Union (EU), have systems to safely recycle what can be used again and properly dispose of what is no longer usable or safe to throw away. Developing nations have fewer or no such laws in place, and recycling is often done by hand in junkyards, with no protection for workers or nearby residents.

The County of San Mateo in California's Bay Area has stepped in to get ahead of this growing problem by partnering with the corporation HMR, Inc., and monitoring the recycling plant. Since the plant opened in 2002, it has processed 6.5 million pounds of electronics. With an estimated 6,000 computers becoming obsolete in California every day, the material stream for recycling companies will only grow. By 2012, in addition to California, 24 other states had some type of electronic waste legislation.

to a large outbreak of *Coccidioidomysis*, or valley fever, a respiratory illness, from the distribution of fungal spores. In the eight weeks following the earthquake, there were 203 cases directly associated to this event. There were also three deaths from the disease, or four percent of the total deaths as a result of the quake, recorded in the eastern part of Ventura County, Simi Valley, near the epicenter. The spores were kicked up by the landslides triggered by the quake, creating large dust clouds. The CDC was able to detect a pattern connecting whether someone was directly exposed to a dust cloud outdoors and how long they stayed in the cloud to their risk of contracting valley fever. This was the first known case of a series of events started by an earthquake leading to an outbreak of a disease, and it caused the CDC to alert public officials about the opportunity for the future **endemic**, or localized spread, of a disease from a dust cloud after an earthquake.

ENDEMIC Restricted to a single locality or region.

GLOBALIZATION AND THE WORLDWIDE EFFECTS OF REGULATION

A common difference between those with ample financial resources and those with far less, whether it is on a personal or a national level, is that those with wealth have more ability to bargain for a good deal. Those without resources can find themselves at the mercy of those who have the resources to lend. The golden rule that often governs international relations is: "He who has the gold makes the rules." However, developed nations have a long history of extensive foreign aid, going back to when the French military aided the US to win the American Revolution. In the twentieth century, the US returned the favor by helping France during both world wars, and by creating the Marshall Plan to help rebuild Europe following the devastation of WWII. Secretary of State George Marshall, who served during the Truman presidency, instituted the largest financial relief program to date, setting aside $13 billion in aid. The Marshall Plan went on until 1951 and resulted in the rapid rebirth of European nations. Japan received similar assistance to become a democratic, industrialized powerhouse.

However, many countries throughout Asia and Africa have not fared as well over the years. These developing nations are still in need of financial aid from outside sources, such as the World Bank, the United Nations (UN), and other non-government organizations (NGOs). Many of these nations have an impoverished human populace and often poor to nonexistent infrastructure, such as roads or schools, and a weak government and law enforcement institutions. Yet they may be rich in natural resources, such as diamonds, minerals, oil, or fertile soil, that are in demand by developed nations. These countries can be in a poor position to negotiate with developed nations to make a deal that benefits both sides equally.

For example, China currently leases vast amounts of fertile land in West Africa for growing crops that are shipped back to China, while at the same time food aid is being sent to the local African population in countries such as Ethiopia and the Sudan. Such arrangements can leave the local African population without the land, the food, water, or the chance for economic development when local needs are ignored. China also purchases millions of tons of soybeans each year from South America to feed its livestock, which results in significant destruction of the South American rainforests.

However, in cases where different populations across multiple countries have competing interests, the ideal course of action can be difficult to discern. For

Field in Mongolia

example, China's leasing of African farmland does benefit the local population when African workers are hired to work at the farms. To help find ways to strengthen developing nations and benefit all populations, governmental institutions such as the World Bank or the IMF, public companies such as Bank of America, and private organizations such as Feed the Children can lend money, provide needed resources including food and clean water, or institute policies without an underlying agenda of maximizing another nation's advantages.

The loss of farmland in China is an example of the consequences of inadequate land management and planning. Decades of land mismanagement and deforestation have turned vast areas of China into a desert that may last for generations, shrinking the amount of usable farmland and water resources. Even with the relatively recent historical example of the Dust Bowl in the US as an object lesson in ill-considered land exploitation, Chinese leaders failed to recognize that similar land use policy decisions were leading them toward their own version of the Dust Bowl—60 years after the American calamity. China may reverse the damage and the decimated farm land may return to China's bread basket if they enact policies similar to the policies enacted by the US after the Dust Bowl. The consequences of the same lack of thoughtful land use planning started to appear as early as the late 1990s, as the topsoil started to erode and blow into the air.

The current crisis began in 1994 when China instituted the rule of land offset, which meant that for every acre of farmland that was taken for construction an equal amount had to be set aside for farming somewhere else. China was also experiencing a sudden, booming middle class, and millions were leaving their farms for the chance at better jobs in cities, which made new housing a priority for the government. The coastal provinces of Guandong, Shandong, Xheijiang and Jiangsu saw the fastest growth, as they quickly transformed ancient farmland to newly constructed high-rise condominiums. As a result, provinces in the northwest, such as Gansu, Zinghai, Ningxia, Xinjiang, and especially Inner Mongolia—with a 22 percent increase in farm acreage—were paid to offset land for farming, which initially raised their economic standards as well.

The land offset policy went into effect at the same time as an economic reform that removed controls put in place in the late 1970s on the number or size of herds or flocks that could be maintained on a piece of land. As a comparison, there were 9 million sheep and goats and 98 million head of cattle grazing on US land in 2001, compared with China's 279 million goats and sheep and 127 million head of cattle. Consider the grasslands in Gonge County in the Quinghai Province; they are believed to be capable of sustaining 3.7 million sheep, but in 1998 there were 5.5 million sheep on the land. The strain devastated the local ecology and created **desertification**, or the removal of topsoil.

Some solutions to the China's complicated problem of desertification may also be found in looking back at the American Dust Bowl. The balance between new construction of urban high-rise buildings and usable farmland will have to be a priority, and some of the eroded farmland has to be converted back into grassland or forests. The herds and flocks need to be reduced as well to give the land an opportunity to recover. The Chinese hope to create a continuous stretch of what is being called a "Green Wall" of trees that will eventually cover over 3,500 square miles and nine

DESERTIFICATION The removal of topsoil, generally from extended drought, overgrazing, or overfarming.

million acres, stretched across northeastern China. In the 1930s, farmers in the US also planted tree belts along the countryside that created wind barriers and helped end the dust storms, and increased seasonal moisture. For the moment, however, China is looking to other nations to help feed its population while it seeks solutions to its farming problem.

A combination of government negotiations and business arrangements are required to import more Chinese workers and export more African harvests. More arrangements may become necessary as China continues to change from an agricultural society to an urban, industrialized nation, displacing millions more Chinese farmers who will need work. The head of China's Export-Import Bank, Li Ruogu, said in a speech that he believes that more than 12 million Chinese farmers will have to leave their land by 2020. Li suggested that leaving China altogether would be easier than looking for work at home. He also pledged the bank's financial support to help any Chinese farmer with a capital investment in order to get started abroad.

This may be good news for Chinese citizens, but these plans bear further review for the affected African nations, whose citizens will not receive the same economic support to start their own business or even see the profits or produce remain within their country. Kenya has recognized the possible shortfalls for the indigenous population and has instituted levies of 50 percent of any profits for all crops. Kenya has also made it difficult for Chinese citizens to obtain travel visas to Kenya, forcing China to stay on the other side of the Kenyan border in Uganda.

China is not the only country making an agricultural footprint on the continent of Africa. Saudi Arabia, India, Kuwait, and even the US are hedging the potential problem of food shortages and negotiating with a variety of African nations for land leases. China's success despite disease and civil warfare has even encouraged other governments to explore the possibilities.

Hedge funds are also entering the market, looking for new and fertile investments after the collapse of the housing market that drove a worldwide recession. The Oakland Institute, an independent policy think tank, has been following the purchase of over 148 million acres of fertile soil in Africa—an area larger than the state of California—that is being used to produce biofuel, flowers, and specialized food. All of it is exported to other countries, and, according to the Institute, the project has displaced millions of Africans. A review of the contracts showed a clause that allowed the export of up to 80 percent of the harvest, even if the host country is experiencing food shortages.

A continent that has historically seen occupation by European colonial powers may decide to stop their natural resources from being used for the benefit of foreign nations. There is also a long history of civil war and violent conflict in many of the countries in Central Africa that continues to this day. It is a very delicate balance that older, established governments with a trained diplomatic force find difficult to navigate.

The global system includes groups such as the World Bank, which have representation of many countries on their boards, balancing out any one country's influence and offering a measure of protection to developing nations. Just like the aid that was given to Europe after WWII benefited everyone, there is much to be said for lending a hand to Africa through diplomatic or NGO sources and assisting this region to become a continent of more developed nations. If the African countries can become developed, they can better meet their own population's needs and contribute to global needs.

MID-CHAPTER QUESTIONS

1. What is China building to combat the growing problem of desertification in its country?

2. What are some of the causes of the desertification across China?

3. What are some of the risks for African countries who agree to lease their farmland to foreign countries or businesses?

CONSUMPTION

The period of global recession that began in earnest in early 2008 has caused worldwide economic crises—particularly in the developed countries of Spain, Greece, and Italy—and challenged many established countries' willingness to lend funds while simultaneously testing the limits of their ability to put their own financial systems back on a healthier path. Consumer consumption, as expected, has also dipped. But again, this is true mostly in developed nations. According to a study by The Nielsen Company, developing countries, particularly in the East, have shown a healthy growth in consumer spending despite the recession. The study also shows that the problem for some countries—including the US—continues to be the consumer's ability to find or keep employment.

Developed nations that are not yet advanced, such as South Korea and Brazil, are able to attract manufacturing companies that want access to a cheaper labor force. As a consequence, these nations are experiencing positive growth.

Brazil has been named the seventh strongest economy in the world by the World Bank, replacing Italy. That means Brazil has not only been able to weather the worldwide economic conditions but also overcome its own recent history of high inflation and deforestation in the Amazon rainforest. The country has become an interesting case study of what can drive a nation's fortunes down as well as what can move an economy forward.

While most of the rest of the world has been struggling with chronic poverty, such as Haiti, or are dragging, older economies, such as Italy or Greece, Brazil's economy dipped for only two quarters in 2008, according to the World Bank, and has been plowing forward ever since, with no signs of a loss of economic momentum. The Nielsen study also shows that a higher degree of consumer confidence has led to an increased rate of consumer spending not dependent on special promotions or sales from retailers and manufacturers. Brazil's GDP was $2.1 trillion in 2010, with a growth rate of 7.5 percent, according to the World Bank, making it the largest economy in Latin America and the Caribbean, with the highest population.

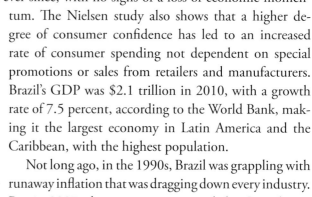

Not long ago, in the 1990s, Brazil was grappling with runaway inflation that was dragging down every industry. But in 2007, the government started the Growth Acceleration Plan in order to increase investments in a crumbling infrastructure and to provide tax incentives to businesses to spur economic growth. Infrastructure

BUSINESSES GOING GREEN: PLUMROSE USA

Most consumers do not think of sandwich meat when they think of environmentally green companies. But Plumrose USA, a 75-year-old meat products manufacturer with facilities in Mississippi, Indiana, Vermont, and Iowa, actively looks for ways to improve its products while respecting and preserving the environment. The company's newest $70 million cold-cut slicing facility in Council Bluffs, Iowa, is LEED-certified (Leadership in Energy and Environmental Design) which means the building meets the highest green buildings standards. And, when it opened it created 100 new jobs.

The company rethought its packaging, leading to the reduction in the use of cardboard by 35 percent throughout the company's plants, saving over 17,000 trees per year. New policies also reduced water consumption during processing by 9 million gallons per year, and company leaders are working on a project to reduce the amount of transportation required throughout the entire process to save on fuel and emissions. The company even has programs in place to teach employees about green practices that they can engage in at home.

All of this is made possible while still managing to save one million dollars per year that goes back into the company and creates jobs in a down economy. The company also improved its product for consumers by reducing salt, cholesterol, and fat. This gained the company a certification from the American Heart Association.

Plumrose is one of the leading meat product manufacturers, but says it prefers to advertise only through retailers, spending nothing on traditional advertising in the media. The company says the money that would have gone toward advertising is put back into the manufacturing of the product.

Plumrose's daily practices show that it is possible to be environmentally conscious, reduce the carbon footprint of a corporation, assist a large employee pool in learning how to use those practices at home, provide an even safer work environment that was built and operated in a sustainable way, and make an even bigger profit while turning out a good product that consumers continue to buy.

needs—such as roads and updated sewer systems—are also being met with development spurred on by two worldwide events that are scheduled to be held in Brazil: the World Cup in 2014 and the 2016 Olympic Games. These events will attract millions of visitors to the country and bring in millions of dollars of consumer spending. But without the right preparation, these events could prove disastrous. However, the government appears to be spending funds where they will do the most good by reinforcing the infrastructure, which also has the positive consequence of creating jobs. The improved roads, hospitals, and other infrastructure will benefit not only the visitors brought by these events but also the native population for years to come.

Moderate poverty, defined by the World Bank as living on two dollars or less per day, has fallen sharply in Brazil, from 21.7 percent of the population in 2003 to 9.9 percent in 2009. Absolute poverty, which applies to those living on only $1.08 or less per day, has fallen from 10 percent in 2004 to only 4 percent in 2009. Between 2001 and 2009, when the stranglehold of inflation began to wane, the poorest segment of Brazil saw the greatest economic increases. Their incomes grew by 7 percent, compared to an increase of 1.7 percent among the wealthiest.

This explains, in large part, why Brazil's rate of consumer spending has been so high—those who previously owned very little suddenly have buying power. This is also part of the reason the recession was over so quickly in Brazil, despite the rest of the world's economic woes. Once a large segment of the population rose above poverty level and were no longer concerned exclusively with basic survival, they started to buy goods that were previously beyond reach. This had the positive effect of getting more money circulating in the economy, ultimately creating more jobs.

The World Bank, which is made up of contributions from developed nations, has also contributed to Brazil's economic revival by funding 59 different projects at a cost of $9.6 billion dollars. The World Bank is funding another 21 projects aimed at improving the environment; these are estimated to cost $334.65 million dollars.

In contrast, domestic consumption in the US has slowed down during the Great Recession, with a growth rate of 1.7 percent in 2011. The growth rate was predicted to improve only slightly in 2012 to around 2.3 percent, according to the Kiplinger Report. Many Americans also began saving more in order to make up for the value lost during the housing crash, or to protect against a job loss. Some spending, such as for new cars, increased in 2012, but not as much as economists had hoped.

It may be more than just fewer available dollars to spend that is influencing a drop in consumer spending. According to a study done at the University of Houston's C.T. Bauer College of Business, even those whose economic status is unchanged or improved slowed down their spending when the majority around them stopped buying goods or services. The study called this a reverse form of that old cliché about "keeping up with the Joneses," in that members of a community don't want to appear to have risen too far above or be too different from those who live and work around them. This study suggests that the desire to fit in is stronger than the desire to spend.

The Great Recession has been over since 2010, but the return to a more vibrant US economy has been slow to occur, with some severe setbacks such as a faltering job market. There are signs of further recovery, such as new equipment orders in manufacturing to expand production, which is expected to have a ripple effect on the rest of the economy and will encourage consumers to spend more of their money.

MID-CHAPTER QUESTIONS

1. Why did lesser-developed countries appear to have the advantage during the Great Recession beginning in 2008?

2. What are some of the reasons the US has not recovered as quickly?

3. What segment of the population in Brazil has benefited the most from that nation's economic recovery?

PRESERVATION: PROJECT REDD

An emerging preservation program known as Reduced Emissions from Deforestation and Forest Degradation (REDD) is showing some success at preserving large forests around the globe. The UN administrates the REDD Programs.

Some scientists believe that 20 percent of carbon dioxide (CO_2) released as a result of human activity can be traced directly to the loss of rainforests. The trees take in CO_2 and release oxygen as the other part of the cycle that keeps the atmospheric carbon levels in balance. The natural consequences of taking down large expanses of forest area loss of habitat for some endangered species, a reduced water table as discussed earlier in the chapter, and a change in weather patterns known as global climate change.

Preservation initiatives often work best when the concerns of the local human population are taken into consideration and respected just as much as the endangered flora or fauna. Conservation efforts have proven difficult in projects that don't have the cooperation of the people who live nearby. The Gordon and Betty Moore Foundation, dedicated to environmental conservation, offers REDD programs in the form of grants to help educate people on the advantages of preserving rainforests. The country of Gabon in the Congo region of Central Africa is home to one of the largest expanses of virgin rainforest on Earth. It covers 80 percent of the country with 8,000 plant species, some of them found only in this rainforest, 200 animal species, and 600 bird species.

In March 2009, the Moore Foundation gave the government of the Gabonese Republic over $300,000 to study just how much the trees of Gabon contribute to the quality of the oxygen needed for humans to sustain life. A key part of any REDD is to show the economic feasibility—or in this case the ability to preserve life—that comes with keeping the trees rather than tearing them down for lumber or to create farmland. The US has also contributed financial aid, such as $75 million in 2002 that assisted the government of Gabon in preserving 10 percent of the land as national forests. As a result, there were 13 national parks created in 2002, and Gabon is now seen as a world leader in conservation. REDD programs are also being used in other parts of the world to grant aid to local populations that helps raise the quality of life while motivating them to preserve the natural resources of rainforests for the future.

Another initiative benefits local populations by offering debt relief in exchange for conservation efforts. The Tropical Forest Conservation Act (TFCA) enacted in 1991 supports local foundations and NGOs in their conservation efforts in the communities they serve while forgiving debt owed to the US government in exchange. By 2010, 14 countries had participated in this program, resulting in $266 million for total forest conservation.

CHAPTER SUMMARY

The developing and developed nation classification system takes into account a wide variety of criteria that measure both economic activity and human welfare. These measures include personal income, access to health care and education, life expectancy, and GNP. The World Bank was originally formed to help fund the rebuilding of European nations after WWII, and lists eradicating poverty as its main goal.

Before a nation can address its environmental problems, basic needs must be met. Interactions between nations can be complex, requiring government oversight to balance the variety of social and business interests involved in addressing environmental issues or basic human needs, which are often very connected. A clean water and food supply, adequate shelter from the elements, and access to education and healthcare are high priorities for developing nations trying to eradicate poverty and create a stable and productive economy.

The World Bank, the UN, NGOs, and charities provide financial aid to countries in need. Globalization has also provided opportunities in areas such as food distribution and environmental preservation that can greatly benefit local populations. Some of these countries can be in a poor position to negotiate with developed nations to make deals that benefit both sides equally. Sometimes a wealthier nation benefits from activities such as land leases or manufacturing in an area that can provide an inexpensive labor force where the local populace does not gain an equitable or sustained reward.

The period of global recession that began in earnest in early 2008 continues to affect many nations' ability to lend aid as they struggle to stabilize and grow their own financial systems. A recent study shows that some developing countries, particularly in the East, have shown a healthy growth in consumer spending despite the recession.

REFERENCES

Anbumozhi, V., & Bauer, A. (2012). *Impact of global recession on sustainable development and poverty linkages.* Tokyo, Japan: Asian Development Bank Institute. Retrieved from http://www.adbi .org/working-paper/2010/07/08/3933.impact.global.recession.dev.poverty.linkages/

Asante-Darko, K. (2009, September 4). *Africa, the global recession and climate change.* EastWest Institute. Retrieved from http://blog.nielsen.com/nielsenwire/consumer/the-state-of-the-global-consumer-spending-trends/

Birn, A-E., Pillay, Y., & Holtz, T. H. (2009*). Textbook of international health: Global health in a dynamic world* (3rd ed., pp. 150–153). New York, NY: Oxford University Press

Brown, L. R. (2001, May 29). China's dust bowl is growing at an alarming rate. *Grist.* Retrieved from http://grist.org/article/grossman-bites/

California Department of Food and Agriculture. (2012). California agricultural production statistics. Retrieved from http://www.cdfa.ca.gov/statistics/

The Carter Center. (n.d.). River Blindness Program. Retrieved from http://www.cartercenter.org/ health/river_blindness/index.html

Central Intelligence Agency. (2012). *The world fact book, 2012–2013.* Retrieved from https://www .cia.gov/library/publications/the-world-factbook/appendix/appendix-b.html#D

Colorado River Management, Arizona Department of Water Resources. (2012). Lower Colorado River Multi-Species Conservation Program. Retrieved from http://www.azwater.gov/azdwr/ statewideplanning/crm/environmentalprograms.htm

Greenpeace International. (2009, February 24). Where does e-waste end up? Retrieved from http://www.greenpeace.org/international/en/campaigns/toxics/electronics/the-e-waste-problem/ where-does-e-waste-end-up/

Kamakura, W. A., & Du, R. Y. (2011). How economic contractions and expansions affect expenditure patterns. *Journal of Consumer Research, 39.* Retrieved from http://www.bauer .uh.edu/rexdu/how%20economic%20contractions%20and%20expansions%20affect%20 expenditure%20patterns.pdf

Erasmus, M. (2011, July 18). Feeding China: Africa's other natural resource. *Consultancy Africa Intelligence.* Retrieved from http://www.consultancyafrica.com/index.php?option=com_content &view=article&id=796:feeding-china-africas-other-natural-resource&catid=58:asia-dimension-discussion-papers&Itemid=264

Feenstra, G., Ingels, C., & Campbell, D. (n.d.). What is sustainable agriculture? UC Sustainable Agriculture Research and Education Program. Retrieved from http://www.sarep.ucdavis.edu/concept.htm

George C. Marshall Foundation. (2009). The Marshall Plan. Retrieved from http://www .marshallfoundation.org/TheMarshallPlan.htm

Gordon and Betty Moore Foundation. (2009). Environmental conservation, program grants: Reducing emission from deforestation and forest degradation (REDD). Retrieved from http://www.moore.org/project.aspx?proj=2964&id=2964

Heakal, R. (2011, July 31). What is the World Bank? *Investopedia.* Retrieved from http://www .investopedia.com/articles/03/042303.asp#axzz1lRen1REM

Hedge funds buying massive tracts of African farmland. (2011, August 10). *Here and Now, Public Radio International.* Retrieved from http://www.pri.org/stories/world/africa/hedge-funds-buy-massive-tracts-of-farm-land-5343.html

The History Place. (1996).The rise of Adolf Hitler: Hitler named chancellor. Retrieved from http://www.historyplace.com/worldwar2/riseofhitler/named.htm

International Monetary Fund. (2011, August 31). The IMF and the World Bank. Retrieved from http://www.imf.org/external/np/exr/facts/imfwb.htm

Nielsen. (2010, September 10). The state of the global consumer: Spending trends [Web log post]. Retrieved from http://blog.nielsen.com/nielsenwire/consumer/the-state-of-the-global-consumer-spending-trends/

Nielsen, L. (2011, February). *Classifications of countries based on their level of development: How it is done and how it could be done* (IMF Working Paper No. WP/11/31). International Monetary Fund.

OECD iLibrary. (2011). Society at a glance 2011: OECD social indicators. http://www.oecd-ilibrary.org/sites/soc_glance-2011-en/04/01/g4_ge1-01.html?contentType=&itemId=/content/chapter/soc_glance-2011-6-en&containerItemId=/content/serial/19991290&accessItemIds=/content/book/soc_glance-2011-en&mimeType=text/html

Pan, X-R., Yang, W-Y., Li, G-W., Liu, J., & National Diabetes Prevention and Control Cooperative Group. (1997). Prevalence of diabetes and its risk factors in China, 1994. *Diabetes Care, 20,* 1664–1669. Retrieved from http://care.diabetesjournals.org/content/20/11/1664.short

Patton, D. (2008, April 7). Africa at large: China eyes idle farmland. *Afrika.no: The Norwegian Council for Africa.* Retrieved from http://www.afrika.no/Detailed/16472.html

Plumrose. (n.d.). Sustainability. Retrieved from http://www.plumroseusa.com/sustainability.php

Plumrose USA breaks ground on $70 million facility. (2012, 1st quarter). *View Point: Council Bluffs, Iowa Chamber of Commerce Newsletter.*

The Rain Forest Foundation. (n.d.). Gabon [Fact sheet]. Retrieved from http://www.rainforestfoundationuk.org/Gabon

Recycle Works. (n.d.). Old computers are not deleted: The electronics recycling process. Retrieved from http://www.recycleworks.org/ewaste/ewaste_process.html

Schwartzman, S. (2000). Brazil: The social agenda. *Daedalus, 129*(2), 29–56. Retrieved from http://www.schwartzman.org.br/simon/daedalus.htm

Urban Habitat Chicago. (n.d.). True nature foods rooftop garden. Retrieved from http://www .urbanhabitatchicago.org/projects/true-nature-foods/

Welby, C. W., & Gowan, M. E. (Eds.). (1998). *A paradox of power: Voices of warning and reason in the geosciences.* Boulder, CO: The Geological Society of America.

World Health Organization. (n.d.). Water sanitation and health: Water related diseases. Retrieved from http://www.who.int/water_sanitation_health/diseases/oncho/en/

The World Bank. (2012, February). Brazil country brief. Retrieved from http://web.worldbank.org/ WBSITE/EXTERNAL/COUNTRIES/LACEXT/BRAZILEXTN/0,,menuPK:322351~page PK:141132~piPK:141107~theSitePK:322341,00.html

The World Bank. (2012, February). Data: Brazil. Retrieved from http://data.worldbank.org/country/ brazil

The World Bank. (2011, May 17). *Emerging market growth poles are redefining global economic structure.* Retrieved from http://web.worldbank.org/WBSITE/EXTERNAL/COUNTRIES/ LACEXT/BRAZILEXTN/0,,contentMDK:22916098~menuPK:322347~pagePK:1497618~pi PK:217854~theSitePK:322341,00.html

CHAPTER

5

Food Production

THE SONOMA COMPOST COMPANY

The practice of collecting and disposing of paper products, fruit and vegetable scraps, grass clippings, and fallen leaves has been employed by gardeners for generations. **Composting** is an effective way to create an inexpensive and highly beneficial fertilizer while reducing waste. When "brown" organic material is layered with "green" organic material and allowed to decay in a ventilated outdoor area, rich, organic black compost forms in a few weeks. Brown materials include dead leaves, branches and sticks, and manure from herbivore livestock. Green materials include grass clippings, vegetable wastes, and coffee grounds. These materials are high in nitrogen, phosphorus, and other minerals essential for plant growth.

Some companies are turning this into a profitable business that also benefits local food growers. Sonoma Composting Company, in Sonoma, California is doing this by creating and selling compost along with providing recycling services. They provide ready-made organic compost, mulch, firewood, and biofuels to local residents and commercial customers such as grape and other food growers, and they donate these materials to school gardens. Sonoma Composting Company collects donations of recyclable materials to turn them into organic material for reuse, diverting 1.2 million tons of waste since 1993.

In 2011, the company expanded its mission with a pilot program in conjunction with Sonoma County Waste Management and about 20 local restaurants. They began collecting waste from

COMPOSTING The practice of layering "brown" organic material with "green" organic material and allowing it to decay in a ventilated outdoor area, creating an inexpensive and rich fertilizer while reducing waste.

local kitchens, where almost 90 percent of the waste is compostable food. Food waste in a landfill is responsible for producing high levels of methane gas, a greenhouse gas that is 21 times more potent than carbon dioxide (CO_2). The Environmental Protection Agency (EPA) estimates that in 2010, food waste accounted for 34 million tons of waste in the United States (US)—more than any other type besides paper.

Food waste to be composted (anything but meat or dairy—even paper napkins can be recycled) is collected by kitchen staff and local Sonoma Waste Management delivers it to Sonoma Composting Company. This cooperation results in keeping reusable material, especially food waste, out of landfills and provides local food producers with rich organic fertilizer, improving the soil throughout the community.

GENETICALLY MODIFIED ORGANISMS

The term **genetically modified organism**, including genetically modified food, refers to an organism that has had its DNA altered through the addition or subtraction of specific genes. Genetically

GENETICALLY MODIFIED ORGANISM An organism that has had genes added or deleted for specific results.

modified crops have been grown on a large scale since the 1990s, usually as a method to increase food production. This is just the latest in a series of technological break-throughs throughout history that have

allowed human beings to increase the amount of food produced from growing crops. This chapter discusses the agricultural techniques of splicing, cross pollination, pesticides, and irrigation. But before these methodologies can be explained, it is important to understand the history and development of agriculture.

The History of Crop Modification

Early humans lived primarily in hunter-gatherer societies. These people made rudimentary tools to spear, trap, and carry their food. The bulk of their diet was often high in calories and fat from protein sources. Early humans were generally nomadic, searching for food over large expanses of land. They often hunted large animals with wide habitat ranges, such as deer and bison, and also gathered grains and fruits.

A key to transitioning from a nomadic lifestyle to a more agrarian lifestyle was the cultivation of food sources. As early humans experimented with foods and cooking, there was a new emphasis on developing a constant food supply, which led to the domestication of plants and animals. Early humans began by domesticating grains such as wheat and oats as well as animals such as dogs, goats, pigs, and sheep. This domestication required humans to transition from tools used to acquire food, such as spears and traps, to tools that allowed people to produce food, such as hoes and plows. As early agriculture

1. What are some benefits of composting?

2. What kind of cooperation from local residents and businesses is necessary for companies like the Sonoma Composting Company to remain successful?

3. Why might people be resistant to implementing composting in place of traditional trash collection, in which waste is hauled to landfills?

developed, it drastically changed human interaction and society as a whole. Instead of living in nomadic clans, people began to live in much larger groups in developing villages and towns. By 4500 BCE, the ancient city of Sumer was founded and in 3000 BCE the first city-state was founded in Mesopotamia.

Agriculture remained fairly similar to this early model for thousands of years, with only minor developments in tools and the use of animal-driven equipment—such as plows and mills—until the early nineteenth century. The agricultural revolution, beginning in the eighteenth and continuing into the nineteenth century, saw increases in production as farm implements such as plows began to be produced and sold on a large scale. As Europe began to enter the Industrial Revolution, fields such as genetics, **agronomy**, and botany rapidly added to the human understanding of plant and animal biology, and the face of food production would change forever. Animal husbandry and cross-pollinating became important tools to increase production, as did the development of chemical fertilizers and motorized farming equipment. Slowly, small family farms and household gardens began to wane and large commercial farms increased.

As the need for mass production increased, so did the need for more efficient plant varieties with larger, hardier crops such as hybrid corn and soybeans. This need inspired drastic changes from the most basic version of agriculture.

Splicing

A common form of genetic modification is the use of **splicing**, also known as grafting. It was one of the first methods of genetic modification. Splicing itself can actually describe several different techniques used to combine two or more individual plants together. In general, splicing refers to joining the root of one plant, known as a **rootstock**, with a portion of another plant that includes a branch with a growing bud, known as a **scion**. The rootstock, sometimes simply known as the stock, includes both the root and some trunk or stem. Through splicing, the rootstock's genetic code is muted, and the fruits, leaves, branches, and seeds show only the genetic code of the scion because only the scion's genetic material creates the majority of the part of the plant above the ground. This occurs because even though the roots support the plant, collecting nutrients and water, the branches, leaves, and buds all grow from the scion's initial **apical bud**. The stock remains permanently in the ground and is selected for its roots, while the scion is chosen for its leaves, fruits, or appearance. However, it should be noted that in some cases the scion is added to a full-grown plant and is merely an addition. This is done in several different ways, including bark grafting (where a scion is added underneath a slit cut into an existing tree's bark), side veneer grafting (where a notch is cut out of an existing plant and a scion is added into the notch), and budding (which is similar to bark grafting except that instead of an entire scion, only a bud is added).

There are several reasons splicing may be used. Some plants are spliced to help grow scion varieties in climates or soils that are not suitable for them; in these cases, the rootstock is well suited for propagation in that climate or soil. Some plants are spliced because they are difficult to grow from seeds, or the seeds are scarce. Some splicing occurs to get several different varieties of a similar plant from one tree. For example, some apple trees with splicing on them can produce different varieties of apples, and Rose-of-Sharon bushes may be spliced to produce several different colors

AGRONOMY The science of agriculture and its economic values.
SPLICING Method of artificially creating desired plant effects by joining a scion from one plant to the rootstock of another.
ROOTSTOCK The portion of a plant used in splicing that includes the roots and a portion of trunk.
SCION A portion of a branch with growing buds that is attached to the rootstock during splicing.
APICAL BUD The end or terminal bud of a branch or stem.

of flower on the same bush. Sometimes splicing is used to create oddities, such as tomato vines spliced to potatoes to create both crops from one plant. Splicing can also be used to graft one or more healthy scions onto a diseased or dying stock to bring new life to the plant.

Splicing can be divided into two main types: splicing involving scions of small size in relation to the rootstock, and splicing in which the scions and rootstocks are about the same size. The major difference between these two styles is that when rootstocks and scions are the same size, only one scion can be added directly to the rootstock because of the size of the scion compared to the size of the rootstock. However, when scions are smaller, a number of scions can be grafted to the same rootstock. Rootstocks and scions of similar size are spliced together by creating interlocking notches on each piece. These notches are inserted into one another, sealed with grafting wax (a wax made from rosin, tallow, bees wax, or similar substances), and taped with grafting tape in order to heal and grow. Splicing is done during the dormant season so the plant does not die from the cutting involved.

Historically speaking, splicing is an ancient tool for cultivation. The splicing of olive trees is mentioned in the Bible, and an ancient Greek treatise, dated around 424 BCE, specifically describes the process of grafting:

> "Some trees however, grow from grafts implanted into other trees: they live independently on these, and the fruit which they bear is different from that of the tree on which they are grafted. This is how: first of all the graft produces buds, for initially it still contains nutriment from its parent tree, and only subsequently from the tree in which it was engrafted."

Because of the depth of understanding of the technique of splicing evident in this passage, it is safe to assume that the act of splicing was a common agricultural method even prior to 424 BCE.

Cross-Pollination

Cross-pollination, or the selective breeding of plants to create certain traits, is a cultivation technique that people have used for thousands of years. Ancient Assyrian art depicts the artificial pollination of date plants and dates back to 870 BCE. Cross-pollination creates faster-growing plants with larger or sweeter yields. However, until Gregor Mendel's work on pea plants in the 1860s, there was limited understanding of the genetic effects of cross-pollination.

Mendel, an Austrian monk, is often considered the father of genetics. Mendel's work included cross-pollinating specific pea plants to determine if certain traits were expressed more than others. Through his multiple crosses of his pea plants, he soon learned that some traits were in fact **recessive** while other traits were **dominant**. A recessive trait is one that is only expressed when there are no dominant genes present. Meanwhile, a dominant trait is one that is expressed as long as there is one dominant gene present. These types of traits are commonly seen in all organisms. A good example of dominant and recessive traits can be seen in hairlines. A widow's peak hairline is a dominant trait while a hairline that goes straight across the forehead tends to be recessive. If a woman with a widow's peak and a man without one were to reproduce, the child would have a higher probability of having a widow's peak, because that characteristic is dominant. Mendel's work, which was not formally published until after his death, founded the science of genetics and revolutionized plant breeding.

There are two distinct types of cross-pollination: **interspecies** and **intergenus**. Interspecies cross-pollination involves members of the same species. In interspecies cross-pollination, individual plants are selected because they possess certain desirable

traits, such as flower color, size, or yield. These individuals are cross-pollinated with the intention of producing offspring with the best traits from both plants. A similar example can be seen in dogs. All dog breeds are members of the same dog species, *Canis familiaris*, and therefore can be bred together to produce fertile offspring. Over generations, certain traits were selected for and bred repeatedly, eventually creating dramatically different-looking breeds, such as the Chihuahua and the golden retriever. For example, a popular dog breed in recent years is the Labradoodle, a mix between a Labrador and a Poodle. The Labradors are selected for their gentle demeanor, while Poodles are selected for their hypoallergenic coats. Plants have been selectively bred in similar ways throughout human history.

Intergenus cross-pollination occurs with members of the same genus of plant, such as the Loganberry, created by crossing a raspberry and a blackberry. While they are closely related, they do not share enough genetic similarity to be classified in the same species. This type of pollination can occur naturally, but most examples of intergenus cross-pollination occur artificially. The major difference between intergenus and interspecies cross-pollination is found in the offspring. Because of the distinct genetic differences between species in intergenus cross-pollination, the offspring are hybrids of both species and are sometimes sterile, meaning they cannot reproduce. This style of cross-pollination can limit the generational returns from a single plant, but is often used to produce specific flowers or yields.

Pesticides

Pesticides are a type of chemical used in many agricultural settings to control a variety of organisms that can cause harm to crops—including slugs, insects, molds, and many others. Pesticides have been used in one form or another for millennia. The first known example of pesticide use dates as far back as 4500 BCE in ancient Sumer. The Sumerians used sulfur compounds to dust for insects and mites. Later, the ancient Chinese, Greek, and Romans used pesticides and insecticides to control a variety of pests. During this time, many of these pesticides were derived directly from plant or animal products. For example, Pyrethrum, a compound still used today, is created from a variety of daisy and has been used as an insecticide for more than 2,000 years. Not until the 1940s were pesticides frequently created synthetically. During this period the benefit of perhaps the most well-known pesticide was discovered, DDT. DDT was very efficient in controlling insects, especially malaria-carrying mosquitoes. Unfortunately, overuse of DDT would ultimately grow strains of resistant insects. Worse, the toxins in DDT worked their way up the food chain, producing devastating effects in large predatory birds like the bald eagle. It became evident that the presence of DDT caused eggshells of these birds to become fragile, and as the adults would roost on the eggs, they would break, and entire clutches were lost.

Pesticide manufacturing and application have evolved greatly since the days of DDT. Today, new pesticides are evaluated prior to commercial use and testing continues once they are in broad use to ensure and maintain product safety. The most modern types of pesticides are genetically engineered pesticides, or **plant incorporated protectants** (PIPs).

PLANT INCORPORATED PROTECTANTS Genetically inserted proteins that aid a plant in resistance to a pest.

"Pesticides are a type of chemical used in many agricultural settings to control a variety of organisms that can cause harm to crops—including slugs, insects, molds, and many others. Pesticides have been used in one form or another for millennia. The first known example of pesticide use dates as far back as 4,500 BCE in ancient Sumer."

Within PIPs, specific genes that code for the production of proteins that are toxic to selected insect pest species are inserted into the genome of many crop species. These genetically modified crops produce insect-specific pesticidal proteins, which help to control insect pest populations to increase crop yields.

These PIPs, like other pesticides, are regulated by the EPA, but they have caused concern among different groups because the pesticides are added at the most basic biological level. Apart from the effect that these PIPs may have on people ingesting the fruits of the plants, there is also concern regarding the effects on pollinators. In recent years there has been a noted decline in the number of honeybees around the world, and some concern has risen about the correlation between these PIPs and the phenomenon known as **colony collapse disorder (CCD)**. At present, the EPA and the US Department of Agriculture (USDA) are monitoring pesticides and their effects on both honeybees and other pollinators. If an entire species of pollinator were lost, it could be catastrophic for plant and crop production, as these pollinators are essential for many plants to reproduce.

Irrigation

Perhaps the most important requirement for a plant's growth is water. In fact, some plants are grown without soil, but they still need water to thrive. Therefore, early humans required a constant and manageable supply of water in order to produce enough food to eat. Irrigation is believed to have started simultaneously around 6000 BCE in both Egypt and Mesopotamia. These two early civilizations were centered around the Nile and Tigris rivers, respectively, both of which flood on a regular basis. Early farmers diverted this floodwater to fields near the river for periods between 45 and 60 days and would then divert it back to the river at key times in the growing season. Irrigation techniques would continue to develop. In 3100 BCE, a large canal project built in Egypt eventually formed a reservoir at Lake Moeris. Romans used cement pipes to move water as early as 2000 BCE, and among other laws given by Hammurabi in 1792 BCE were laws governing irrigation canals.

COLONY COLLAPSE DISORDER A term first used in 2006 to describe the significant loss of bee colonies in North America. There are many proposed reasons for such disappearances, such as biotic pathogens or Varroa mites, or environmental stresses such as malnutrition and pesticides.

Irrigation continued to progress into the twentieth century, with major technological advances such as the ones listed here. Today an estimated 600 million acres of irrigated farmland exist globally.

However, over-irrigation and mismanagement of irrigation has become a real concern, especially in developed countries with abundant irrigation systems. Erosion and increases in soil salinity (the salt content found in the soil) caused by irrigation are great concerns, but a greater concern is the depletion of fresh water. An estimated 70 percent of fresh water used by human beings annually goes to farmland irrigation. However, as urban populations increase, the demand for fresh municipal water increases, as does demand for greater food production, which results in an even greater need for irrigation water supplies.

Because of the growing demand for food, as well as the growing demand for fresh water, scientists have turned to genetically modified plants to help. By altering the genomes of plants and isolating specific traits, scientists have begun developing several different vegetable varieties that can thrive on less water. For example, researchers have discovered they can modify the gene that produces a stress hormone in plants, making them resistant to drought conditions. While only recreated in the lab with the *Arabidopsis,* a plant related to mustard that is commonly used in experiments, breakthroughs like these types of very beneficial genetic modifications will help food production keep up with demand, even in times of environmental stresses.

Genetic Engineering

The genetic engineering of plants is a recent development in agriculture and, as mentioned earlier, may be the key to solving a number of issues, including fresh water depletion and increasing food requirements. By altering specific genes from plants, certain traits of these crops can be expressed or repressed. For example, scientists have genetically engineered varieties of tomato plants to survive with moderate levels of saltwater irrigation, rather than freshwater. As with most plants, normal tomatoes cannot tolerate even minute levels of **salinity** before they begin to wilt and die from water loss. However, with these new varieties, tomatoes can be grown with less freshwater irrigation and in new locations where saltwater intrusion may be a factor. In most cases of genetic engineering, genes of one variety of plant are added to another plant.

International Regulations of Genetically Modified Foods

In the US, the Food and Drug Administration (FDA) is responsible for regulating foods through lab trials, monitoring and testing, and the creation of harvesting guidelines. Nearly half the world's genetically modified crops are grown in the US—almost 170 million acres were planted with such crops in 2012. Most of the rest of the world's other genetically modified foods are grown in developing countries. Critics of GMOs claim that they may be harmful to humans or animals. Proponents of GMOs point out that most gene additions come from plants that are edible themselves. Since the FDA first began regulating GMOs, over 20 new varieties of these crops have been approved for planting, mostly soybeans and cotton.

China's farmers also grow GMOs. But China has an extensive regulation process that often hampers imports from countries like the US, and, in 2001, new regulations caused great concern that US exports of soybeans would be affected. In China, before a GMO is approved, lab research must first be conducted, followed

SALINITY Concentration of salt found in a solution, generally measured in parts per thousand (ppt).

ENVIRONMENTAL MISCONCEPTIONS: GENETICALLY MODIFIED FOODS AND HUNGER

Breakthroughs in the development of genetically modified foods have created potential solutions to end hunger and sustain populations in impoverished areas. Genetically modified corn and soy strains have proven resistant to herbicides. These products are often suggested as a solution to increase yields in developing countries, potentially increasing food availability and reducing hunger.

There has been an increase in the use of GMOs in developing countries in recent years, especially in Brazil, which is now second to the US in GMO production. Some developing countries, however, do not have access to this technology due to cost barriers.

While producing crops resistant to herbicides and pesticides is beneficial in many geographic regions, the promise of higher crop yields may not be met. A misconception regarding GMOs is the assumption that they dramatically increase food production through larger yields. One recent study indicated that this is not necessarily the case. Research conducted by the Union of Concerned Scientists showed that even though genetically modified foods have been used commercially for more than 13 years, there has been no significant increase in yields. In fact, Bt corn (a GMO variety of corn that has genes taken from the bacteria *Bacillius thuringiensis*, which makes the corn resistant to several different insects) has increased in yield by an average of only 0.2 to 0.3 percent each year. Meanwhile, traditional corn crops increase annually by an average of 1 percent. The recommendation of this group is that scientists continue to do research into GM technology but also continue to spend time cultivating organic and traditional farming methods to increase yields instead.

by field tests, controlled environmental releases, and finally pre-market testing before there is an actual market release. This process can take three to five years.

GMOs approved by the US include sugar beet, alfalfa, canola, corn, cotton, flax, potato, rice, soybean, tomato, papaya, potato, squash, rice, corn, and others. Many other plants are now approved and the government is considering approving genetically modified animals, such as fish. Typical traits of GMS include resistance to herbicides, resistance to diseases, change in oil content, and change in ripening time.

Potential advantages of GMOs include improved consistency, taste, and quality; increased nutrients, yields, and stress tolerance; increased food security for growing populations; new products and growing techniques; increased food output; and conservation of soil, water, energy.

Some disadvantages of GMOs include potential increased food allergies and antibiotic resistance in humans, and unknown risks from consuming new genetic combinations. In addition, genetic homogenization makes food supplies vulnerable to new strains of disease. Finally, since GMOs are created by large corporations, some fear that control of the world's food production could be left in the hands of a small group of companies and developing countries could become more dependent on a few developed countries.

Other countries and unions have been slow to accept GMOs. For example, the European Union (EU) requires any company or entity desiring to import a GMO into a member state to send a detailed description and background on the genetic alterations, and foods containing GMOs must disclose this information on the label. Before approval, a risk assessment is conducted to identify any harmful reactions, such as rashes, irritations, or other serious allergic reactions. The findings are passed to the general committee for a vote. If there are concerns, the committee forms a panel to review the approval and vote again. Plants that have been passed through this testing and approval process in Europe include varieties of soybeans, cotton, and corn that are resistant to herbicides like glyphosate salt, as well as cotton and corn that are resistant to Lepidopteran pests (butterflies and moths). In 2010, the first approval for a genetically modified crop—a genetically modified potato (which is not designed for human consumption but for starch used in paper products)—was approved after a 12-year moratorium on new approvals. This and other commercially used GMOs in Europe must pass a risk assessment test to screen for the plant's effects on local biodiversity through cross-pollination, effects on non-target animals, and any other potential harmful effects on humans or animals.

Dealing with Increasing Food Needs

On October 31, 2011, the human population of the Earth crossed the 7 billion mark. As the planet's population increases, the demand for food around the world increases as well. There is a need to develop more sustainable and available food supplies for this growing population. While the development of some GMOs shows promise in helping to deal with some of the issues that demand attention, there are concerns regarding these technologies. Some critics of GMOs point to the loss of non-hybrid plants that can produce fertile offspring, human and animal reactions to these new genetically engineered plants, and, in the case of pesticide-resistant GMOs, the development of stronger, more dangerous pests that would be poised to cause even greater plant destruction. Other issues, such as the availability of natural resources like water and nutrients, as well as financial resources to purchase new plants, will need to be addressed as well.

MID-CHAPTER QUESTIONS

1. Name one benefit of grafting.

2. Describe three ways that humans have altered the way food is grown.

3. What are some benefits and challenges to genetically modifying foods?

ORGANIC FOODS

Due in part to concern over the modifications to the food production system described in the previous section, there is growing demand for organic and naturally produced foods. Before exploring the ways in which food is produced organically,

it is important to understand how organic food is defined. Guidelines for organic certification were established in 1990 under the Organic Food Production Act. Under this law, the USDA devised standards that a food producer must maintain before it can be certified organic. Third-party certifiers such as Oregon Tilth and California Certified Organic Farmers act as extensions of the USDA. These extensions inspect and monitor farms seeking certification.

There are differing levels of certification that a food producer can receive:

- 100% Organic
- Organic (made with 95% organic food)
- Made with Organic Material (between 74-90% organic)

The USDA considers organic agriculture to be an:

"ecological production management system that promotes and enhances biodiversity, biological cycles, and soil biological systems. It is based on minimal use of off-farm inputs and on management practices that restore, maintain, and enhance ecological harmony."

Attempting to maintain this definition can be difficult, and the requirements for certification are fairly extensive. As with most legislation, the requirements are extremely specific, ranging from where seeds originate, how fields are laid out, how crops are rotated, and how compost is created. For example, compost must maintain a ratio of carbon to nitrogen of between 25:1 and 40:1; if the compost is being turned, it must be turned a minimum of five times; and the compost must maintain a temperature of between 131 °F and 170 °F for 15 days. Requirements like this are in place for all aspects of vegetable farming, as well as livestock and poultry farming. Farmers and growers must maintain documents to prove that they adhere to the USDA standards in order to be certified and remain certified. With these stringent regulations in place, the USDA organic label is a valuable marketing tool for farmers and food producers.

Putting aside the finer points of organic certification, one key to understanding the difference between conventional and organic agriculture is the use of manufactured products versus natural products to increase yields. Each method has its advantages and disadvantages (see Figure 5.1).

Proponents of organic methods of agriculture say that one benefit is that its methods produce less runoff of harmful chemicals such as phosphates. Runoff occurs when loose soil (and any residual chemicals such as pesticides on the plants or attached to the soil) is removed from an ecosystem during times of heavy precipitation, irrigation, or high winds. However, scientists are still studying whether the differences in runoff lead to an environmental benefit. Organic farmers may make lower monetary investment in production and replacement of lost nutrients and soil. Even with reduction in runoff, organic farms must be as vigilant as conventional farms in controlling their runoff. Any runoff of manure used as fertilizer or natural pesticides still contaminates waterways and surrounding soil. For example, Rotenone, a plant extract used as a natural pesticide, is known to be toxic to fish. Runoff can create dead zones, like those found in the Gulf of Mexico, as a result of excess nutrients such as phosphorous and nitrogen that make their way

CONVENTIONAL AND GMO AGRICULTURE	POTENTIAL ADVANTAGES	POTENTIAL DISADVANTAGES
Apply chemical fertilizers to provide nutrients to plants	Increased yields, quickly fertilize soil to replenish nutrients	Runoff can alter and damage surrounding environment, destroy microbes in the soil
Use chemical insecticides to control pests	Increased yields, effective way to reduce pests, inexpensive	Insecticides may harm pollinators and other insects that ensure crop yields; can reduce total insect population
Use chemical herbicides to control weeds	Increased yields, effective, inexpensive	Herbicides can be toxic to humans and other animal populations; runoff can alter and damage surrounding environment
Use of antibiotics, growth hormones, and medications for livestock for health and growth	Increased yields, reduction in disease, requires large amounts of animal feed	Animals can be crowded or mistreated, animal waste contributes to water contamination, antibiotics may be present in product consumed by humans
Genetically modified crops	Production can be more manageable and inexpensive, crops resistant to insects and disease, require less water and fuel resources	Disease-resistant traits can be passed onto other plant and animal organisms
ORGANIC AGRICULTURE		
Apply raw manure and natural fertilizers such as compost to provide nutrients to plants	Produce is free of man-made chemicals, can provide nutrients to soil, increases microbes in the soil	Runoff can alter and damage surrounding environment, fertilizers can carry dangerous bacteria such as E. coli, organic herbicides and fertilizers can be expensive, can cause people to become sick due to pathogens in manure
Use of natural insect and bird predators and traps	No man-made chemicals released into the environment	Time consuming to manage, may damage organisms that are helpful
Use of crop rotation and tilling to replenish nutrients in soil and control weeds	No artificial chemicals released into the environment, replenishes nutrients to soil, reduces erosion	Time consuming to manage, large farm equipment uses fossil fuels, crop rotation does not replenish all nutrients in soil, requires excess water
Access to outdoor grazing or free range of livestock, rotational grazing, and use of clean housing for health and growth	Humane treatment of healthy animals, reduces carbon emissions	Requires more land and can lead to deforestation and smaller production, can contribute to overgrazing, animal waste may contribute to water contamination

FIGURE 5.1 Differences, advantages, and disadvantages in conventional and organic agriculture

down the Mississippi River from farms in the Midwest. These nutrients, washed down by floods in the spring, create an environment where algae grows in excess, starving other plants and animals of oxygen, a process called eutrophication.

One aspect of organic agriculture is the use of open pollinating plant varieties. Conventional agriculture often makes use of hybridized plant varieties that can tolerate environmental changes such as mild droughts. Hybrid varieties offer other beneficial traits as well, including resistance to bacteria and other pests. Open pollinating plants, on the other hand, are true varieties of the plants, and when fertilized these plants produce viable seeds. These seeds can then be collected, preserved, and replanted the following season. While these plants may not have the hardiness of some of the hybrid versions, when collected properly the seeds can produce food over and over again.

Are organic foods healthier? Both the USDA and the Mayo Clinic assert that there is no evidence that organically produced food is more nutritious than other foods. However, conventionally grown foods tend to have chemical residues and additives, while the fertilizers used to produce organic foods may carry harmful bacteria, such as E. coli.

Organic foods have other drawbacks. First, the practice of organic agriculture is typically more labor-intensive and requires more man-hours to harvest. Organic farms are also smaller and make up a smaller market share of agriculture. This raises the price of organic food. Another key reason for the price is the lack of food preservatives. Harvested crops do not last as long without the use of preservatives, which can create a larger loss if foods do not sell quickly. Finally, organic farming may require more land to produce the same level of crops, resulting in deforestation.

Even with these limitations, organic agriculture may be a viable way of producing food in underdeveloped countries. Due to limited environmental, financial, and scientific resources, many developing countries struggle to produce enough food for their growing populations. Organic agriculture and its simple farming techniques may be able to increase food production especially in nations that most need it.

US Food Sources

The majority of Americans get their grains and vegetables as produce that was grown on large, open farms throughout the US. The trend since the end of WWII and the start of industrialization has been toward larger, industrial, massive-output farms that make it possible to feed more people for less cost, with a wider variety of produce and a smaller workforce. However, in the 1990s a new trend started to emerge among smaller farms that are also finding niche opportunities, such as growing organic produce or less-common varieties, such as heirloom tomatoes, to create a thriving business and serve their local community. This is another example of how human beings can interact with their environment to bring about solutions while creating jobs and boosting the local economy.

Monoculture (a single crop species planted over a large area for many years) agriculture can be susceptible to crop and economic failure if insect pest or disease outbreaks occur and cannot be controlled. Polyculture (multiple crop species in a given area) may protect against monoculture failures, due to crop diversification.

Polyculture is part of the trend known as sustainable agriculture, which is an approach to farming that also takes into consideration the local needs, much like a corporate farm would grow what can efficiently be sold on a national level. Limitations such as an adequate work force or water supply go into deciding what kinds of crops to farm. This comprehensive overview is known as a **systems perspective**.

The use of farmland is one of the most direct ways human populations interact with their environment as a means to create a sustainable quality of life. History shows that the communities, states, and countries that can most efficiently use their land and natural resources to feed their populace are most likely to be able

SYSTEMS PERSPECTIVE
Used in sustainable agriculture to make operating decisions based on the local ecosystem, the needs of the surrounding community, and governing bodies overseeing a farm.

to also sustain their way of life. Therefore, resources such as water and its proper management become essential to even the most advanced and developed countries and the subject of negotiated and enforced treaties.

MID-CHAPTER QUESTIONS

1. How will the growth in world population affect how food is grown in the future?

2. What are some limitations to organic farming?

3. What is sustainable agriculture?

BUSINESSES GOING GREEN: ORGANIC DAIRIES

Instituting organic processes can be very beneficial for agricultural businesses. An example of a very lucrative type of organic food is organic dairies. Ken Preston, a dairy farmer in Vermont, switched his dairy farm to organic in 2005, and his profits quickly increased 20 percent. Preston, like many other organic dairy farmers, found that supermarket orders skyrocketed. In fact, sales of organic milk grew from 60 million pounds of product in 2006 to nearly 150 million pounds just before 2009.

However, in recent years a major increase in the cost of organic cattle feed has left many organic dairy farmers unsure about the future. Because of the cost of feed and stringent standards that organic farmers need to comply with in order to be certified organic by the USDA, organic milk has become nearly twice as expensive as non-organic milk. As more and more Americans began to watch their budgets during the recession that began in 2008, organic milk began to be considered by many as an extravagance, and demand began to decline. One dairy farmer in Wisconsin watched his income fall 40 percent within a year.

Larger processors have not been immune to the recession of 2008, either. Organic Valley, a nationwide co-operative of farmers, watched as growth fell in 2008 from 20 percent to nearly zero within six months. Many of these large processors were forced to end contracts and decrease production to survive.

To make matters worse, some farms made large investments in their operations in order to convert them into organic dairies. Craig Russell, an organic dairy farmer from Vermont, was $500,000 in debt in 2009, mostly from the conversion to organic he implemented in 2006. Farmers like Russell face an uncertain future due to changes in production, continued increases in costs for organic feed, and large contracts coming to an end.

INTERNATIONAL FOOD DISTRIBUTION

The distribution of food across the globe differs greatly depending on several factors. Each factor weighs differently on food production and distribution. These include the regional biome, infrastructure, poverty level, global economic climate, and governmental factors, including war, closed borders, and corruption.

As discussed in Chapter 2, the Earth consists of seven distinct biomes distributed unevenly across the globe. Of the world's biomes, grasslands, tropical rainforests, and temperate deciduous forests have long growing seasons, warm or moderate temperatures, ample rainfall, and fertile soils. These primary characteristics provide the most ideal climate for food production.

Infrastructure is also a key component of food production, and thus determines whether a nation can grow its own food and provide its citizens access to it. Even countries located in biomes favorable to agriculture that struggle to provide their people access to clean abundant water, equipment, and supplies struggle to produce enough food to feed their people. Coupling this with poor roads and lack of efficient transportation avenues can leave the population undernourished.

The poverty level of a nation also can factor into its distribution of food. According to the World Bank, more than 1.3 billion people across the world live on less than $1.25 a day. This number also coincides with the number of people who are undernourished, 1.02 billion, according to the Food and Agriculture Organization (FAO) of the United Nations (UN). Although related, food insecurity and poverty are not the same. Unemployment rather than poverty is a stronger predictor of food insecurity. In the US, 50.1 million residents lived in food insecure households. Without the ability to purchase supplies or seeds, these numbers will remain high.

The global economic climate also can dictate how food is distributed. From 1997 to 2007 food distribution and donations rose, and those that were undernourished dropped to as low as 792 million people in developing countries around the globe. However, as global financial markets crashed in 2008, the levels of undernourishment rose again. By 2010, the number of undernourished around the globe had risen to 925 million.

Finally, governmental factors affect food distribution and production. Bureaucratic corruption can often divert food away from those who most need it. Furthermore, governments may have sanctions imposed upon them by other

"According to the World Bank, more than 1.3 billion people across the world live on less than $1.25 a day. This number also coincides with the number of people who are undernourished, 1.02 billion, according to the Food and Agriculture Organization (FAO) of the United Nations."

nations prohibiting international trade. Governments may also voluntarily close their own borders to other countries.

For developing countries, food aid, while a necessary short-term solution in times of drought or civil war, can limit local prosperity and sustainability over time. Recent changes to the more common model of developed countries providing large drops of food aid to developing nations are due to higher transportation costs, higher cost for bioengineered foods, and the overall desire for local economies to be self-supporting. The EU, for example, has begun to facilitate "triangular" purchases in which it helps one developing country provide food to another. The World Food Program, a UN program, states that "Sustainability is achieved by contributing to the economies of developing countries through local food procurement rather than obtaining food aid from already developed countries."

Of course, geography plays a role in the variety and type of food available. Different regions, depending on their biome, climate, rainfall, and soil types, are better for growing different types of food. Perhaps most notable is the rice industry of Southeast Asia. The climate of this region provides warm growing seasons and abundant rain. Couple this climate with many generations of farmers perfecting rice cultivation and it is understandable why rice grows so well here. Similarly, the Midwestern United States is known for its ability to grow corn and wheat. Again, consistent, moderately dry, warm seasons aid in the growing of this staple food. This distribution is not limited to continental regions. Consider the types of plants that grow in the US. In the Southeast—such as Florida—citrus fruits and warm-climate plants like tomatoes and strawberries thrive. The Midwest is known for its grains, and central and northern California, with its Mediterranean-like climate, is perfect for growing grapes. While these regions are all within the boundaries of one country, if the US were made up of several smaller nations based on geographic similarities, these food varieties could be distributed unevenly.

People benefit nutritionally from the world food trade as the variety of food available increases with this access to foods from other geographic regions. However, this trade comes at an environmental and economic cost. Transporting food across long distances burns fossil fuels and some food is damaged or spoiled during transport. Purchasing local and seasonal produce can reduce these issues and support local growers, in the US and across the globe.

In fact, the FAO has assessed the food **commodities** produced by countries around the world. This collection of data, which shows the amount produced by monetary value and by metric ton, explains this scenario in great detail. For example, the top five food commodities in the US are maize (corn), beef, milk, chicken, and soybeans. Many processed foods contain soy as filler or for protein enhancement. China is another developed nation with a similar latitude range as the United States, and the top five commodities in China are rice, unspecified vegetables, chicken eggs, maize (corn), and wheat. In the Democratic Republic of Congo (DRC), a developing nation in central Africa, the top five commodities are cassava (a tuber), plantains, groundnuts, game meat, and wheat.

These distributions are starkly different from one another, and a few conclusions might be drawn from comparing these countries. First, both China and the DRC rely much less on high-protein food commodities than the US does (although pork consumption in China has significantly increased in recent years). Also, the DRC's main commodities indicate that industrial agriculture is not well developed there. Finally, regardless of country, high-energy foods form the top of their commodities list. High-energy, carbohydrate foods such as corn, rice, and cassava are an essential part of a

COMMODITY An item that has a marketable value.

healthy diet and in agricultural sense produce more calories per acre than other foods. It should be noted, however, that just as the variety of commodities varies from country to country, the amount produced by each country also varies. The amount of food supplies varies greatly depending on both population and (perhaps more so) economic development.

Increasing Access for the World

Several factors hamper the industrial model abroad. First is the access to resources, both natural resources, such as water for irrigation or abundant rainfall, and financial resources. Areas such as those in and around the Sahara desert are prime examples of a **limiting factor**. These arid areas do not support the large-scale farming operations that produce food in other places. Furthermore, desert areas have limited amounts of fertile land for agriculture. In some cases where land and natural resources are available, financial resources become limiting factors. Developing nations such as Mongolia, Angola, and Cambodia often lack the infrastructure and finances, both on a governmental and individual level, to purchase large-scale equipment or irrigation systems.

Because of these socio-economic factors facing developing nations, smaller, more intensive forms of agriculture and gardening may be the answer for feeding undernourished populations. Intensive forms of agriculture rely on **successive planting**, space-saving techniques, and **companion planting**. These techniques, coupled with organic measures, can help produce ample food supplies with little financial input and limited arable land.

Successive planting actually encompasses two different characteristics of crop production: successive planting and **relay planting**. Successive planting involves rotating different varieties of plants out of the same location in the garden in the same season. In most temperate climates, including the majority of the US, the growing season can be divided into three parts: spring, summer, and fall. Each of these sub-seasons of the larger growing season can be used to grow specific plants that thrive during these sub-seasons. Spring and fall crops can be very similar to one another since both of these seasons characteristically have shorter days with moderate daytime temperatures and brisk nighttime temperatures. There are a number of plant varieties that grow well in these cooler temperatures but struggle or even die as the warmer summer months arrive. Crops such as *Brassica* plants (kale, turnips, cabbage, broccoli, and Brussel sprouts), lettuces, and different pea varieties all do well in cooler temperatures.

As the season warms, crops such as tomatoes, peppers, and high-energy plants such as beans and corn are more suitable for growing. As this season continues and cools, new cooler-weather plants can be planted again. The key to successive planting is to have young seedling plants ready to replace plants that have finished producing their fruit, which provides a variety of crops throughout the year.

Akin to successive planting is relay planting. Relay planting involves staggering the same plants throughout a particular growing season in order to have harvests throughout the season. For example, growers with small plots may begin growing corn at the beginning of a summer season and then plant seeds approximately every two weeks to create a continuous crop that can be collected throughout the season.

LIMITING FACTOR Something that restricts the growth of a desired entity.

SUCCESSIVE PLANTING A method of agriculture in which different varieties of plants are rotated in and out of the same location.

COMPANION PLANTING A method of agriculture in which plants that grow well and benefit from one another are planted in close proximity.

RELAY PLANTING A method of agriculture where the same plant variety is planted over a staggered time period to ensure crop yield throughout the growing season.

Space-saving techniques involve several ways to grow plants that maximize the soil in small garden plots to produce the largest yield per square foot. These techniques include square-foot gardening, vertical gardening, and raised-bed gardening. Space-saving techniques like these often are implemented together. Square-foot gardening is the notion of creating a grid over the garden area, either on paper during layout of a garden or directly on the garden itself. Then, within each square-foot grid space, crops are planted based on previous research that determined how many plants of each variety can fit inside a square foot. For example, one broccoli plant can grow well in a square foot but 16 carrots can grow well in the same space. By planting using this data and planting crops that work well together, no space is wasted and maximum yields can be obtained. If the crop density is too high, failures are likely because too many plants are competing for limited resources, such as water, light, and nutrients. Also, if weeds are present, the weeds will compete for the same resources, leading to reduced yields or crop failures. Optimal crop density techniques apply to all levels of farming, whether home gardens or massive industrial-scale production farms.

Vertical gardening is often used in conjunction with square-foot gardening to help increase the amount of vining plants that can be grown in an area. Commonly, plants like tomatoes are caged or trained up trellises to not only support the plant but to create ground space as well. Traditionally plants like cucumbers and melons, both vining plants, are run on the ground and may grow to be several feet long. This can limit the number of individual plants as well as the space for different plants. However, by training vining plants to grow vertically, these plants can be spaced just a few inches apart, thus leaving greater area open for other varieties.

Both square-foot gardening and vertical gardening are often used with raised beds. Raised-bed gardening uses a simple, constructed frame (generally no larger than four feet by eight feet) filled with soil that sits on top of any surface. Raised beds allow gardens to be placed where they otherwise may not succeed, and they minimize the amount of equipment needed to tend the plants. Between the beds are often walkways to get to all four sides, which creates easy access to all plants and, because it is raised, helps keep some pests out of the garden.

Companion planting is also a space-saving technique that is often used alongside the methods described above. Companion planting involves planting crops that grow well beside each other and that may even benefit one another. A prime example of this is carrots and leeks; both grow well mixed together. However, there is an added benefit to planting them together. Carrots are often preyed upon by the carrot fly, and leeks' most common pests are the leek moth and onion fly. When planted together, the combined plant smell does not attract any of these pests and thus acts as a natural pest deterrent. There are many examples of different vegetables and herbs that when planted together not only help each other grow but deter pests from one another in a symbiotic way.

One of the major advantages of this style of agriculture is that it can be done in small areas with little money. Coupling these methods with organic techniques reduces the financial investment required. As mentioned above, two of the most common aspects of organic gardening are the creation of a gardener's own fertilizer by making compost and open pollinating of non-hybrid seeds. By creating compost using animal waste, leaves, grasses, and the remains of vegetables, even a fairly inhospitable soil can be made fertile, which in turn maximize yields. And by using open-pollinating, non-hybridized seeds, even an impoverished family can continue to grow vegetables year after year with only a small initial investment. Another benefit to using this type of seed is that the plant produces an overabundance of seeds that in turn can be passed on or swapped for different varieties, while maintaining enough seeds to continue growing. This bartering style of seed sharing can create a diverse diet in a community with very little invested monetarily.

Another benefit to both organic gardening and the use of space-saving gardening is a decrease in use of resources, such as water. The addition of organic matter to a soil system has a myriad of benefits. Besides increasing the soil's natural fertility, it also increases beneficial bacteria growth, such as bacteria that are responsible for **nitrogen fixation**, it increases the holding capacity for a number of beneficial minerals, and it buffers the soil temperature from both hot and cold extremes. An additional benefit to the addition of organic material to a soil is increased water-holding capacity. When water-holding capacity of soil is increased, the amount of water needed per area can be reduced. Because more water is able to absorb into the soil, runoff is diminished. Using space-saving techniques, more plants are located in a compact and centralized area, which also decreases the need for water and also decreases the distance that the water must be transported to benefit different crops.

This style of gardening is also well-adapted to urban settings where land parcels are extremely tiny and population density is high. The Dervaes Institute in Pasadena, California, and Growing Power in Milwaukee, Wisconsin, are examples of this intensive organic gardening. The Dervaes Institute is a small, self-sustaining farm in downtown Pasadena, sandwiched between several major highways, 30 minutes north of Los Angeles and just minutes from the Rose Bowl. The entire lot, including the house, takes up only one-fifth of an acre; the garden plot consists of just one-tenth of an acre. Yet on a plot of less than 4,000 square feet, the farm is able to produce more than 6,000 pounds of food annually, from over 400 varieties of plants. Not only does the Dervaes Institute grow that much produce, but staff also collect over 2,000 chicken eggs a year; produce up to 50 pounds of honey; raise tilapia (a species of fish) in a self-sustaining **aquaponic system**; and make their own bio-diesel for fuel. This output is not only able to sustain a family of four throughout the year, but also grosses over $20,000 annually from produce sales.

Growing Power runs a nonprofit urban farm on two acres of ground that is the only remaining active greenhouse in Milwaukee. It is also the largest year-round grower in the state of Wisconsin. The Milwaukee facilities include six traditional greenhouses, nine hoop houses, 14 beehives, poultry houses, livestock pens for goats and turkeys, fish ponds, and a retail store. There is also an aquaculture system set up to raise both tilapia and yellow perch. The aquaculture system is filtered through different raised beds of watercress, a green leafy vegetable, and then returned back to the ponds. Using this method of filtration cuts the cost of aquaculture while simultaneously fertilizing the watercress. Growing Power also creates compost from its own and other local sources, such as restaurants and breweries, that is used to fertilize the vegetables and is sold to the public. The two-acre farm is able to raise one million pounds of food annually, which is sold to various restaurants and the public.

In 2005, Urban Habitat Chicago (UHC) proposed to a local organic cooperative—True Nature Foods—a unique opportunity to rehabilitate an old automotive shop in a Chicago neighborhood to create a sustainable urban garden. The site was chosen because it was originally used as a victory garden during WWII to

NITROGEN FIXATION Biological process in which bacteria living in soil (and symbiotically with plants) transform and store nitrogen compounds that can be readily used by plants.

AQUAPONIC SYSTEM An agricultural production technique in which plants and aquatic animals are raised in a symbiotic manner. Animal waste is used to fertilize the plants, and the plants then serve as a filter to produce clean water that is returned to the animal tank.

help provide families with fresh vegetables during a period of wartime food rationing. The brick building was largely unusable due to a lack of insulation in a city with extreme winters. The project was originally meant to be a beta test to see what kind of retrofitting could be done to green a building on a limited budget.

The project was designed to take place in phases, with the first phase focused on winterizing, to make work in the building bearable during the winter months. Next, the plan called for south-facing trellises with vines dangling from the roof garden to create a natural awning during the hot summer months. There would also be solar curtains to work with the sun, planters as benches to help with temperature swings, solar heaters, and raised planting beds. The organizers, along with UHC, applied for local and federal grants to help with funding the variety of projects and also sought assistance from a local architecture firm to ensure their plan was structurally sound.

This project is a good example of how it is possible to take a sustainable idea and work with a variety of business and government organizations in a cooperative effort to ensure success. The Victory Garden, as it is now known, has been successfully planting a rooftop garden—largely with the use of volunteers—for years. The success has encouraged volunteers to expand their idea of what's possible by incorporating innovative ideas like a rooftop irrigation system.

These examples could be and are being used across the globe to answer the food needs of impoverished people. Even in large urban areas, small gardens in raised beds or containers can provide ample food for individual families with little monetary investment. Raised beds or containers can also help gardeners in small villages where water access is limited.

Some developing countries have also taken to GMOs as a solution to increase domestic yields, reduce money spent on fertilizers and pesticides, and increase productivity. As of 2010, the International Service for the Acquisition of Agri-biotech Applications (ISAAA), a nonprofit that monitors international GMO use and production, reports that developing countries now grow half of the world's genetically modified crops, led by Brazil and followed by Argentina, India, and China. Most of these efforts to increase production of GMOs are local, such as in China where the government, late in 2009, approved some strains of genetically modified rice. This could have a significant impact on feeding China's growing population.

Hunger, Malnutrition, and Famine

While there are key difference between **hunger, malnourishment**, and **famine**, they are interconnected. It is important to understand the definitions and difference that each of these terms entail. Equally important is to understand how they connect to one another. In the context discussed here hunger does not refer to common hunger pangs or a bodily desire to eat a meal. In this context hunger relates to the lack of food or the scarcity of food and generally refers to the amount of available food in a country or region.

Malnourishment can result from extended periods of hunger. Malnourishment in most basic terms is the lack of proper nourishment. The general types of malnourishment are nutrient- and vitamin-deficient (which will be addressed later) and **protein-energy malnourishment (PEM)**. PEM is the most lethal type of malnourishment because proteins and their building blocks—amino acids—drive the cellular reactions in an organism's body. A lack of these amino acids and proteins can cause organ failure and anemia, among other serious illnesses. Increasing the problem of PEM is that due to the general lack of food, those suffering from it usually lose a great deal of weight,

HUNGER Lack of food for a region or group of people.

MALNOURISHMENT Lack of food and proper nutrition and its effect on people.

FAMINE Widespread lack of food caused by climatic and/or political policies.

PROTEIN-ENERGY MALNOURISHMENT The most dangerous form of malnourishment, caused by a lack of sufficient protein.

FAO focuses primarily on agriculture and often works with impoverished people to help them develop their own agricultural industry. This can be in the form of small microgardens in urban settings, larger greenhouse systems, or agricultural development on a larger scale in more rural areas. Their work revolves around helping those who are hungry become more self-sufficient. Their primary goal is to help all people obtain food security.

The World Food Program (WFP) focuses its attention on global emergency relief efforts. Since the FAO helps later in the process, after the crops mature, the WFP meets the impending need for immediate nourishment. In this role, the WFP donates an average or 3.7 million tons of food annually to 73 different nations, following a five-point mission:

1. Save lives and livelihoods during emergencies.
2. Prepare for emergencies.
3. Restore and rebuild lives after emergencies.
4. Reduce chronic hunger and undernourishment.
5. Strengthen the capacity of countries to reduce hunger.

The US government has several entities that both provide food and help encourage agricultural development in developing countries. The US military has long distributed food supplies in countries facing famine events. Two specific organizations addressing world hunger within the confines of the US government are Food Aid and the Peace Corps.

The US Food Aid and Security Coalition is a conglomerate of three different programs that have been signed into law over the years. Food Aid works in conjunction with NGOs and the USDA to operate the Food for Peace, Food for Progress, and Food for Education relief organizations.

Food for Peace is a program signed into law by President Dwight D. Eisenhower and later restructured by President John F. Kennedy. Its main goal is to promote food security in developing countries. Food for Progress, which was signed into law in 1985, is run through the USDA's Foreign Agricultural Service. The organization strives to help emerging democracies develop free market agricultural industries. Food for Education was founded in 2002; it focuses on increasing nutrition and education in impoverished countries and is also run by the USDA's Foreign Agricultural Service.

The Peace Corps is a volunteer outreach of the US. It maintains a variety of projects around the globe, ranging from basic education to health training to business leadership development to agricultural projects. The Peace Corps' agricultural extension works with farmers around the world to develop sustainable methods of agriculture. These include vegetable garden development, animal husbandry, conservation projects, agroforestry initiatives, and food security projects. By working with local farmers, Peace Corps volunteers enable the local population to be self-sufficient.

NGOs can include faith-based organizations and non-faith based service organizations. They also often work in close proximity with world and local governments to maximize their efforts. Examples of these types of organizations include the Resource Center for Urban Agriculture and Food Security (RUAF) Foundation, Food for the Hungry, the Islamic Relief Foundation, and perhaps the most well-known anti-hunger organization, Feed the Children.

Some groups like the RUAF coordinate with other organizations to encourage and develop urban gardens in some of the most impoverished countries. Through their seven different resource centers, they have helped create food-producing centers in the heart of cities in over 15 countries. Not only are they concerned with decreasing hunger in these urban areas, but also decreasing poverty by developing employment opportunities at gardens and markets. RUAF does this while attempting to develop complete self-sufficiency among the people of these developing countries.

There are numerous faith-based organizations addressing hunger that span all religions. Two well-known Christian organizations are Food for the Hungry and Feed the Children. Both of these organizations work to help the hungry, but, like the difference between the WFP and FAO, they also serve different roles. Food for the Hungry's mission revolves around four different tenets:

- Food Security
- Food Access
- Food Availability
- Food Utilization

These tenets are addressed by working with the poor and hungry to increase crop production, teach them beneficial animal husbandry skills, develop working water wells, inspire entrepreneurial endeavors, and develop cash crops. These and other activities performed by Food for the Hungry help increase food yield while they work to decrease poverty.

Feed the Children—a faith-based organization founded in 1979—has long-been one of the top ten international charities based in the US. Funded on private donations, their mission is to provide hope and resources to those without life's essentials. The group follows this mission by delivering food, medicine, clothing and other essential equipment to people in all 50 US states and throughout the globe. In 2010, Feed the Children distributed over 133 million pounds of food and supplies internationally.

As mentioned before, faith based organizations are not limited to just Christian organizations. Islamic Relief Worldwide is a non-profit organization based out of the United Kingdom (UK) that works to aid the hungry and impoverished. However, their scope of work goes beyond food. They also provide small business loans

MID-CHAPTER QUESTIONS

1. Describe two limiting factors associated with food distribution worldwide.

2. What are the differences between hunger and malnourishment?

3. What are some ways that malnourishment is being dealt with around the world?

to impoverished areas, work to dig clean wells to give the poorest people access the clean drinking water, and offer a host of health initiatives globally.

FOOD SECURITY

Contrary to what it sounds like, food security does not refer to the safety of food alone. According to the World Food Summit, food security is defined as "when all people at all times have access to sufficient, safe, nutritious food to maintain a healthy and active life." Not only are there a staggering number of people struggling with malnutrition, but they are also often burdened with food-borne illnesses that cause potentially fatal bouts of diarrhea.

Because of this twofold issue, the World Health Organization (WHO) identified three separate requirements for true food security:

- **food availability**—sufficient quantities of food available on a consistent basis
- **food access**—having sufficient resources to obtain appropriate foods for a nutritious diet
- **food use**—appropriate use, based on knowledge of basic nutrition and care as well as adequate water and sanitation

Meeting all three of these requirements is necessary before food security can be achieved.

It should be noted that even though an area or family has ample amount of food, they may still suffer from malnutrition. It is important to understand that malnutrition does not equate always to a lack of food but can also be the lack of a nutritious diet. This requires a diet to be balanced with ample amounts of fruits, vegetables, meats, fats, dairy products, and carbohydrates. Even in developed nations like the US, this type of malnutrition can affect large populations of people. This occurs especially in urban areas where fresh produce is not available and incomes are low, as well as in very rural areas where access to stores is limited due to distance. These areas are referred to as food deserts and often contain a high number of fast-food restaurants and small convenience stores with few grocery stores or fresh produce markets. This type of malnutrition can be difficult to diagnose because there is often an abundance of calories but not enough nutrients.

All global food relief efforts must be cognizant of the normal dietary staples for the recipients. Many people around the world are not able to adapt to an "American" or "European" diet. Also, many people, particularly adults in some African nations, do not possess the proper digestive enzymes to effectively process dairy products. In

"A recent FAO report estimates that over 1.3 billion tons of food—about one third of the food produced globally each year—is wasted when food that is still edible is discarded."

effect, they are lactose-intolerant. So, the best intentions to provide milk to starving people can actually do more harm than good.

Contrasting issues such as malnourishment due to a lack of food and malnourishment because of an abundance of food with low nutritional value have created a debate about food security globally. The argument has been made that there is an abundance of food for the Earth's entire population; the problem is the inequality in the distribution of the food. A recent FAO report estimates that over 1.3 billion tons of food—about one third of the food produced globally each year—is wasted each year when food that is still edible is discarded. The case for poor distribution can be made by noting that people in wealthy countries waste nearly the same amount of food annually as the entire food production of the sub-Saharan region: 222 million tons wasted in wealthy countries compared to 230 million tons produced in the sub-Saharan region.

Food supplies are squandered in one of two ways: through loss or through waste. Losses occur primarily during the harvesting and processing steps. Meanwhile, waste occurs when both retailers and consumers dispose of edible food, usually due to appearance issues, like skin blemishes and spots. Per capita, consumers in Europe and North America waste on average between 209 pounds and 253 pounds of food annually. Unfortunately, it is difficult to transport fresh food from one continent to another. Aside from the logistics of transporting that volume of food, maintaining freshness and preventing rot would be nearly impossible. Developing better ways of distributing food to areas that suffer shortages could help move the global population towards food security.

The global food trade is important to food security as it contributes to the food supply, makes use of resources and reduces waste, and can provide economic advantages to participating countries. However, developing countries rely heavily on food imports to reduce undernourishment and the economics is not sustainable. Experience has shown that to increase food security, a country must have some agricultural development that provides for the local population and produces exports for additional economic stability.

Another issue that is part of food security is food safety. The ability to protect people from food-borne pathogens is paramount in combating malnutrition. *E. coli* poisoning, *Listeria*, and Salmonella are common diseases that are caused by the mishandling of food and undercooking of meats. These types of disease affect people in both developed countries and developing countries—especially at-risk populations such as those with existing illnesses—and the very young and very old. However, due to a lack of medical aid and previous malnourishment, food-borne pathogens and their subsequent diseases can have a deadlier effect on populations in developing nations.

There are approximately 31 different varieties of food-borne pathogens that can cause illness in humans. In the US alone, 48 million people—the equivalent of 1 in 6—get sick from food-borne pathogens annually. Of these 48 million, 128,000 people are hospitalized and 3,000 eventually die from these diseases. Outbreaks of food-borne pathogens occur often.

For example, in the US there were 26 different food recalls issued for the month of October 2011. One of the most well-known of these was the Listeria outbreak that occurred in October 2011, caused by improperly handled cantaloupes. Investigators are still not sure how the bacteria first contaminated the farm, but they theorize that a dump truck that was used to take poor-quality cantaloupes to a nearby cattle farm may have brought back the bacteria with it. Within a span of approximately two months, 133 cases of Listeria spanning 26 states had been identified, with 28 confirmed deaths. To protect the population from such food-borne threats, developed countries, especially, have very stringent regulations that govern the production, packaging, and transportation of food. Unfortunately, outbreaks of food-borne disease occasionally occur even with such safeguards in place.

The number of outbreaks of food-borne disease is much higher internationally, exacerbated in developing nations by these countries' limited financial and manpower resources to inspect farms and processing centers for bacteria and handling procedures. In 2005, an estimated 1.8 million people worldwide died from a diarrheal disease associated with contaminated food or drinking water.

Perhaps the best way to promote global food security is not large-scale aid or agriculture but to help individuals provide themselves with food. Sometimes large-scale aid results in local farmers no longer being able to sell their crops. They then look for other work, resulting in fewer small farms and an increased dependency on food aid. Small-scale production like the Dervaes Institute in Pasadena, California, and microgardens in Africa are examples of economical self-sustaining agriculture that can provide enough produce for a family and have supplies left over. Not only would ample food grow, but also a well-balanced nutritional diet would be created. Creating avenues for people living in poverty to sustain themselves also acts as a buffer against a global economic crisis that could drive more into poverty.

MID-CHAPTER QUESTIONS

1. Describe the difference between food availability, food use, and food access.

2. What are two issues that affect food safety?

3. Think of some ways that food waste can be eliminated or reduced.

CHAPTER SUMMARY

Since humans began the transition from hunting and gathering to an agrarian lifestyle, people have attempted to modify the plants they cultivate to maximize crop yields. Splicing plants is a method humans have used to obtain specific results or to raise plants that are difficult to grow from seed. Splicing involves splicing the scion of one plant onto the rootstock of another plant. Another method of achieving plants with certain characteristics is cross-pollination. Interspecies cross-pollination involves members of the same species and is commonly used to maximize a desired trait that each plant shares. Intergenus cross-pollination involves plants that are closely related but are members of different species. They are used to produce non-viable offspring with specialized traits. Other agricultural advancements include pesticides,

PRESERVATION: MAINTAINING SOIL HEALTH

Due to limited financial and material resources in many developing nations, simple small food plots are key to growing food. Since these food plots are generally small and urban in nature, it is necessary to intensively tend these areas using techniques like successive plantings, replay plantings, and vertical gardening. In order to maximize yield, good soil health is paramount.

Throughout a growing season, nutrients, especially the essential elements nitrogen (N), phosphorus (P), and potassium (K), are constantly being drawn out of the soil to feed plants.

In industrial farming systems, large amounts of these fertilizers, many of which are synthetic chemicals, are applied to replenish soil nutrients. However, in poor countries with little resources available, these nutrients must be replaced in other ways, such as by the addition of organic material and compost.

The addition of **organic material** is a cheap, accessible, and highly efficient way of replenishing nutrients in the soil. Organic material can be comprised of animal waste, plant or grass clippings, and mulch. Organic material increases the soil's **water holding capacity**, which means that water stays near the surface longer, where plants can use it.

Organic material also increases microbial activity in the soil. There are in fact a number of beneficial bacteria found in soil. These bacteria, through a process called **mineralization**, convert organic forms of N, P, and K into inorganic forms, such as nitrogen found in manure into NO_3, (or nitrate). Plants can absorb these inorganic forms of nitrogen, which are water-soluble and can be distributed through the root system.

Organic material also buffers the soil from temperature changes during night and day cycles. Because organic material is dark in nature, it absorbs and holds thermal energy throughout the night better than soil alone, much like insulation in a home. This temperature buffering action allows plants to grow healthier and protects the plant from extreme temperature swings.

ORGANIC MATERIAL
Carbon-based material generally from a plant or animal.

WATER HOLDING CAPACITY The ability for a soil to retain water from rain or irrigation events.

MINERALIZATION The transformation, (by specialized bacteria), of organic forms of nitrogen, phosphorus, and potassium into inorganic forms that can be absorbed by plants.

irrigation, and genetic engineering, the latter of which is the most modern and involves adding or deleting specific genes in plants. Examples include Bt corn (insect pest resistant), salt water-tolerant tomatoes, and drought-tolerant corn.

Along with the emergence of genetically engineered plants, there has been an increased interest in organic gardening and agriculture. Organic agriculture involves limited or no chemical additions to plants in the form of pesticides, herbicides, or fertilizers. Characteristics of organic agriculture include composting of dead organic material, open or free-range livestock, open pollinating seeds, and sometimes, intensive gardening methods. These methods include successive planting, relay planting, and space saving methods.

Even with these advancements, hunger and malnourishment exist worldwide. In 2010, an estimated 925 million people worldwide were undernourished. The majority of these people are found in heavily populated regions of Asia and the Pacific and dry and arid regions of sub-Saharan Africa. These regions are often home to developing nations that are densely populated and very poor. Because of these factors, access to food and food security itself is not easily obtainable. Organizations such as the FAO, WFP, USAID, Feed the Children, and others work to provide food to those who are malnourished and help these communities move toward becoming self-sustaining with regard to food production.

REFERENCES

The adoption of genetically modified crops: Growth areas [Web log post]. (2011, February 23). *The Economist online.* Retrieved from http://www.economist.com/blogs/dailychart/2011/02/adoption_genetically_modified_crops

Agropolis Museum. (2011). History of food and agriculture. Retrieved from http://museum.agropolis.fr/english/pages/expos/fresque/la_fresque.htm

Bloy, M. (2002, October 11). Irish potato famine. *The Victorian Web.* Retrieved from http://www.victorianweb.org/history/famine.html

Centers for Disease Control and Prevention. (2011). Food borne pathogens. Retrieved from http://www.cdc.gov/foodborneburden/index.html

Cendrowicz, L. (2010, March 9). Is Europe finally ready for genetically modified foods? *Time Business.* Retrieved from http://www.time.com/time/business/article/0,8599,1970471,00.html

Coleman-Jensen, A., Nord, M., Andrews, M., & Carlson, S. (2011, September). *Household food security in the United States in 2010* (USDA Economic Research Report No. ERR-125). Retrieved from http://www.ers.usda.gov/publications/err-economic-research-report/err125.aspx

Dervaes Institute. (2011). Food production. Retrieved from http://urbanhomestead.org/urban-homestead

Environmental Protection Agency. (2013, January). Plant incorporated protectants. Retrieved from http://www.epa.gov/oppbppd1/biopesticides/pips/

European Commission. (n.d.). Health and consumers: Food: Genetically modified food and feed—What are GMOs? Retrieved from http://ec.europa.eu/food/food/biotechnology/gmo_en.htm

Food and Agriculture Organization of the United Nations. (1999). Agricultural trade fact sheet: Agricultural trade and food security. Retrieved from http://www.fao.org/docrep/003/X6730E/X6730E03.HTM

Food and Agriculture Organization of the United Nations. (2005). Food Commodities by Country. Retrieved from http://www.fao.org/es/ess/top/country.html;jsessionid=D4F0856C80F7F6076552D1CA714FF9F8

Food and Agriculture Organization of the United Nations. (2011). Somalia famine. Retrieved from http://www.fao.org/news/story/en/item/89101/icode/

Genetically engineered tomato plant grows in salty water. (2001, July 25). *UC Davis News and Information.* Retrieved from http://www.news.ucdavis.edu/search/news_detail.lasso?id=5840

Growing Power. (2011). Milwaukee farm. Retrieved from http://growingpower.org/headquarters.htm

Highfield, R. (2007, November 26). GM plant grows with 1/3 of usual water. *The Telegraph.* Retrieved from http://www.telegraph.co.uk/science/science-news/3316059/GM-plant-grows-with-13-of-usual-water.html

Irrigation Museum. (2013). History of irrigation. Retrieved from http://www.irrigationmuseum.org/exhibit2.aspx

Kaufman. L. (2011, June 2). Chemicals in farm run off rattle states on the Mississippi. *New York Times.* Retrieved from http://www.nytimes.com/2011/06/03/science/earth/03runoff.html?pagewanted=all

Meng, X., Qian, N., & Yared, P. (2011, November 22). *Institutional causes of China's great famine, 1959–1961.* Retrieved from http://federation.ens.fr/ydepot/semin/texte1213/NAN2012INS.pdf

Mudge, K., Janick, J., Scofield, S., & Goldschmidt, E. E. (2009). *A history of grafting.* Retrieved from http://www.hort.purdue.edu/newcrop/janick-papers/c09.pdf

Pesticide Management Education Program, Cornell University. (1993, September). Extension toxicology network: Rotenone. Retrieved from http://pmep.cce.cornell.edu/profiles/extoxnet/pyrethrins-ziram/rotenone-ext.html

Shuping, N. (2011, March 7). China GMO corn hits policy deadlock. *Reuters*. Retrieved from http://af.reuters.com/article/cameroonNews/idAFTOE72604L20110307?pageNumber=2&virtualBrandChannel=0

Union of Concerned Scientists. (2009, April 14). Genetic engineering has failed to significantly boost U.S. crop yields despite biotech industry claims. Retrieved from http://ucsusa.org/news/press_release/ge-fails-to-increase-yields-0219.html

United Human Rights Council. (n.d.). Ukrainian famine. Retrieved from http://www.unitedhumanrights.org/genocide/ukraine_famine.htm

United Nations. (2009). *Report to the General Assembly on food procurement in developing countries.* Retrieved from http://www.amun.org/uploads/09_Final_Report/WFP-I-Report.pdf

Unsworth, J. (2010, May 10). History of pesticide use. Retrieved from http://agrochemicals.iupac.org/index.php?option=com_sobi2&sobi2Task=sobi2Details&catid=3&sobi2Id=31

U.S. Department of Agriculture. (n.d.). Biotechnology. Retrieved from http://www.usda.gov/wps/portal/usda/usdahome?contentid=BiotechnologyFAQs.xml&navid=AGRICULTURE

U.S. Department of Agriculture. (2012). Key statistics and graphics. Retrieved from http://www.ers.usda.gov/topics/food-nutrition - assistance/food-security-in-the-us/key-statistics-graphics.aspx#insecure

U.S. Food Aid and Security. (2010). Food aid programs. Retrieved from http://foodaid.org/food-aid-programs/food-aid-facts/

World Health Organization. (2011). Food security. Retrieved from http://www.who.int/trade/glossary/story028/en/

World Hunger. (2010). World hunger statistics. Retrieved from http://www.worldhunger.org/articles/Learn/world%20hunger%20facts%202002.htm

Zexima, K. (2009, May 28). Organic dairies watch the good times turn bad. *New York Times.* Retrieved from http://www.nytimes.com/2009/05/29/us/29dairy.html

Water

The Aral Sea

THE DISAPPEARANCE OF THE ARAL SEA

The Aral Sea, located on the border of Kazakhstan and Uzbekistan, was once the fourth largest inland lake in the world. Supported by freshwater inflows from the Amu Darya River to the south and the Syr Darya River to the east, the Aral Sea sustained a vast ecosystem of aquatic life as well as the economies of fishing communities surrounding the rivers and lake. Changes to the Aral Sea began with the Soviet Union's decision to divert water from the Amu Darya and Syr Darya Rivers. Increased demand for agricultural production in the Soviet Union, which required additional water resources, began a sequence of events that markedly change the composition of the Aral Sea, culminating in its near-disappearance in 2005. At this time, the Aral Sea had lost half of its surface area, exposing more than 30,000 square kilometers of its lake bed. Destruction of the lake resulted in the devastation of the ecosystems supported by the Aral Sea as well as the loss of hundreds of thousands of jobs related to the fishing industry.

While the loss of ecosystems and livelihoods represent substantial problems in and of themselves, the disappearance of the Aral Sea has exposed other threats to environmental and human health. The revealed lake bed left communities exposed to dust storms, which continue to pose a significant health hazard. The use of the Amu Darya and Syr Darya Rivers for agricultural development resulted in the dumping of large amounts of chemicals (such as pesticides and fertilizers) in the lake. As the lake dried up, the water and some of the liquid chemical solvents evaporated, but the chemical solids remained behind. The soil in the lake bed became contaminated with these chemicals. Thus, the resulting dust storms produce toxic dust that has been linked to numerous health problems including cancer, respiratory illness, kidney disease, and liver disease.

PERSPECTIVES ON WATER POLLUTION

Water pollution occurs when foreign materials are discharged into water. Foreign materials can include a wide range of substances, such as sewage, industrial waste, agricultural waste, and oil. The Environmental Protection Agency (EPA) classifies water pollution as originating from point sources or non-point sources. **Point source** pollution originates from specific locations and is released in quantities above a particular threshold or standard. Point source pollution can be traced back to a point of origin, such as a smokestack, sewage treatment plant, or industrial complex. Local, state, and federal laws have been established to help regulate the emission of point source water pollutants. In most instances, potential point sources of water pollution are regulated so that water emitted from these points is treated before it is released from its source. Water treatment reduces pollution levels to help ensure that the water is safe for the environment.

Non-point source pollution is a less discrete and less localized form of water pollution that is more difficult for regulators to control. In its simplest form, non-point source water pollution is any type of water pollution that does not meet the criteria for point source pollution. Non-point source pollution occurs when water from agricultural runoff, precipitation, or drainage filters through land and collects pollutants that have been left in the environment. It also occurs when pollutants in the air become trapped in precipitation and are returned to the Earth's surface (e.g., acid deposition). Pollutants collected from non-point sources become part of the water cycle and are deposited into rivers, streams, lakes, and coastal waters. Examples of non-point source water pollution include excess fertilizers and livestock waste from agricultural lands that become trapped in water runoff; excess oil and chemicals released from energy production that have polluted the soil and become trapped in rain or melting snow; and water drainage through abandoned mines that deposits chemicals into groundwater systems.

Non-point sources of water pollution contribute substantially to water quality problems and the contamination of potable drinking water supplies. Because the origins of non-point source pollution can be difficult to identify, reducing non-point source water pollution requires a comprehensive approach to reducing all environmental pollution, including soil and air pollution. Individuals can help reduce non-point

WATER POLLUTION Foreign materials added to water.

POINT SOURCE Pollution released in quantities above a particular threshold or standard and that can be traced back to a point of origin.

NON-POINT SOURCE Water pollution that cannot be traced back to a single point of origin.

1. How have chemicals such as pesticides and fertilizers impacted the health of communities living along the borders of the Aral Sea?

2. Could the disappearance of the Aral Sea have been prevented? How?

source water pollution by recycling chemicals such as oil used in automobiles rather than releasing it into the ground. In addition, non-point source water pollution can be reduced when individuals use fertilizers and lawn chemicals responsibly and use detergents that are low in phosphorus. By reducing the amount of chemicals released into the environment, these actions help ensure that non-point source water contamination is controlled over the long term.

Although it can be classified as point source or non-point source, water pollution can also be classified by type. While nearly any foreign material dissolved or suspended in water can be considered a pollutant, water pollution falls into several common types based on the substances involved.

Sewage and Wastewater

In most developed nations, sewage and wastewater, including laundry waste, is removed from buildings through sewage systems. Sewage is then transported to a local treatment plant where environmental contaminants are removed. In developing nations, sewage systems are often non-existent, allowing sewage to contaminate the soil, ground water, and air. Wastewater contamination of drinking water supplies can result in diseases such as dysentery and typhoid fever, which are common in many developing nations.

Industrial Waste

Industry is a substantial source of water pollution because it produces wastes that are significantly harmful to the environment. Many industrial facilities use fresh-water from rivers and lakes in their operation. When this water is released back into the environment after use as industrial wastewater, it typically contains chemicals used in the industrial processes. Examples of pollutants emitted from industrial facilities include asbestos, lead, mercury, nitrates, phosphates, and oil. The chemicals used for hydraulic fracturing (fracking), which is a natural gas and petroleum extraction process, can contaminate soil and water, if improperly handled.

Each of these pollutants has the potential to cause substantial harm to drinking water systems via point and non-point sources.

Nuclear Waste

Nuclear waste is produced in operations that use radioactive materials. Although it is not a central energy resource in the United States (US), nuclear power supplies most of the energy consumed in France. In other nations such as China, South Korea, and India, nuclear power has become more widely used, and new reactors are currently being built. Nuclear waste produced by power plants can pollute water systems. Nuclear waste from power plants in Europe has become one of the largest sources of waste in oceans surrounding the European Union (EU).

Petroleum

Oil from spills, shipping, runoff, and dumping is also a substantial source of water pollution. Water pollution caused by oil often represents a localized problem that can have catastrophic consequences for marine ecosystems. One high-profile example is the BP oil leak that occurred in the Gulf of Mexico in April 2010. This underwater leak unleashed millions of gallons of crude oil into the ocean, killing large numbers of fish, birds, dolphins, and turtles and impacting wetlands, fisheries, and human communities along the Gulf Coast.

Atmospheric Deposition

Greenhouse gases such as carbon dioxide (CO_2), sulfur dioxide, and nitrogen oxides are most commonly associated with air pollution. However, when these gases mix with water vapor in the atmosphere, they produce acids. These dissolved acids can then be deposited back on the Earth's surface in the form of precipitation, commonly known as "acid rain" (though it can also be in the form of snow). Such atmospheric deposition can adversely impact aquatic ecosystems and render groundwater resources non-potable.

Other Sources

In addition to several substances that can contribute to the pollution of water resources, there are many natural and man-made events that contribute to the development of water pollution. For instance, marine dumping has become a substantial source of water pollution in recent years. Marine dumping occurs when trash is released into water systems such as lakes or coastal areas. The most prominent example of marine dumping can be seen in the Great Pacific Garbage Patch. This floating mass of trash stretches across the North Pacific Ocean and includes various types of garbage, especially plastic. Plastic poses an immediate threat to marine animals, which can die if they ingest this material. Plastic takes up to 400 years to degrade, making this material a long-term threat to marine ecosystems.

Increased fertilizer use has also contributed to water pollution problems. Fertilizer used for agricultural activities can be discharged into local waterways, including lakes and coastal areas. Fertilizers contain nutrients that make the water nutrient rich and increase algae levels. Often, the end result is an algal bloom, in which phytoplankton (phyto Greek; plant) reproduce rapidly. Increased algae growth disrupts ecosystem function by limiting surface oxygen available to other forms of aquatic life. Over time, this can result in the death of many species of plants and animals, causing substantial damage to the ecosystem. If left unchecked, algal blooms can also produce toxins that are harmful to animals living near the water source. Animals that rely on a lake or stream may be poisoned as a result of the toxins.

Underground storage leaks have also been found to contribute to increased water pollution. Many industrial facilities dispose of waste by placing it in containers that are stored underground. Although underground storage facilities are designed to prevent leaking of materials, in recent years scientists have found that many containers used for underground storage have eroded, releasing toxic chemicals into the soil and groundwater. As containers used for underground waste storage continue to age, the amount of toxins released from them will increase. Over time, this will have implications for the environmental health of groundwater supplies and soil integrity.

Agricultural production, or farming, can also have notable implications for the development of water pollution. Farming typically involves the use of fertilizers, herbicides, and pesticides that can contaminate groundwater and soil. While chemical pollution of water systems is a significant source of water pollution, agricultural production can also result in soil erosion. Each year millions of tons of soil are eroded in the US as a result of agricultural activities. Soil erosion results in the deposition of sediment in waterways including streams, rivers, and lakes. Increased sediment can block sunlight in water systems, making it difficult for aquatic plants to reproduce. Marine animals that rely on aquatic plants for food may not be able to survive in water with high amounts of sediment. Additionally, increased sediment in water systems can suffocate fish by blocking their gills.

MID-CHAPTER QUESTIONS

1. What is the difference between point source and non-point source water pollution?

2. What are some of the most common sources of water pollution?

NATURAL WATER CYCLE AND HUMAN IMPACT

Water in the environment is in constant motion. Water that falls to the Earth's surface as precipitation may have been part of a lake several days earlier. The flow of water can be tracked through a process known as the natural water cycle. The natural water cycle, or **hydrologic cycle**, provides an overview of the continuous movement of water across the surface the planet, in the atmosphere, and underneath the Earth's surface. Although various models for the natural water cycle have been developed, all models contain some basic elements that are foundational to understanding the movement of water. These elements include evaporation, condensation, and purification. Beginning with evaporation, it is possible to understand how the natural water cycle occurs.

Evaporation in the hydrologic cycle occurs when water from the Earth's surface (including oceans, lakes, and rivers) is heated from a liquid into its gaseous state. As water vapor rises into the atmosphere, it cools and condenses back into its liquid state. Water droplets suspended in the upper levels of the atmosphere come together to form clouds. When enough condensed water produces a cloud, precipitation in the form of rain, snow, or sleet falls back to Earth. Precipitation that lands on the ground is filtered through the soil, resulting in purification of the water. Purified precipitation often becomes part of the groundwater system and can be used by humans as a potable water source. Ground water that is not used for human consumption flows beneath the Earth's surface until it reaches a river, lake, or ocean. Here, the water is reincorporated into surface water and evaporates, condenses, and is purified once again.

The hydrologic cycle is an integral part of human survival. It replenishes freshwater sources that can be consumed by humans and animals. Human activities

HYDROLOGIC CYCLE The continuous movement of water above, below, and on the surface of the Earth, in gaseous, liquid, and solid form.

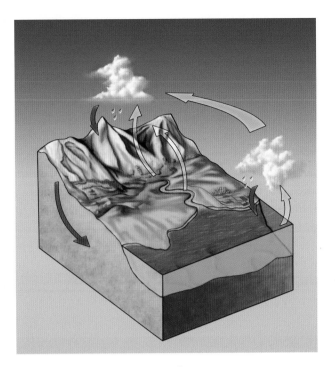

FIGURE 6.1 The hydrologic cycle

that impact the natural water cycle can have significant implications for access to clean, safe drinking water. One human impact on the natural water cycle occurs with regard to the greenhouse effect. The burning of fossil fuels increases the release of greenhouse gases, limiting surface cooling of the Earth and raising the Earth's temperature. As the temperature increases, the amount of water evaporated from the surface of the Earth increases. Increased evaporation can result in droughts in areas of the country that typically have abundant precipitation. Increased evaporation has also been associated with increased precipitation in certain areas, sometimes resulting in devastating storms and floods.

Deforestation has also been implicated in disruptions of the natural water cycle. Deforestation involves the removal of trees from large areas of land. Trees emit water vapor into the atmosphere, which condenses to form precipitation. When large numbers of trees are removed from a particular area, the amount of water vapor available for condensation decreases. Over time, this can lead to shortages in precipitation or droughts. Evaporated water vapor from the trees is needed to support the flow of water through the natural water cycle.

Irrigation has also been noted as a significant human threat to the natural water cycle. Irrigation is commonly used by farmers to provide water to crops that do not receive enough natural precipitation. Irrigation activities have increased over the course of the twentieth century, as farmers grow more crops to feed an expanding population. Demand for food has also prompted the development of farms in arid (dry) regions, requiring irrigation as a principle resource for maintaining crops. Irrigation removes water from the surrounding region, reducing the amount of water that can be evaporated into the hydrologic cycle. As the amount of evaporated water declines, so does the amount of precipitation. Over time, droughts can result in regions that are affected by these changes.

Irrigation poses additional challenges for preserving the hydrologic cycle. Agricultural activities typically involve the use of chemicals for fertilizing plants

DEFORESTATION The removal of trees from large areas of land.

or pesticides to protect the plants from insects and bacteria. Irrigation provided to agricultural lands often results in runoff that is heavily polluted with these chemicals. Water containing pollutants that is evaporated into the atmosphere can fall to Earth as polluted rain. Even when precipitation is allowed to filter through the soil into the groundwater system, the soil may not be able to remove the harmful chemicals. In these instances, pollutants may end up in drinking water supplies.

Other changes in land use by humans have also impacted the natural water cycle. In particular, the damming of rivers and streams to produce hydroelectric power has had an impact on the natural flow of water. Damming rivers and streams to produce power can be an effective way to generate electricity. However, the damming of waterways reduces the amount of water available for evaporation into the system because it reduces the total surface area of the river or lake. As the amount of water available for evaporation declines, the natural water cycle is disrupted and less precipitation is produced. In areas affected by this change, droughts can result.

MID-CHAPTER QUESTIONS

1. Explain the natural water cycle using the terms evaporation, condensation, and purification.

2. What human activities impact the natural water cycle? List three.

WASTEWATER

Wastewater is a broad term that can be applied to any water that people have used and that is found to contain materials or substances that are harmful to human and/or environmental health. Examples of wastewater include sewage, effluent from industrial processes, and drainage from agricultural irrigation and mining activities. Common contaminants found in wastewater include heavy metals such as cadmium, lead, and mercury; oils; phosphates; and nitrates. Each of these contaminants poses unique threats and each must be addressed when wastewater is released into the environment. **Wastewater treatment** is typically used to remove contaminants before water is discharged into waterways such as lakes, rivers, or streams.

In most wastewater treatment activities, the goal is to reduce or eliminate the

amount of toxins in the water such that the remaining water, or effluent, can be safely discharged back into the environment. Wastewater effluent that is safe for the environment can be reincorporated into the natural water cycle to sustain life on Earth. The treatment used for wastewater is contingent upon the particular contaminants found in the water and the environmental and human health risks posed by those contaminants. Wastewater treatment can be a useful process that not only protects the environment but also provides a valuable resource for certain industrial or farming activities. Treated wastewater can be recycled and used for crop irrigation in areas where precipitation and freshwater resources are scarce.

Which Countries Treat Their Water and Which Do Not?

Even though wastewater treatment is viewed as essential to the protection of human and environmental health, many countries do not require or regulate wastewater treatment. Developing nations that do not have access to the economic resources to establish safe and secure drinking water systems typically do not have wastewater treatment programs in place. In these countries, there is a host of barriers prohibiting the effective development of wastewater treatment facilities. For instance, developing nations without access to basic water infrastructure do not have the resources or the technology needed to establish wastewater treatment plants. Further, because developing nations do not currently have wastewater treatment plans in place, they lack the technical expertise and experience needed to establish and operate these types of facilities.

The implications of a lack of wastewater treatment facilities in developing nations are apparent in some of the public health issues faced by residents of those countries. Water-borne diseases such as dysentery, typhoid fever, and Hepatitis A are commonly found in countries that do not have access to wastewater treatment facilities. These diseases take a substantial toll on human life, reducing life expectancy and increasing infant mortality. In these nations, wastewater is mixed with drinking water supplies, resulting in the widespread outbreak of water-borne diseases. Water-borne diseases are most commonly found in the poorest of developing nations.

Although very poor developing nations typically have no wastewater treatment facilities, more affluent developing nations such as Brazil and India have implemented some wastewater treatment policies. Typically, these nations provide basic wastewater treatment but do not regulate or monitor the quality of drinking water supplies. Developed nations with high levels of economic affluence, such as the United States, Canada, and Great Britain, have the highest standards for wastewater treatment. In these countries, wastewater is consistently monitored to ensure that it is properly treated and discharged. Careful regulation of wastewater in developed nations has enabled scientists to establish recycling programs for wastewater use. Using treated wastewater for agricultural irrigation is one such example. Similar programs cannot be efficiently used in developing nations due to a lack of water quality monitoring to ensure the safety of recycled wastewater.

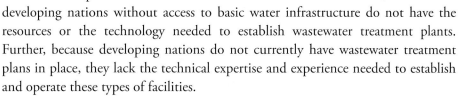

MID-CHAPTER QUESTIONS

1. **What are some examples of wastewater?**

2. **What barriers exist to wastewater treatment in developing countries?**

DRINKING WATER

Americans consume more than one billion glasses of water each day. While the US enjoys one of the safest drinking water supplies on the planet, contamination of drinking water supplies does occur in the US, creating the need for consistent

COMMUNITY WATER SYSTEMS Direct, in-home, year-round water service; the principle source of drinking water for most US residents.
PUBLIC WATER SYSTEMS Water systems that provide water service to at least 25 individuals or have 15 service connections and operate at least 60 days a year.
GROUNDWATER Water located beneath the Earth's surface, typically collected in aquifers or wells.
SURFACE RUNOFF Excess water that cannot be absorbed into the soil and remains on the Earth's surface.

monitoring of drinking water safety. The EPA is charged with monitoring and regulating community water systems (CWS) and public water systems (PWS).

- ■ **Community water systems** are the principle source of drinking water for most US residents and include direct, in-home, year-around water service. There are currently 54,000 CWS in the US that serve approximately 268 million individuals.
- ■ **Public water systems** are defined as water systems that provide water service to at least 25 individuals or have 15 service connections and operate at least 60 days a year. Currently there are 161,000 PWS in the US.

Most drinking water consumed in the US comes from groundwater or surface runoff. **Groundwater** refers to water found beneath the Earth's surface that collects in aquifers or wells. Underground pipes route groundwater to treatment plants, where it is treated and purified for human consumption. **Surface runoff** is excess water that cannot be absorbed into the ground. Surface runoff can occur during a flood, when large amounts of rain falls at one time, or when heavy rains have previously saturated the land, preventing the absorption of even small amounts of precipitation as it falls. Surface water is also captured and routed into a water treatment plants for purification.

Despite the fact that such a large amount of drinking water is consumed each day, only one percent of the available water on the Earth's surface can be accessed for drinking. Ninety-seven percent of the Earth's water is saltwater, which makes it undrinkable. The other two percent of the Earth's water supply is trapped in ice

ENVIRONMENTAL MISCONCEPTIONS: WATER, WATER EVERYWHERE

When you turn on the tap, water typically flows freely. The availability of water in the US creates the misconception that clean, safe drinking water is readily available in all areas of the globe. As noted earlier in this chapter, only one percent of the Earth's water is available for human consumption. Most of the Earth's water is saltwater, which is unusable for human consumption. Water scarcity impacts 1.2 billion people across the globe, or more than one-sixth of the Earth's current population. An additional 500 million people are at risk for water scarcity. Almost one-fourth of the world's population (1.6 billion people) faces economic water shortages. Economic water shortages occur when governments lack the basic infrastructure to deliver potable water to communities and homes. Unfortunately, water use continues to increase at twice the rate of population growth. As the population and water consumption increases, regions of the globe impacted by water scarcity will multiply.

The reasons for water scarcity are both natural and man-made. While natural changes in the Earth's environment cannot be altered, man-made changes, including pollution levels, can be curbed. Too much of the world's water is being wasted or polluted, making it difficult for some regions of the globe to access needed water resources. In order to reduce water scarcity, individuals and communities must recognize that water is not an abundant resource and that, over time, water sources can be substantially degraded and/or depleted. Only by recognizing these issues in the present and taking the needed steps to preserve water sources will it be possible to prevent water scarcity in future. Failure to address the man-made sources of water scarcity will further deepen the crisis, making it difficult for all nations to secure the water needed for survival.

caps and glaciers. As the world population continues to increase, safe and readily available drinking water becomes scarcer. This increases the need to protect freshwater resources from harmful contaminants.

Human Threats to Clean Water

In developed nations such as the US, contamination of drinking water is rare. However, when drinking water contamination does arise, the sources of pollution are either naturally occurring or generated by humans. Naturally occurring threats to clean water include microorganisms from the soil or rocks that contaminate the water, as well as heavy metals such as arsenic, lead, or selenium from underground rocks. Most water treatment and purification systems remove these toxins before they enter the drinking water supply. However, if water supplies are not properly treated or disinfected, naturally occurring threats to water safety can impact human health.

While naturally occurring threats to water safety can be addressed through proper treatment and purification of water supplies, human threats to clean water are often more difficult to control. Some of the most common human threats to water safety include chemicals that are improperly discharged into the environment, untreated sewage that is released into waterways, and wastes that are stored or injected underground. Each of these contaminants can enter surface runoff systems or underground aquifers, contaminating the drinking water supply. Although many of these threats are mitigated through the use of water treatment and purification systems, as the population increases, so, too, does the quantity of toxins that threaten the water supply. Thus, reducing human threats to safe drinking water supplies requires efforts to prevent chemicals and toxins from entering the environment in the first place.

Disposed Medicines

Although many of the chemicals and toxins released from human activities can be effectively removed to provide safe drinking water, pharmaceutical medications released into the water system pose an emerging threat. Medications consumed by humans and animals are found in sewage. Also, countless unused and outdated medications are discarded in sinks and toilets. Although sewage is wastewater that is treated to remove harmful contaminants, filters for separating out medications have not yet been developed. Tests of watersheds from sewage treatment plants indicate high levels of medications and hormones such as estrogen, commonly found in birth control pills. While the direct impact of these medications on the environment is still unknown, there is growing concern about the environmental and human impact of these substances.

Antibiotics, which have been found in high levels in water sources downstream from sewage treatment plants, represent an issue of particular concern. Antibiotics are typically used to fight infectious diseases, but the overuse of antibiotics in recent years has prompted the development of antibiotic-resistant bacteria. The concern is that with such large amounts of antibiotics being discharged into the environment, the number of drug-resistant bacteria strains will increase, making it difficult for medical professionals to fight infectious diseases. Conditions such as tuberculosis that can be effectively treated with antibiotics may become resistant to treatment, creating widespread threats to public health. While antibiotic-resistant tuberculosis strains have been identified, the fear is that antibiotics in the water supply will accelerate this antimicrobial resistance before new cures can be found.

Safe Drinking Water Act (SDWA)

Early civilizations recognized the need for safe drinking water and organized communities around potable water sources. In spite of the fact that drinking water was recognized as a vital component for the sustenance of human life, it was not until the 1900s that efforts were made to regulate water safety. Beginning in 1914, the US Public Health Service (PHS) set regulations regarding bacteria levels in drinking water. These regulations only applied to interstate water transport systems such as trains, ships, and buses. By 1962, the PHS had identified 28 different substances that were harmful to humans, including arsenic, cadmium, and cyanide. Even though regulation of these substances had been put in place, it was not until the passage of the **Safe Drinking Water Act (SDWA)** in 1974 that the most comprehensive regulations for safe drinking water were adopted.

The principle goal of the SDWA is to ensure that all public water supplies meet national standards to protect individuals from harmful contaminants that can enter the drinking water system. The SDWA accomplishes its goals by requiring the EPA to regulate contaminants that are known or likely to occur in public drinking water systems. The EPA is charged with the responsibility of establishing maximum contaminant level goals (MCLGs) for each contaminant.

Maximum contaminant level goals (MCLGs) provide a threshold for measuring the level of contaminants in drinking water; these numbers represent levels at which the contaminant poses no known health risk to humans. MCLGs are not enforceable by the EPA. The SDWA also requires the EPA to set enforceable limits for contaminants known as maximum contaminant levels (MCLs).

The **maximum contaminant level** is the highest amount of a contaminant that can be present in drinking water used for human consumption. MCLs are based on an assessment of the contaminant to human health and cost considerations for removing the contaminant from the drinking water supply.

Even though the EPA is responsible for setting water quality standards, the SDWA contains provisions that allow the EPA to delegate the physical regulations of public water systems (size, capacity, volume, etc.) to the states. Under the provisions of the SDWA, the EPA is authorized to provide states with grants to test and monitor water quality. Public water systems are required to collect water samples at specific locations and intervals. The samples are then sent to a state-approved testing laboratory. The results obtained by the lab are sent to the state to determine if the public water system is in compliance with the SDWA. If a public water system is in violation of the SDWA, it is required by law to report the issue to the public. States must report violations of the SDWA to the EPA on a quarterly basis. These reports are warehoused in a federal database known as the Safe Drinking Water Information System. Information in this database is used to monitor national water quality and to identify trends in contaminants that may require additional regulation.

MID-CHAPTER QUESTIONS

1. What is the difference between groundwater and surface runoff?

2. Why do medicines in the water supply pose a potential risk to human health?

3. What does the Safe Water Drinking Act (SWDA) do?

WATER TREATMENT

Wastewater includes liquid waste that is produced from any commercial, residential, or industrial operation. Businesses, homes, and factories generate wastewater. Although the term **sewage** is often used interchangeably with wastewater, sewage is actually a subset of wastewater that contains the human wastes urine and feces. Most wastewater is primarily composed of water, contaminated with small amounts of pollutants. However, when wastewater is released into the environment in large quantities, the environment is not always able to effectively remove harmful contaminants, possibly creating substantial threats to environmental and human health. For instance, wastewater containing pesticides can pollute groundwater, resulting in harmful health effects for plants, animals, and humans that consume this groundwater.

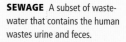

SEWAGE A subset of wastewater that contains the human wastes urine and feces.

In an effort to protect the environment from the harmful effects of wastewater, treatment of the water is needed. Wastewater treatment involves the removal of pollutants from the water such that the effluent can be discharged back into the environment safely. Wastewater treatment not only removes pollutants from the water, but also puts dissolved oxygen back into the water. The addition of oxygen to wastewater helps to ensure that the effluent can be used to support different types of plant and animal life. Wastewater treatment is essential for protecting the environment and ensuring that polluted water does not adversely impact human health or fragile ecosystems.

Process

Wastewater treatment is typically carried out in a treatment facility. While each facility and the processes used for treatment differ based on the type of wastewater being processed, many of the same processes and technologies are used at all wastewater treatment plants. The diagram in Figure 6.2 represents a typical wastewater facility and the treatment processes involved.

Wastewater Facility Technology

As demonstrated in Figure 6.2, wastewater treatment involves four treatment steps:

1. *Coagulation:* The wastewater treatment process begins with coagulation. Coagulation refers to the removal of dirt and other solid particles suspended in the wastewater. Chemicals such as alum are used to create sticky particles known as "floc" that attract the solid material.

2. *Sedimentation:* Once the solid particles have attached themselves to the floc, the wastewater is subjected to sedimentation, in which the dirt and floc are removed from the wastewater.

3. *Filtration:* Filtration occurs next and involves the use of specialized filters designed to remove smaller pollutants from the water. Sand, gravel, and charcoal are materials that are typically used in wastewater filtration systems.

4. *Disinfection:* In this final stage of wastewater treatment, the water is subjected to different chemical processes to remove (destroy) harmful bacteria and microscopic pathogens.

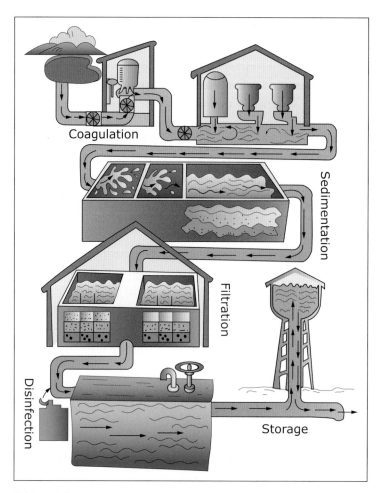

FIGURE 6.2 Wastewater treatment process

Once wastewater is treated, it can be released into the environment or stored for later use. Reclaimed water from wastewater treatment can be used by communities to help conserve freshwater resources. Specifically, reclaimed wastewater can be used for irrigation and industrial purposes, reducing the amount of freshwater resources that are used for these activities. Examples of how reclaimed wastewater can be used include irrigation for golf courses, irrigation of landscaping along highways and roads, and cooling ponds used by power generation plants.

Some homes and businesses have installed "gray water" recovery systems. Waste water (gray water) from sinks, bathtubs/showers, and washing machines is collected, the solids are removed, and the water is reused to flush toilets, water landscape plants, or wash vehicles, which saves some money and promotes recycling.

The Economic Impact of Desalination

While the use of reclaimed wastewater can be useful for conservation of freshwater resources, in some areas of the world, such as Saudi Arabia, freshwater resources are scarce enough that communities need to practice desalination in order to provide life-sustaining drinking water. Desalination refers to a process of purifying ocean water by removing its dissolved salt. Humans cannot consume saltwater, but removal of the salt provides communities with a viable water resource capable of sustaining life and ecosystems that rely on freshwater. Because 97 percent of all the Earth's water is from the ocean, desalination continues to grow in popularity as the need and demand for freshwater resources increases.

Even though desalination has important benefits for sustaining human life and the environment, the process of desalination raises many economic challenges. In particular, the costs associated with the production of desalinated water prompt questions about the sustainability of desalination in the economic development of communities. For economic growth in a community to thrive, community leaders must be able to provide businesses with affordable infrastructure and resources such as water and power. In many instances, the costs associated with desalination make water more expensive to deliver to the customer. If water costs in a community that uses desalination are higher than those in a community that does not use this technology, the economy of the community using desalination may suffer.

Effective management of desalination costs requires consideration of the size and location of the community. Communities located close to oceans may have an economic advantage compared with communities that do not have access to this resource. Poor communities without access to basic infrastructure for transporting water will also face challenges in developing desalination operations. Even though desalination offers a viable alternative for providing needed water resources, the socioeconomic status of the community and its location must be considered when establishing desalination plants. In certain communities, this type of technology may not be feasible to address water needs.

Economic challenges for desalination are also present in managing energy inputs and waste outputs that result from the process. Desalination requires extensive energy requirements in order to produce freshwater resources. In energy rich countries such as Saudi Arabia, desalination can be easily undertaken. This process may not be viable for countries with less access to the energy to produce freshwater in this way. Desalination also results in the production of concentrated salt water, or **brine**. This brine must be stored or treated so the effluent can be released into the environment. Both processes carry substantial economic costs.

Desalination of ocean water also has hidden costs that may not be known for years to come. Desalination is often undertaken through the burning of fossil fuels. Because significant amounts of fossil fuels are needed to operate a desalination plant, greenhouse gas emissions increase, with the potential of long-term implications for the Earth's environment. Changes in the greenhouse effect as a result of greenhouse gas emissions were discussed earlier in this chapter. Even though desalination plants produce water resources needed to sustain life and the environment, over the long term these plants may have a damaging impact on the environment; one that needs to be considered when developing this technology.

Storm Water

Most wastewater is treated and then reclaimed for use in activities such as irrigation. While most types of wastewater can be captured and monitored, storm water represents a unique form of wastewater that can be difficult to manage and treat. **Storm water** is water produced during precipitation (e.g., rain or snow) as well as water from melting snow and ice. Storm water is typically not a pollution threat if it is absorbed into the ground, becoming part of the groundwater system. However, this type of water has the potential to become harmful to the environment if it becomes surface runoff.

Surface runoff that travels over surfaces contaminated with various chemicals, such as gasoline, oil, and other vehicle fluids on the road, or pathogens (from

BRINE Salt water.
STORM WATER Water produced during precipitation (e.g., rain or snow) as well as water that originates from melting snow and ice.

many sources, including animal wastes) has the potential to absorb and dissolve the contaminants and pollute water. For example, surface runoff that travels over concrete surfaces that have been treated with chemicals many result in the pollution of the runoff with residual chemicals in the concrete. If the storm water is not effectively captured and managed, the end result will be the pollution of areas where the runoff enters the environment. Polluted runoff deposited into a stream, for instance, may transmit harmful chemicals that kill certain aquatic species. Polluted runoff deposited on land may result in pollution of the plants and soil as the water filters through the ground.

In order to prevent these events from occurring, effective management of storm water is needed. Communities typically install and route storm water into storm drains so that the water can be collected and treated before it is released into the environment. Additionally, watersheds or natural catchments can be used to collect storm water so that it can be separated from freshwater resources. Depending on the composition of the water, runoff collected in watersheds can be used for a number of different purposes, including irrigation and industrial processes. Storm water management also includes the development of wetlands that act as natural biofilters to help separate out sediment and pollutants from runoff. Wetlands contain important plant, stem, root, and soil structures that help to filter out contaminants that pollute water systems.

While effective storm water management tools provide needed supports for managing water pollution caused by precipitation, reducing pollution caused by surface runoff requires the responsible use of chemicals that are harmful to the environment. Pollutants on most surfaces, including concrete and soil, can be absorbed by surface runoff. As such, reducing pollutants present on the ground is imperative for reducing pollution in storm water. Storm water is an increasingly important environmental resource as freshwater resources become scarce. Unpolluted storm water that is collected can be used for irrigation without the need for treating the water beforehand. Thus, improving the quality of storm water is imperative for preserving and conserving freshwater resources.

Industrial Wastewater

Industrial wastewater is also an issue of concern when developing wastewater treatment guidelines and facilities. Most industrial processes utilize freshwater resources to remove wastes from their operations. Examples of pollutants in industrial wastewater include organic chemicals and animal waste that are absorbed by surface runoff used in irrigation; sediment and metals, such as zinc, and oxides that are produced from mining activities and discharged through surface runoff; and chemicals produced in paper mills that use water as a central component of the manufacturing process. Companies that produce wastewater as a result of their operations are required to treat their water or manage water flows in order to prevent polluted wastewater from entering the groundwater system. Industrial wastewater differs from household waste in terms of the type of pollutants and their concentration. While household wastewater may contain high levels of biological waste, this type of wastewater typically does not have the high concentrations of toxic chemicals or organic materials present in industrial wastewater.

The specific methods used for the treatment of wastewater are contingent upon the particular type of waste generated from the industrial process. For instance, mining companies concerned about surface runoff may choose to establish a watershed to capture the polluted water before it enters the environment. Other industrial facilities may have a water treatment plant onsite that provides the technology to eliminate contaminants before the effluent is released. While the specific processes used by each industrial wastewater treatment facility will be different, the following processes are most commonly found in industrial wastewater treatment facilities:

Primary Treatment

Primary treatment of industrial wastewater consists of processes used to remove solid particles and materials. Sedimentation, which includes filtering out solids, is often used in combination with skimming. Skimming includes the use of filters to remove materials such as oil and grease that float on the surface of the wastewater.

Secondary Treatment

The purpose of secondary treatment is to remove residual materials and solids suspended or dissolved in the wastewater. In industrial wastewater treatment plants, there are a host of technologies that are used in secondary treatment. Examples include:

- *Activated Sludge:* Activated sludge involves aeration of the wastewater with microorganisms that oxidize residual organic products. The sludge produced from this process is allowed to settle and separate from the effluent. The effluent can then be released into the environment or subject to further secondary treatment.

- *Trickling Filters:* Trickling filters are biofilters that contain materials capable of capturing microscopic contaminants dissolved in the wastewater. Wastewater is passed over the filters and pollutants are removed.

- *Rotating Biological Contactors:* Rotating biological contactors or RBCs are similar to trickling filters; RBCs rotate through flowing wastewater to remove pollutants.

Tertiary Treatment

In some industrial processes, tertiary or advanced treatment is needed to remove contaminants not removed through primary and secondary treatment. Chemicals such as phosphorous or heavy metals (such as lead) may require combination techniques (e.g., activated sludge and RBCs) or additional cycles of secondary treatment in order to remove them from the wastewater.

MID-CHAPTER QUESTIONS

1. What are the four common processes used in wastewater treatment?

2. How does storm water differ from groundwater?

3. What are the advantages and disadvantages of desalination?

FRESHWATER CAPACITY AND FUTURE WATER AVAILABILITY

Even though water is one of the Earth's renewable resources, it remains one of the most difficult to secure over the long term. Changes in the environment and disruptions to the natural water cycle as a result of human development have taken their toll on human populations and the environment. Population growth continues to impact the consumption of freshwater resources, limiting their supply. In addition, human development continues to place pressure on the natural environment, creating water shortages in areas where water was once abundant. In order to better understand freshwater capacity and future availability of water, it is pertinent to review the implications of these issues.

Example: Las Vegas (Water in the Desert)

Despite its location in one of the most arid regions of the US, Las Vegas continues to thrive as a metropolitan area. When Las Vegas was first founded as a central rail-road hub in the 1800s, the region had ample water supplies to meet the needs of residents. The Las Vegas Valley—located between the Great Basin and the Mojave Desert—was home to deep aquifers that could be accessed to provide needed water resources. Rapid development of Las Vegas in the mid-twentieth century caused a reduction in available groundwater resources. In response to this problem, community leaders built a pipeline from Las Vegas to nearby Lake Mead and, later, a pipeline to capture water from the Colorado River. Even though these resources continue to provide water for residents, Las Vegas continues to face water shortages as its population grows. Improving outcomes for the future of Las Vegas will require city leaders to consider how to better use water resources so that scarce freshwater supplies are not depleted.

Example: Gasoline vs. Bottled Water

The issues of freshwater capacity and future water availability can also be seen when comparing the costs of bottled water to gasoline. Over the course of the last several years, the cost of gasoline has increased to well over $3.00 per gallon in most regions of the US. While this cost is considered to be quite high for many, consumers often do not think twice about purchasing a liter of bottled water for $2.50, or an 8-ounce bottle of water for $1.00. When the price of water per liter is converted to gallons, this means that a gallon of water costs about $10. When the cost of a gallon of gasoline is compared to the cost of a gallon of bottled water, the gasoline is clearly a bargain. Despite the substantial costs of a gallon of bottled water, many consumers recognize the importance of this resource. Estimates indicate that bottled water has become so popular that 41 billion gallons of it are consumed annually around the globe.

From another perspective, the cost of bottled water vs. municipal water is very high. Municipal water costs vary great across the US, depending on availability and processing costs. As an example, assume municipal water costs $10 per 1,000 gallons. The equivalent amount of

Lake Mead, outside of Las Vegas, Nevada

bottled water (at $2.50 per liter; about 0.26 gal) from the example above would cost:

1 liter of bottled water ~0.26 gallons = $2.50

1,000 gallons municipal water ~3,785 liters bottled water

3,785 liters of bottled water × $2.50 per bottle = **$ 9,462.50!!!**

MID-CHAPTER QUESTIONS

1. What can cause saltwater intrusion?

2. Is water worth more than gasoline? Why?

THE OCEANS

The oceans are a prominent water resource essential to sustaining the environment and human health. The importance of the oceans can be seen in the case of the British Petroleum oil leak that occurred in the Gulf of Mexico in April 2010. The discharge of oil into the Gulf, as well as chemical dispersants used for clean-up, was directly implicated in the death of fish and coastal wildlife living in the region. In addition, there were concerns regarding human consumption of fish and shellfish exposed to the oil leak. Contamination of food resources in the Gulf resulted in economic losses, as fishing companies were unable to work during the crisis and during the clean-up. Given the importance of the oceans, it is pertinent to consider some of the water issues that have implications for these valuable water resources.

OVERFISHING A situation in which excessive amounts of fish are captured, reducing the fish population to unsustainable levels.

Overfishing

Overfishing occurs when excessive amounts of fish are extracted, reducing the fish population to unsustainable levels. Although overfishing is a modern problem, examples of overfishing can be seen as far back as the 1800s. At that time, whales, sought for their oils, were hunted almost to extinction. Because of overfishing, the whale population was decimated, threatening the long-term survival of this species. While overfishing can result in the extinction of a species, the practice can also result in substantial alterations of marine ecosystems. When too many fish are removed from a particular environment, organisms that rely on the fish for food may also become extinct. Other smaller species may also produce in abundance if a fish that used to feed on them is reduced in numbers. One example of an imbalance of this nature occurred on the Alaska Aleutian Islands. Here, decimation of the seal population resulted in orcas preying on sea otters for food. Over time, the sea otter population also began to decline. Overfishing must be controlled in order to sustain fish populations and the ecosystems in which these fish live. In Alaska's Prince William Sound, the king crab fishing industry collapsed as a result of overfishing.

Even though overfishing is typically associated with extracting too many fish, scientists have identified three different types of overfishing: growth, recruitment, and ecosystem overfishing. **Growth overfishing** refers to the capture of young fish before they grow to a reasonable size. Growth overfishing reduces the number of future recruits or fish that will be included in future fish populations. **Recruitment overfishing** occurs when too many mature parents from the species are extracted. When recruitment overfishing occurs, there are not enough adult individuals left to propagate the species. **Ecosystem overfishing** refers to the destruction of an entire ecosystem as the result of removing too many of one species from an environment.

Aquaculture

Seafood is an important component of the modern diet because it is rich in nutrients and vitamins vital to human health. Increased demand for seafood has led to overfishing, and in an effort to combat this trend, aquaculture or aquafarming has become an alternative for securing needed seafood resources. **Aquaculture** involves the cultivation of aquatic (freshwater) and marine (saltwater) organisms for human consumption. Aquaculture is conducted under controlled conditions in which aquatic or marine organisms and fish are bred, reared, and harvested; it is analogous to agricultural farming, with the difference that all plants and animals are cultivated in either a fresh or salt water environment.

Although aquaculture provides access to needed fish resources without the need for overfishing, there are some drawbacks to this technique. Aquafarms require the use of vast fresh or seawater resources. In order to sustain these farms, various chemicals must be used. These chemicals have the potential to pollute the natural water systems in which seafood grow and develop naturally. Aquafarms also change the landscape of the local flora and fauna, which may have widespread impacts on the aquatic ecosystems in nearby areas. Sustainable aquaculture systems must be established to increase access to seafood while minimizing the impact of aquafarms on the environment.

Bycatch

Bycatch refers to any water-dwelling species unintentionally extracted and discarded during the effort to capture a specific type of fish. For instance, fishing operations focused on capturing shrimp will often capture other types of marine life, such as tuna. Bycatch can also occur when undersized members of the target species are harvested. Extraction of young fish can result in growth overfishing, which can limit the maturation of the fish population in the near future. Bycatch is often discarded and therefore provides no economic benefits while contributing to species decline and overfishing.

Because bycatch is often discarded, reducing the amount of discarded aqua life collected during fishing expeditions is imperative. In order to mitigate the amount of bycatch, various changes to fishing operations have been implemented. In particular, fishing is banned in certain geographical areas that are known for high levels of bycatch. Additionally, fishing companies limit bycatch by using larger nets that allow smaller fish to escape before being harvested. Given the extent of bycatch that can result from some fishing expeditions, many companies now collect bycatch and sell it as food, fertilizer, pet food, or soil sediment for aquafarms. Using the undesired and unsellable catch helps to ensure that bycatch is not wasted.

Marine Dumping

Marine dumping refers to the discarding of trash into the ocean. The practice has short- and long-term implications for marine life and ecosystems. Trash dumped in the ocean can directly harm marine life. For example, plastic can become lodged in the blowholes of dolphins. This limits air flow for the dolphins, often causing death by suffocation. Trash that does not pose an immediate harm to marine wildlife may decay over time, resulting in the release of harmful chemicals such as polystyrene and bisphenol-A (BPA) into marine ecosystems. Metal products in garbage that contain lead or mercury can erode, unleashing harmful toxins into the ocean. These heavy metals can be harmful to humans if they are absorbed by fish that are captured and consumed.

Because of the severity of the hazards posed by marine dumping, the practice is banned worldwide. Despite bans on marine dumping, large amounts of garbage continue to make their way into the ocean. Shipping accidents and a lack of enforcement for marine dumping laws mean garbage continues to accumulate in the oceans. The Great Pacific Garbage Patch, noted earlier in this chapter, is an example of what can occur when marine dumping becomes excessive. As the human population increases, the need to dispose of waste may result in increased marine dumping, which has implications for marine life and human health.

Coastal Development

Coastal areas account for approximately 20 percent of the total land area in the world. Despite the relatively small size of coastal areas, the populations in these regions continue to increase significantly each year. As more individuals inhabit coastal areas, development, including the construction of homes and commercial buildings, continues to have a significant impact on these regions. One particular issue that has come to the forefront in coastal development is beach erosion.

Beach erosion is a natural process in which coastal storms redistribute sediment to form sloping beaches that dampen wave energy. Beach erosion replenishes the sediment and helps to protect the coastline from destruction caused by waves. Coastal development has altered the landscape of many beaches and can change the natural beach erosion process. When sediment is not properly distributed, wave energy may cause more substantial erosion, impacting the ecosystem and reducing the integrity of the beach's natural defenses. Removal of the beach as a barrier can make storms such as hurricanes more devastating for coastal communities. Because the beach is unable to reduce wave energy associated with the storm, waves can be more destructive to the beach, resulting in greater property damage. Unfortunately, the popularity of coastal areas continues to foster growth in these regions that can be difficult to address through sustainable development practices.

Sustainable Seafood

Clearly, there are a host of issues that can impact the integrity of seafood supplies. Overfishing and the problems associated with aquaculture highlight the need for sustainable seafood resources. Not surprisingly, this need to acquire seafood that is safe and produced in environmentally sensitive ways has resulted in the development of the sustainable seafood movement. **Sustainable seafood** refers to seafood products obtained from fishing or aquaculture organizations that do not jeopardize the environments in which they operate. Organizations such as the Marine Stewardship

MARINE DUMPING The discarding of trash into the ocean.

SUSTAINABLE SEAFOOD Seafood products that are obtained from fishing or aquaculture organizations that do not jeopardize the environment.

specific crops and use vast amounts of water just to provide food resources for their citizens. Virtual water comes in three "colors" (classes) related to agriculture:

- Green – evaporated rainwater during the production process
- Blue – evaporated ground and surface water during the production process
- Gray – the water that is contaminated or polluted during the production process

Use Low-Water Sanitation Options

Sanitation systems use millions of gallons of water each day. Low-water sanitation products such as low-flow toilets can dramatically reduce the amount of water used in sanitation activities. Consumers and businesses need to be encouraged to adopt this technology in order to reduce the amount of freshwater used for waste removal.

Improve Desalination Technology

As previously noted, 97 percent of the world's water is saltwater. Although desalination plants can be effective in providing water resources to sustain life, the economic costs associated with this technology are quite high. Investments in desalination technology may help improve the process, lower the cost, and reduce the impact of the process on the environment. Innovations in desalination technology could vastly improve access to potable drinking water and allow communities to preserve existing drinking water supplies.

The process of preserving existing freshwater resources requires a consideration of the changes to policy and practice that can be reasonably made without negatively impacting the environment. This is well illustrated in the recommendation to improve desalination technology. Even though desalination is a viable means for acquiring potable drinking water, the process has a number of drawbacks and can be detrimental to the environment. Improving desalination technology would enable the establishment of water preservation efforts that are practical for implementation.

MID-CHAPTER QUESTIONS

1. Name three water preservation activities.

2. Why is it important to reduce virtual water?

CLEAN WATER ACT

While the SDWA provides clear guidelines for regulating safe drinking water, the **Clean Water Act (CWA)** establishes regulations for the discharge of pollutants into water systems as well as regulations for quality standards for surface water. The basic foundations of the CWA were established in 1948 under the Federal Water Pollution Control Act. In 1972, the act was reorganized and expanded. Additional amendments made to the legislation in 1977 resulted in a change in legislation's name to the Clean Water Act. Additional amendments were made to the CWA in 1987 under the Water Quality Act.

CLEAN WATER ACT (CWA) Establishes regulations for the discharge of pollutants into water systems in the US and sets regulations for quality standards for surface water.

BUSINESSES GOING GREEN: PFIZER

As one of the world's largest pharmaceutical manufacturers, Pfizer utilizes millions of gallons of water in its research and development and manufacturing operations each day. In an effort to mitigate its impact on the ecosystems in which it operates, Pfizer made a formal commitment to environmental sustainability, one that includes specific water commitments and actions to preserve water resources, evaluate the organization's global impact on water sources, and expand opportunities to address the global issue of access to clean, safe drinking water. Some of the specific actions taken by the organization to achieve these goals include developing partnerships with government and non-governmental organizations (NGOs) to evaluate water resources; increasing water preservation through community outreach; evaluating the organization's water footprint in distressed areas to reduce consumption; re-circulating wastewater for additional industrial purposes; repairing leaks in water systems that supply the organization's facilities; collecting storm water to replenish the industrial water supply; and improving technology to use less water in industrial processes.

In order to ensure that Pfizer continues to pursue sustainable water solutions and a program of environmental stewardship, the organization voluntarily reports its monitoring results to various public and private entities. Results from the organization's environmental programs are regularly reported to the United Nations (UN). In addition, the organization provides organizational stakeholders with annual reports about its environmental programs via its website. Pfizer also participates in environmental sustainability surveys undertaken by companies such as the Carbon Disclosure Project, Bloomberg (Climate Innovation Index), and *Newsweek* (Green Rankings), which compare environmental initiatives of Fortune 500 companies.

Because of Pfizer's commitment to preserving water resources, the organization has become one of the most environmentally conscious companies operating in the world economy. Other organizations seeking to establish a water commitment program could learn a considerable amount from the program at Pfizer.

Under the CWA, pollutants are classified into three groups: priority pollutants, conventional pollutants, and non-conventional pollutants.

Priority pollutants pose a substantial risk to human and environmental health and include radioactive materials as well as organic and non-organic chemicals. Identification of priority pollutants in water indicates that significant environmental contamination has occurred.

Conventional pollutants can be treated through the use of conventional water treatment systems and include solid wastes, oil, grease, and fecal coliform.

Non-conventional pollutants are not classified as priority or conventional pollutants. Examples include manganese and ammonia.

Integral to the Clean Water Act is the National Pollutant Discharge Elimination System (NPDES). This system oversees the discharge of wastewater into navigable waters, including direct discharge or point sources (e.g., pipes or sewers). Companies seeking to discharge wastewater into navigable waterways must obtain a permit from NPDES. Once a permit is issued, the company is responsible for establishing a pollutant monitoring system and reporting monitoring results to the EPA.

PRIORITY POLLUTANTS
Pollutants that pose a substantial risk to human and environmental health.

CONVENTIONAL POLLUTANTS Pollutants that can be treated through the use of conventional water treatment systems.

NON-CONVENTIONAL POLLUTANTS Pollutants not classified as priority or conventional pollutants.

Discharge limits for pollutants established under the CWA must be followed in order to retain a permit.

The CWA also contains provisions for monitoring storm water discharge. Organizations with storm water discharge can apply for a permit to release this water into the environment. Most industrial facilities, manufacturing plants, and raw materials storage areas must obtain a NPDES permit for storm water. In order to qualify for a permit, companies seeking these permits must develop and implement a pollution prevention plan to limit pollutants that may contaminate storm water.

PRESERVATION: INDIVIDUAL WATER CONSUMPTION

While water preservation is a process that must be addressed on a community level and activities such as increasing water rates and improving water delivery infrastructure must be implemented by community leaders and policymakers, there are a number of actions that individuals can take to preserve water resources in their homes. Water preservation is a collective process that includes a number of activities that can be carried out at the individual level to reduce water consumption and prevent pollutants from entering the water system. Water preservation must be viewed as an integral part of daily life if water resources are to be effectively preserved and protected. In general, most water preservation techniques used in the home are easy to implement and vital to water preservation efforts across the globe. As an added benefit, water preservation efforts in the home can save consumers money.

One of the most notable preservation techniques that can be used in any home is to fix leaky faucets. Small drips from a water faucet can result in the loss of up to 20 gallons of water each day. Larger leaks can result in the loss of up to 100 gallons per day. Additionally, water can be preserved through taking shorter showers and turning the water off when washing. A four-minute shower in which the water is turned off while washing can save between 20 and 40 gallons of water each day. Turning the water off while brushing teeth can save up to 8 gallons of water per day. When washing a car, turning off the water while soaping the car can save as much as 150 gallons of water. Using a broom rather than a hose to clean driveways and sidewalks not only reduces water consumption but also reduces the amount of pollutants that are absorbed into the runoff. Finally, individual water preservation efforts can include educating others about water use and the savings that can be acquired by making small changes in the home.

Permits for point source effluent and storm water discharge ensure the EPA is able to monitor the water that flows into the groundwater system. Once the water enters groundwater aquifers and is accessed for drinking water, regulations established under the SDWA are used to monitor and measure the safety of the water.

CHAPTER SUMMARY

Water is a vital resource essential for all life on Earth. Even though more than 70 percent of the Earth's surface is covered with water, only three percent of this water is fit for human consumption, and most of this water is trapped in ice caps and glaciers. Freshwater resources remain under siege from a host of pollutants and human activities. Water pollution can be addressed in two ways: by preventing contaminants from entering the groundwater system and by using water treatment facilities to purify water for human consumption. Both processes require a number of different activities and consideration of how to reduce human impact on the environment. Activities such as farming, deforestation, and burning fossil fuels that emit greenhouse gases all have implications for the safety and availability of water.

Protection of water resources is facilitated through the use of formal legislation as well as recommended actions for communities and individuals. The SDWA sets acceptable standards for drinking water while the CWA works to reduce the pollutants discharged into water systems before they filter back into the groundwater system. Human impact on the natural water cycle demonstrates the need for legislation to protect both surface water and groundwater. Community and individual preservation activities include efforts to improve water delivery infrastructure and reduce the use of water in the home.

Even with water preservation efforts in place, there are currently regions of the globe where water scarcity threatens the health and safety of millions of individuals. Although the Earth has enough freshwater to sustain its 7 billion inhabitants, changes in the climate and the environment have reduced water availability in many areas. Moving toward the future, individuals, communities, companies, and governments will need to work cooperatively to protect freshwater resources and to ensure that safe drinking water is available to everyone.

REFERENCES

Alverson, D. L., Freeberg, M. H., Murawski, S. A., & Pope, J. G. (1994). *A global assessment of fisheries bycatch and discards. Food and Agriculture Organization of the United Nations.* Retrieved from http://www.fao.org/DOCREP/003/T4890E/T4890E01.htm#ch1

Bennett, K. (2008, May 23). Disappearance of the Aral Sea. *World Resources Institute.* Retrieved from http://www.wri.org/stories/2008/05/disappearance-aral-sea

Blankenship, K. (2010, July 1). Scientists suspect the decline in herring is result of bycatch in other fisheries. *Chesapeake Bay Journal.* Retrieved from http://www.bayjournal.com/article.cfm?article=3889

Drechsel, P., Scott, C. A., Raschid-Sally, L., Redwood, M., Bahri, A. (Eds.). (2010). *Wastewater irrigation and health: Assessing and mitigating risk in low-income countries.* London, England: International Water Management Institute and International Development Research Center. Retrieved from http://www.iwmi.cgiar.org/Publications/books/pdf/Wastewater_irrigation_and_Health_book.pdf

Fuller, J. (2012). Would you pay $55 for bottled water? *How Stuff Works.* Retrieved from http://money.howstuffworks.com/bling-water1.htm

National Oceanic and Atmospheric Administration. (2012). Description of the hydrologic cycle. Retrieved from http://www.nwrfc.noaa.gov/info/water_cycle/hydrology.cgi

National Oceanic and Atmospheric Administration. (2009). Ocean dumping. Retrieved from http://oceanexplorer.noaa.gov/explorations/deepeast01/background/dumping/dumping.html

National Oceanic and Atmospheric Administration. (2011). What is aquaculture? Retrieved from http://aquaculture.noaa.gov/what/welcome.html

National Pollutant Discharge Elimination System. (2012, July 13). About NPDES. Retrieved from http://cfpub.epa.gov/npdes/about.cfm?program_id=0

National Resources Defense Council. (2009). Sustainable seafood guide. Retrieved from http://www.nrdc.org/oceans/seafoodguide/

Pauly, D. (1984). *Some simple methods for the assessment of tropical fish stocks* (FAO Fish. Tech. Paper No. 234:52). Food and Agriculture Organization of the United Nations. Retrieved from http://www.fao.org/DOCREP/003/X6845E/X6845E07.htm

Pavelko, M. T., Wood, D. B., & Laczniak, R. J. (2000). Las Vegas, Nevada: Gambling with water in the desert. U.S. Geological Survey. Retrieved from http://pubs.usgs.gov/circ/circ1182/pdf/08LasVegas.pdf

Pescod, M. B. (1992). *Wastewater treatment and use in agriculture* (FAO irrigation and drainage paper No. 47). Food and Agriculture Organization of the United Nations. Retrieved from http://www.fao.org/docrep/t0551e/t0551e05.htm

Pfizer. (2012). Key performance indicators. Retrieved from http://www.pfizer.com/responsibility/protecting_environment/key_performance_indicators.jsp

Pfizer. (2012). Water: Commitments and actions. Retrieved from http://www.pfizer.com/responsibility/protecting_environment/water_commitments.jsp

Rogers, P. (2008, July 23). Facing the freshwater crisis. *Scientific American*. Retrieved from http://www.scientificamerican.com/slideshow.cfm?id=facing-the-freshwater-crisis

Side effects of drugs in water still murky. (2013, February 11). *Discovery News*. Retrieved from http://news.discovery.com/earth/drugs-water-pollution-side-effects.html

Urban Land Institute. (2007). Ten principles for coastal development. Retrieved from http://www.uli.org/ResearchAndPublications/Reports/~/media/Documents/ResearchAndPublications/Reports/TenPrinciples/TP_Coastal percent20Development.ashx

U.S. Environmental Protection Agency. (2001). *25 years of the Safe Drinking Water Act.* Retrieved from http://permanent.access.gpo.gov/websites/epagov/www.epa.gov/safewater/consumer/trendrpt.pdf

U.S. Environmental Protection Agency. (n.d.). Coastal zones and sea level rise. Retrieved from http://epa.gov/climatechange/effects/coastal/index.html

U.S. Environmental Protection Agency. (2010). Nonpoint source fact sheets. Retrieved from http://www.epa.gov/owow_keep/NPS/facts/index.html

U.S. Environmental Protection Agency. (2011). Polluted runoff. Retrieved from http://www.epa.gov/owow_keep/NPS/index.html

U.S. Environmental Protection Agency. (2012, March 20). Storm water: Basic information. Retrieved from http://cfpub.epa.gov/npdes/stormwater/swbasicinfo.cfm

U.S. Environmental Protection Agency. (2011). Storm water program. Retrieved from http://cfpub.epa.gov/npdes/home.cfm?program_id=6

U.S. Environmental Protection Agency. (2011). Summary of the Clean Water Act. Retrieved from http://www.epa.gov/lawsregs/laws/cwa.html

U.S. Environmental Protection Agency. (2009). Water on tap: What you need to know. Retrieved from http://water.epa.gov/drink/guide/upload/book_waterontap_full.pdf

U.S. Environmental Protection Agency. (2010). Water pollutants. (2011). Retrieved from http://www.epa.gov/ebtpages/watewaterpollutantcontaminatedsediment.html

U.S. Environmental Protection Agency. (2011). Water treatment process. Retrieved from http://water.epa.gov/learn/kids/drinkingwater/watertreatmentplant_index.cfm

U.S. Geological Survey. (2011). Reclaimed wastewater. Retrieved from http://ga.water.usgs.gov/edu/wwreclaimed.html.

Clean Air

Sunset over Beijing, China

THE 2008 BEIJING OLYMPIC GAMES

When the Summer Olympic Games were slated to open in Beijing in 2008, leaders of the country welcomed the opportunity to highlight the modernity of a city that had once been thought of as the capital of a poor, developing nation. Preparations for the games did indeed showcase some of the best attributes of the city: Beijing's high-speed public transportation system, its modern architecture, and its newly built Olympic facilities. However, some of the city's most significant problems were also highlighted by the international attention. In particular, world organizations had the opportunity to measure limited air and water samples and confirmed the significant water and air pollution common to Beijing's landscape. Although Beijing had made great strides toward modernization, several factors had created an environmental and health threat that could have significantly impacted the health of tourists and athletes visiting the city. These factors included rapid industrialization, an increase in the number of automobiles, and topography in the middle of mountains, which allows for particulates to be trapped in the air surrounding the city.

In an effort to address the problem and meet its promise to the Olympic Committee to improve air quality before the games, the Chinese embarked on an extensive campaign to ensure the air was cleaner for the games. A World Bank study found China is home to 16 of the 20 worst cities for air quality. Three-quarters of the water flowing through urban areas is unsuitable for drinking or fishing. In an attempt to reverse the hazardous air conditions during the 2008 Olympics, half of Beijing's 3.3 million vehicles were pulled off the roads and many polluting factories were shuttered.

Chemical plants, power stations, and foundries left open had to cut emissions by 30 percent and construction in the capital was halted. In addition, 300,000 heavy polluting vehicles—aging industrial trucks, many of which operate only at night—were banned. China only reduced pollution for two months for the games and the air has returned to levels dangerous to living organisms. Given the high levels of air pollution in the city and surrounding communities, the government took decisive action in order to present an image of a cleaner city. Even though the plan appears to have worked temporarily—Beijing saw clear skies for the first time in many years in the days before the games—following the games, most factories resumed production.

AIR TREATMENT

Air pollution has significant implications for human and environmental health. Air pollution has been identified as a key source of various lung diseases, including asthma, bronchitis, and emphysema. Efforts to address air pollution focus on the use of air pollution control strategies. Broadly, **air pollution control** refers to the various policies and processes that have been employed to reduce or eliminate the release of pollutants into the air. While some air pollution control techniques focus on stationary sources of air pollution (and will be discussed in detail later in this chapter) other pollution control measures focus on the development of policy and practice used to reduce mobile sources of pollution. **Mobile sources** of air toxics include highway vehicles and off-road equipment, which release compounds known or suspected to cause cancer or other serious health and environmental effects. Mobile sources are responsible for direct emissions of air toxics and contribute to precursor emissions that react to form secondary pollutants. Examples of mobile source air toxics include benzene, gasoline, paint thinner, dry-cleaning fluid, formaldehyde, acetone, or particulate matter.

Mobile sources of air pollution are important because they account for more than half of all the current air pollution in the United States. Presently, the automobile accounts for 50 percent of all mobile air pollution, even though studies demonstrate that today's automobiles emit 75 to 90 percent less pollution than cars that were manufactured in the 1970s. Improvements in technology—including cleaner gasoline and the use of catalytic converters—have been responsible for the reduction in air pollution from automobiles. Typical pollutants emitted from cars include volatile organic compounds (VOCs), nitrogen oxides (NO_x), and carbon monoxide (CO). Combustion (burning) and fuel evaporation (transformation from a liquid to a vapor) are the two primary processes through which mobile source pollution is

AIR POLLUTION CONTROL The various policies and processes that have been employed to reduce or eliminate the release of pollutants into the air.

MOBILE SOURCES Sources such as highway vehicles and off road equipment that emit compounds known or suspected to cause cancer or other serious health and environmental effects.

1. What causes the high levels of air pollution in Beijing?

2. What other steps could the Chinese government take to reduce air pollution?

3. What could happen to the residents of China if environmental concerns are not addressed long term?

created. Most automobiles generate power by burning fuel such as gasoline, ethanol, diesel, compressed natural gas, or other fuels, or by using green fuel like electricity. In fuel-burning automobiles, evaporative emissions result when molecules from gasoline vaporize and escape into the atmosphere. Evaporative emissions occur when gasoline is spilled or when gasoline becomes hot and evaporates directly from a car's fuel tank.

Although the term "mobile sources" is notably broad, classifications of mobile sources have been developed in order to aid in the identification of these sources. **On-road mobile sources of air pollution** include highway sources of air pollution, such as vehicles, trucks, and motorcycles. On-road pollution results from the different types of fuels used to power engines—including gasoline, diesel, and alternative fuels such as ethanol or natural gas. Additionally, mobile sources can be classified as **off-road mobile sources of air pollution**. Off-road sources include emissions from vehicles and engines that are used in processes such as construction, agriculture (such as farm tractors), and recreation (such as all-terrain vehicles, or ATVs). In addition to emitting pollutants from fuels, off-road mobile sources can also emit other hazardous air pollution, including particulates. **Particulates** are tiny pieces of matter that are released through combustion or industrial activities or from sources such as fires or volcanic activity.

Pollutants generated by mobile and stationary sources can also be classified as either criteria air pollutants (CAPs) or hazardous air pollutants (HAPs). **Criteria air pollutants** are those that can potentially cause adverse health and environmental effects. Health effects include lung disease and respiratory damage, and environmental effects include acid rain and ozone depletion. The six criteria pollutants identified by the Environmental Protection Agency (EPA) are lead, nitrogen dioxide, sulfur dioxide, carbon monoxide, ozone, and particulates. **Hazardous air pollutants**, on the other hand, are significant toxins that can cause severe health problems in humans. These less common but potentially severe health effects associated with HAPs include lung cancer, damage to the immune system, and birth defects. The EPA has identified 189 HAPs, including asbestos, formaldehyde, methanol, and phosphorous.

Because mobile sources of pollution are responsible for such a large part of the total air pollution that occurs in the US, substantial efforts have been made to effectively control this type of air pollution. Specifically, efforts to control mobile sources of air pollution have focused on two areas for policy and practice development: improving fuels used in passenger and transportation vehicles and improving automobile technology to use less fuel and burn it in a more efficient and clean manner.

In efforts to improve the fuel used to power automobiles and trucks, the EPA has adopted a host of policies over many years. One particular area for change spearheaded by the EPA has been the removal of lead from gasoline. Beginning in the mid-1970s, lead phase-out legislation was put in place to limit the amount of lead in gasoline, due to evidence that children were at particular risk of developmental disorders from high levels of lead in their systems. By January 1, 1995, the phase-out was complete. Today, gasoline in the US no longer contains lead, which was found to be a significant air quality hazard. China and other nations continue to add **Tetraethyllead** to gasoline. Tetraethyllead is an inexpensive gasoline additive that increases

ON-ROAD MOBILE SOURCES OF AIR POLLUTION Sources of air pollution such as vehicles, trucks, and motorcycles.

OFF-ROAD MOBILE SOURCES OF AIR POLLUTION Vehicles and engines used in construction, agriculture, and recreation.

PARTICULATES Tiny pieces of matter released into the air through combustion or industrial activities or from sources such as fires or volcanic activity.

CRITERIA AIR POLLUTANTS (CAPs) Substances that can potentially cause adverse health and environment effects such as respiratory damage and acid rain.

HAZARDOUS AIR POLLUTANTS (HAPs) Significant toxins that can cause severe health problems such as cancer and birth defects.

octane and improves combustion. Additionally, the EPA has enacted policy to limit the release of volatile compounds contained in gasoline into the environment. **Volatility** refers to the temperature required for a compound to change from a solid or liquid state to a vapor (gaseous state). For example, water turns to a gaseous form—or steam—when the pressure and/or temperature increases. The use of equipment to limit the volatility of gasoline aids in reducing the amount of gasoline that evaporates into the air (for example, the use of modern gas pumps). Technological improvements in underground storage tanks (USTs) limit leakage, and changes in gasoline pumps create a seal to limit gasoline and vapor from leaking during pumping.

Improvements in automobile technology have also resulted in a reduction of total air pollutants emitted. In addition to designing cars that use fuel more efficiently (i.e., travel farther per gallon of fuel) present-day cars employ technology that removes a large percentage of the pollutants created during the combustion process. **Catalytic converters** are attached to exhaust systems on automobiles to convert toxic air pollutants into nontoxic substances that can be safely emitted into the atmosphere.

The fourth US Climate Action Report concluded in 2007 that US carbon dioxide (CO_2) emissions increased by 20 percent from 1990 to 2007. However, methane decreased by 10 percent and nitrous oxide emissions decreased 2 percent. The declines in methane emissions were due to a variety of technological, policy, and agricultural changes, such as increased capture of methane from landfills for energy, reduced emissions from natural gas systems, and declining cattle populations. At least some of the decline in nitrous oxide emissions was due to improved emissions control technologies on cars, trucks, and other mobile sources.

Although much of the current federal regulation regarding air pollution was enacted in recent decades, the reality is that air pollution control strategies have been in place in the US for more than a century. Formal air pollution control efforts were initially developed along with efforts to control water pollution. However, water pollution was noted to be a problem for human health as far back as the Roman Empire. Because of the recognition of water pollution as a potential health hazard, policies for water pollution treatment and control were enacted much earlier than those for air pollution control. Interestingly, initial efforts to craft air pollution control legislation viewed air pollution as more of a nuisance than a health issue. For instance, in 1306 Edward I of England prohibited the burning of sea coal in craftsmen's furnaces. This prohibition was not undertaken because of a realization of the health hazards posed by sea coal, rather, Edward I enacted this law to reduce the foul-smelling fumes that were produced from burning this fuel.

Although not officially recognized as a health problem in the early 1900s, some measures were established in the US to control pollution produced by smokestacks on industrial plants, mostly to control the amount of smoke produced. Delays in developing formal federal legislation to benefit human health stemmed from a lack of evidence that demonstrated air pollution to be a significant health threat. Air pollution is not as recognizable as water pollution because most gases released into the atmosphere are colorless and odorless. As a result, extensive build-up of pollutants in the air is needed for air pollution to become visible. The first legislative

VOLATILITY The ease with which a liquid evaporates.

CATALYTIC CONVERTER Device attached to exhaust system on an automobile to covert toxic air pollutants into nontoxic emissions.

efforts aimed at air pollution control were developed in California in 1947 when smog became a significant issue for residents. A disaster in Donora, Pennsylvania in 1948, caused in part by a natural weather change that pushed polluted air toward the ground, also prompted the need for air pollution controls. For a few days in Donora, pollution from a nearby steel plant—consisting of fluorine, sulfuric acid, and nitrogen dioxide—hung as thick smog over the town for days. It killed 80 residents and sickened thousands of others. By the 1950s, the federal government began to address the issue of air pollution, resulting in the passage of the Air Pollution Control Act of 1955. This legislation was the first federal law to mandate research programs aimed at understanding the health effects of air pollution. The legislation also authorized the federal government to assist state governments in managing air pollution issues. In 1963, the Air Pollution Control Act was replaced with the Clean Air Act (CAA). The CAA sought to establish criteria for defining air pollution. The Motor Vehicle Air Pollution Control Act (MVAPCA) passed in 1965 established auto emission standards and the Federal Air Quality Act (FAQA) passed in 1967 designated air quality control regions.

The proliferation of air pollution legislation in the 1950s and 1960s prompted President Richard Nixon to create the Environmental Protection Agency (EPA) in 1970. The creation of the EPA had a significant impact on the development of air pollution control strategies. Rather than just establishing standards or criteria for air pollution and air quality, the federal government now had the authority to enforce rules to ensure that air pollution control was achieved. Many of the efforts to improve air pollution control were established under the CAA Amendments of 1970. The CAA Amendments of 1990 further expanded the authority of the EPA to oversee a broader range of air pollutants, including acid rain.

Although mobile sources of air pollution contribute to half of all air pollution, there are other sources of pollution that account for the rest. Specifically, non-mobile, or stationary, sources of air pollution account for most of the remaining air pollution present in the atmosphere. **Stationary sources of air pollution** are non-moving, fixed sites, such as power plants, cement plants, and industrial facilities. Stationary sources of air pollution emit both criteria and hazardous air pollutants.

"The creation of the EPA in 1970 had a significant impact on the development of air pollution control strategies. Rather than just establishing standards or criteria for air pollution and air quality, the federal government now had the authority to enforce rules to ensure that air pollution control was achieved."

Pollution created by stationary sources comes from two activities. First, stationary sources typically use the combustion of fuel such as oil, coal, or natural gas to power their operations. Combustion in power plants produces air pollution in much in the same way that combustion in a car engine produces air pollution. Second, air pollution from stationary sources is generated from emissions that occur during industrial processes. Examples of industrial processes include smelting iron ore, refining crude oil into gasoline, manufacturing, and use of products such as solvents for cleaning, paints, and coatings.

Controlling air pollution in stationary sources is facilitated through the identification of emission points for pollution. **Emission points** are the specific areas or pieces of equipment that emit an air pollutant. Air pollutants in stationary sources can be emitted from smokestacks, equipment leaks, or water treatment areas. Process vents can also be an emission point for air pollution. **Process vents** are openings where gases are vented into the atmosphere.

Control of air pollution from stationary sources can also be facilitated by classifying pollution as point or area sources. **Point sources** are large sources of pollutants that come from specific locations and are emitted in quantities above a particular threshold or standard. **Area sources** are entire facilities that have individual emissions that are not significant enough to be considered point sources by themselves, but when taken together with other facilities represent a significant amount of pollution. Stationary sources of air pollution can also be classified as major and minor sources. Major sources include those that regularly emit or have the potential to emit air pollution levels over a specific threshold, while minor sources refer to those that consistently emit air pollutants below a certain threshold. Classification is essential for developing control strategies that reduce or eliminate air pollution.

Treatment at the Source

In order to address the issue of air pollution, myriad treatments or control strategies have been adopted. These treatments can be very effective. In the northeastern US, EPA regulations limiting sulfur dioxide emissions—mostly from coal power plants— have resulted in a 75 percent reduction in sulfur dioxide levels around coal plants. Equipment and processes known as **control technology** are used to reduce stationary air pollution. The specific control technology used is contingent upon the specific needs of the company, its product, its processes, the types of pollutants emitted, and the ability of a company to adopt specific technologies. Among the specific approaches to air pollution control from stationary sources, there are a host of common-sense practices that can be used by organizations to control air pollution. In particular, some companies can control air pollution through the use of basic operational practices such as plant maintenance, process changes, and standard operating procedures designed to limit pollution. These types of air pollution control strategies do not require additional equipment. Also, **add-on controls** can be added to existing pollution control strategies and are used to destroy or capture pollutants such as particulate and gaseous controls with additional equipment.

PARTICULATE CONTROL METHODS Methods to separate particulate matter from the gases in which these materials are contained.

Treatment of Particulate Matter

As previously noted, particulate matter is typically released during combustion and other industrial activities. **Particulate control methods** typically involve the separation of particulate matter from the gases in which these materials are contained. These techniques focus on collecting the particulate matter from the source. The type of particulate emitted will determine the specific control devices used. Often, more than one particulate control system is employed to increase the efficiency of particulate removal and ultimately, reduce air pollution. The broad range of particulate control devices includes cyclones, electrostatic precipitators (ESPs), fabric filters (bag houses), wet scrubbers, and settling chambers.

Cyclones

Cyclones are commonly used in industrial operations that produce large particulate matter (50 microns or larger) suspended in gas streams. Examples include cotton processing plants and rock plants. Cyclones employ a cylinder in which the particulate-laden gas is whirled rapidly to create centrifugal forces that disperse particles to the sides of the container. Once the particles have been removed, the gas moves up through the cylinder and is released at the top. Overall, cyclones are highly efficient. These devices can remove 90 percent of particles 10 microns or larger, which is the size determined by the EPA to be considered coarse. In contrast, fine and ultrafine particles are smaller than 2.5 microns. Increased efficiency can also be achieved by increasing pressure in the cyclone to create greater centrifugal forces. Even though cyclones are efficient for the removal of particulate matter, they do have some drawbacks. In particular, cyclones may re-circulate particulate matter and can be susceptible to erosion and corrosion. Depending on the type of particulate matter and nature of the gas in the cyclone, any recirculation may corrode the components, making the device less efficient. The collection of particulate matter in the cyclone can also lead to clogging of the device, rendering it incapable of removing further particulate matter.

Electrostatic Precipitators

Electrostatic precipitators, or ESPs, are low-velocity dust collectors that remove particulates utilizing principles commonly seen in static electricity. Electrical charges are passed through the polluted gas to charge the particulate matter. Collection plates attract the charged particulate matter and remove it from the gas. The collection plates are then cleaned by dislodging the particulate matter. ESPs are commonly used in power plants, cement plants, and petroleum refineries. In most industries, a series of collection plates are used to increase efficiency of particulate matter removal. When this is done, ESPs can achieve a 99 percent efficiency rate. Electrostatic precipitators require large installation spaces and problems can arise if the moisture level or resistivity of the particulate matter changes.

Fabric Filters

Fabric filters—also known as bag houses—are typically used in industrial applications that produce a considerable amount of dust, such as coal-fired plants and steel mills. The basic principle behind this technology is similar to that of a vacuum cleaner. Gas filled with dust is passed through fabric bags, where particulate matter is collected on the fabric surface of the bag. Sensors built into the bags indicate when the fabric is clogged and requires cleaning. As the particulate matter on the bags increases, so too does the efficiency of the system. Dust on the bags acts as a filter aid to help remove the particulate matter for some time until there is too much build-up. Various materials can be used for the filter bags, including cotton, fiberglass, and Teflon. Even though bag houses can achieve high efficiency levels for particulate matter removal, these devices have some drawbacks. For example, fabric filters can experience a high level of condensation, leading to corrosion, and may accumulate flammable gases that can cause the bags to catch fire. Additionally, if the composition of the particulate matter changes, unexpected bag failures can occur.

Wet Scrubbers

Scrubbing refers to a physical process in which particulates are removed from gases. Wet scrubbers are a unique type of scrubber for particulate matter and highly soluble gases. In these devices, polluted gas is brought in contact with a scrubbing liquid (most commonly water) to remove the particulate matter. Wet scrubbers are typically used in industrial settings, including coal-burning power plants and concrete plants. These devices have efficiencies of 99 percent or greater for large particles. Unfortunately, these efficiency rates cannot be achieved for smaller particles. Despite this high level of efficiency, wet scrubbers produce contaminated wastewater that often must be treated in order to reuse or discharge the water. Wet-sludge is often produced, requiring additional resources for safe and environmentally friendly disposal or reuse.

Settling Chambers

Settling chambers remove large particulate matter, over 75 micrometers in size. These devices employ a gravity-based technique to remove solids. Gases containing the particulate matter are forced into a chamber, where the velocity of the gas is reduced. Heavier particles suspended in the gas essentially drop out of the gas and are removed. Because settling chambers only remove large particulate pollution, they are typically used in conjunction with one of the other types of particulate removal devices. More specifically, settling chambers may be used in conjunction with ESPs. Once the heavy particulate matter from the gas has been removed by the settling chamber, it is then passed into the ESP where it is further processed to remove smaller particulate matter.

Treatment of Gaseous Emissions

In addition to particulate air pollution, gaseous pollutants are also a concern. **Gaseous emissions** include pollutants such as carbon monoxide, sulfur dioxide, VOCs, and nitrogen oxides that are released during various industrial and manufacturing processes. Gaseous emissions require different types of technologies for removal because they generally are too small to be physically separated from the gaseous wastes produced during industrial operations. There is a broad range of technologies designed to control gaseous emissions by either separating or destroying the pollutant gas. Examples of gaseous control devices include scrubbers, adsorption devices, catalytic reactors, incinerators, and biofilters.

Scrubbers

Wet scrubbers were noted as a prominent technology for controlling particulate matter pollution and gases. Gas absorption scrubbers are typically used to remove gaseous pollutants from gas streams by forcing the polluted gas stream into contact

GASEOUS EMISSIONS Pollutants such as carbon monoxide, sulfur dioxide, VOCs, and nitrogen oxides released during industrial processes.

with water. This process facilitates the transfer of the pollutant into the water droplets. Then, much in the same way that rain falls from a cloud, they are collected as wastewater for further treatment. The gaseous pollutants being removed must be highly water-soluble in order to use this air pollution control device. Several different types of gas absorption scrubbers may be used, including spray towers, packed towers, and spray chambers.

Adsorption Technologies

Adsorption technologies require the use of solids with large surface areas to attract gaseous pollutants such as VOCs. Adsorption agents commonly used include activated carbon and molecular sieves. Adsorption materials provide a surface effect that can cause either chemical or physical attraction of the gaseous pollutant to the adsorption agent. One specific example of adsorption technologies involves activated carbon, a charcoal-like material that is optimized to provide a high surface area and high capacity for the adsorption of VOCs. Once the activated carbon has adsorbed large amounts of gaseous pollutants, the activated carbon can be heated to remove the pollutants, allowing the activated carbon to be reused. Adsorption technologies are typically used in oil refineries and steel mills.

Catalytic Reactors

Catalytic reactors are used in industrial operations to remove nitrogen oxides (NO_x) released during the burning of fossil fuels. Catalytic reactors are also found on most automobiles. In industrial applications, ammonia is mixed with NO_x emissions to form nitrogen and water. These compounds can be safely released into the atmosphere with no environmental harm. Efficiency rates of catalytic converters can reach as high as 99.99 percent. However, catalytic agents can become contaminated over time, reducing the efficiency of these materials. Additionally, poisoning of the catalytic material can result in a breakdown of the device itself.

Incinerators

Incinerators use combustion to destroy organic compounds that are produced in industrial processes. Polluted gases are mixed with air in the presence of heat to physically destroy compounds that would otherwise pollute the air. Ideally, incinerators should produce complete combustion. **Complete combustion** results when the process produces only CO_2 and water vapor. **Incomplete combustion** occurs when products other than CO_2 and water vapor are produced. Incomplete combustion can be seen when smoke is produced as a byproduct of incineration. Incineration can be effective for reducing air pollutants. However, these devices require the burning of additional fossil fuels to heat the gas. Additionally, incinerators can become overheated, creating a potential fire or explosion hazard. The ash created can also contain toxic metals, toxic chemicals that do not burn, or new chemicals from the incineration process, all of which must be disposed of safely.

Three different types of incinerators can be used to combust gaseous waste: direct combustion (flaring) incinerators, thermal incinerators, and catalytic incinerators. The selection of a particular incinerator is based on the types of gaseous pollutants present as well as the needs of the facility, including economic considerations.

■ *Direct combustion incinerators:* These devices use a quick burst or flare of heat to instantaneously combust gaseous pollutants. In this process, VOCs can be destroyed with 98 percent efficiency. Direct combustion incinerators are

ADSORPTION The adhesion of molecules to a surface.

COMPLETE COMBUSTION Combustion that results when incineration of waste, air, and heat produces only CO_2 and water vapor.

INCOMPLETE COMBUSTION Combustion that results when products other than CO_2 and water vapor are produced by incineration.

commonly used when gaseous waste products that include a combustible chemical are produced at the beginning or end of a production process.

- *Thermal incinerators:* Thermal incinerators combust gaseous pollutants using a burner flame, transforming pollutants into emissions safer for the environment. These devices can convert 99 percent of gaseous pollutants when used properly.
- *Catalytic incinerators:* These devices employ a thermal incinerator for initial destruction of gaseous pollution. Once the gas has been combusted it is passed over a catalyst bed, which removes pollutants at a lower temperature. Catalytic incinerators can produce efficiencies as high as 95 percent.

Biofilters

Biofilters are used primarily to remove VOCs from gaseous pollution. Polluted gases are passed through a bed of organic material that can include bacteria or fungi. Ideally, the gases react with the bacteria or fungi and are metabolized and destroyed. Biofilters can have efficiencies of up to 98 percent, depending on the pollutant. The materials used in biofilters need to be replaced over time. Further, biofilters are sensitive to changes in moisture and humidity.

While add-on controls are important for directly addressing various types of air pollution resulting from industrial operations, it is important to emphasize that many of the basic practices used by a facility will significantly impact the level of air pollutants released. For instance, industrial plants that switch from coal power to natural gas significantly reduce the level of particulate pollution emitted from the facility. In some cases, air pollution in industrial operations can be significantly controlled through proper maintenance and inspection programs. These programs ensure that equipment is working properly and not emitting pollutants unnecessarily. Inspection and maintenance programs can be undertaken without the use of add-on equipment to enhance air pollution control.

MID-CHAPTER QUESTIONS

1. What techniques are used to control mobile sources of air pollution? What are the particular challenges to controlling these sources?

2. Other than add-on technologies, what techniques can be used to control stationary sources of air pollution?

3. What technologies are in place where you live to control air pollution?

POLLUTION

Air pollution comes from many sources. However, it is difficult to determine exactly how much each source has contributed to air pollution over time. Human beings have lived for thousands of years, continually undertaking activities that have changed the atmosphere. The burning of trees to clear land is one activity that occurred long before scientists could evaluate the composition of air and identify, much less measure, air pollution. Thus, the composition of

"unpolluted" air is not known. What is known, however, are the chemical components of air needed to sustain human life. Through research and investigation, scientists have discovered the primary components of the air we breathe. Nitrogen (78 percent) and oxygen (21 percent) comprise 99 percent of the air we breathe. The remaining one percent of air is CO_2 methane, hydrogen, water, and gases such as argon, helium, and trace amounts of chlorofluorocarbons (CFCs).

Based on this understanding of the composition of the air we breathe, scientists are able to identify **air pollutants** as those substances that—when present in high concentrations in the air—constitute a threat to human or environmental health. Air pollutants can cause disease in humans and represent an environmental threat when they produce a detrimental change in the natural environment.

Human activity that creates mobile pollution from cars and stationary pollution from power plants as a result of our need to support an ever-growing population is a significant source of air pollution. However, there are natural sources of air pollution as well. Natural air pollution, known as **biogenic pollution**, results from changes in the natural environment. An example of a biogenic pollution source is a volcano that spews lava, gas, and ash into the atmosphere. While these sources of pollution can have a detrimental impact on the environment, biogenic pollution is not as detrimental as human sources of air pollution, also known as **anthropogenic pollution**. Pollution generated by humans negatively impacts the ambient air. **Ambient air** refers to the air accessible to all human beings and animals, or air that is unconfined in the atmosphere. When pollution in the ambient air increases, the implications for human and environmental health can become quite significant.

Factory Scrubbers

Perhaps one of the most recognizable forms of anthropogenic pollution is the thick smoke emitted from smokestacks on industrial facilities such as power plants. Although smoke from power plants does contain pollutants, a significant amount of pollutants is removed before the smoke is released into the atmosphere. Pollutants that remain in the gas released from smokestacks represent a threat to human and environmental health and can be classified as either primary or secondary pollutants. **Primary pollutants** are those that are directly released into the atmosphere, remaining in their original form. Primary pollutants released by power plants include heavy metals such as lead and mercury as well as toxic gases such as sulfur and nitrogen oxides. Recall that sulfur and nitrogen oxides are also criteria air pollutants. **Secondary pollutants** are those that are formed when specific pollutants released via the smokestack interact with other compounds in the atmosphere to create pollutants that harm humans and the environment. One example of a secondary pollutant is ammonia.

In order to control the primary and secondary pollutants that are emitted from power plants, factory scrubbers are typically used. Wet and dry scrubbers were previously noted when looking at the add-on air pollution control strategies for stationary air pollution sources. In power plants, a number of different types of scrubbers are used to help control the release of air pollutants. In particular, wet,

AIR POLLUTANTS Substances that—when present in high concentrations in the air—constitute a threat to human or environmental health.

BIOGENIC POLLUTION Air pollution from natural sources.

ANTHROPOGENIC POLLUTION Air pollution caused by human activity.

AMBIENT AIR Air accessible to all humans and animals.

PRIMARY POLLUTANTS Pollutants that are directly released into the atmosphere, remaining in their original form.

SECONDARY POLLUTANTS Pollutants that are formed when primary pollutants react with substances in the atmosphere.

ENVIRONMENTAL MISCONCEPTIONS: REGULATION MEANS MORE JOBS

The reduction of air pollution and efforts to increase government regulation has resulted in a battle over the implications of government regulation. Many have determined that by increasing federal regulation to protect the environment, the US economy will lose jobs. Others have determined that the jobs lost due to environmental regulations will be replaced by higher technology positions required to monitor, test, and upgrade to meet new requirements.

Between 1990 and 2010, companies increased their spending on environmental protection efforts from 2.1 percent to over 2.8 percent of the total gross domestic product (GDP). The result of this increased spending on environmental protection has actually resulted in an increase of "green jobs." Thousands of jobs have been created in an industry that supports the use of sustainable and renewable energy resources. Examples of these jobs include installers of pollution control equipment, installers of catalytic converters in cars, and workers creating more efficient sewage treatment plants.

On the other hand, thousands of jobs have relocated to nations that do not enforce the environmental policies that companies in the US must meet.

In addition to the fact the environmental regulation has increased the number of green jobs; data regarding the loss of jobs does exist. According to Dr. Margo Thorning of the American Council for Capital Formation (ACCF), by 2014, heightened EPA regulations will cost the nation between 476,000 and 1.4 million jobs and between $47 billion and $141 billion in GDP. Several power plants and industrial operations have closed as a result of increased regulation. If organizations wish to maintain operations within the US, they are required to comply with regulations and employing new technologies to protect the environment. The end result regarding economic activity to support government initiatives aimed at protecting the environment is uncertain.

dry, regenerative, and non-regenerative scrubbers are typically employed to reduce pollution emitted via power plant smokestacks.

Wet scrubbers remove particulate matter and water-soluble gases using water containing a scrubbing agent. Dry scrubbers typically use solid materials that are injected into the polluted gas to absorb the pollutants. These scrubbers can be regenerative—meaning the scrubbing agent is replaced naturally—or non-regenerative, in which case the scrubbing agent must be replaced. One drawback of scrubbers is that they produce wastewater and toxic sludge that need to be safely disposed of.

POLLUTANTS

Air pollution can have detrimental impacts on humans and the environment. In general, the human impact of air pollution is recognized through health issues that develop as a result of people breathing contaminated air. Environmental problems that arise as a result of air pollution are more commonly known as welfare effects. **Welfare effects** refer to the changes that result to land, soil, water, climate, and visibility as a result of air pollution.

The impact of air pollution on human health can be quite extensive. Air pollution can impact a number of different biological systems in the human body,

WELFARE EFFECTS The changes to land, soil, water, climate, and visibility that result from air pollution.

PRESERVATION: CLEANING UP AIR POLLUTION IN LOS ANGELES

The City of Los Angeles is well known for its extensive air pollution. Since 1950, the population of the city has almost doubled. The total number of cars on the highways and increased demand for power are both contributing to increased air pollution in the city. Even though Los Angeles faces some monumental challenges in improving air quality, it has taken several steps to address the problem of air pollution.

The air pollution challenges facing Los Angeles have resulted in the use of policy to effectively reduce particulates, ozone, and smog. In addition to increasing air pollution controls on businesses, the city has also worked to develop new technologies that produce fewer emissions. One pertinent example is the use of low-emitting cars and buses that are used by municipal workers. Additionally, the city has focused on public education and awareness campaigns to increase the use of public transportation, ridesharing, and carpooling. The City of Los Angeles has also established policies with regard to cars sold in the city. These cars must contain pollution controls.

In spite of all the technological advancements Los Angeles has adopted toward reducing air pollution and improving the environment, the city remains one of the most polluted in the US. To further address the issue of air pollution, the city is working on additional improvements that should further reduce emissions from automobiles and industrial facilities. For instance, the city is working to expand its highway system so that cars spend less time idling in traffic. Additionally, the city is considering changes to its public transit system to make it more efficient and environmentally friendly. Improvements in the transit system may encourage more individuals to use public transportation rather than drive.

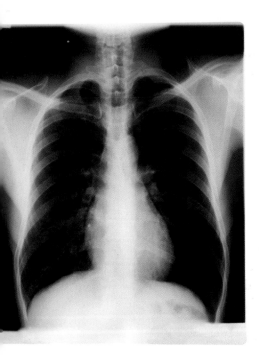

resulting in health problems that range from breathing and cardiovascular illnesses to neurological impairments. Individuals in **high-risk groups** (e.g., children, the elderly, pregnant women, and those with existing health problems) are more susceptible to the health effects of air pollution. In terms of air pollution, children are considered to be a high-risk group because they typically spend a considerable amount of time outside at a time when their lungs are developing.

The effects of air pollution on health can be either acute or chronic. **Acute** health issues are those that impact the individual over the short term. These effects are often immediate and with appropriate intervention, such as removal of the pollutant, can be reversed. **Chronic** health issues are those that impact the individual over the long term. These health issues may not be immediately apparent and cannot be reversed with treatment, even if the pollutant is removed.

While air pollution can have a number of effects on the human body, it has its greatest impact on the respiratory system. Particulate and gaseous pollutants can enter the lungs via the air we breathe. Particulate matter can line the small structures of the lung. Coughing and sneezing help to remove these particles. However, if particulate matter enters into the smallest structures of the lung, known as the alveoli, it can take weeks, months, or years to be removed. Gaseous pollutants can make it difficult for lung structures to function properly. If particulate pollution is present, gaseous

"Over time, exposure of the respiratory system to gaseous and particulate pollution can result in the development of respiratory diseases. Respiratory diseases commonly associated with air pollution include emphysema, asthma, bronchitis, and cancer."

||||||||||||||||||||||||||||||||||||||||||||||||||||||||||||||||||||||||||||||||||||||||||||||||||||||||

pollutants can limit the amount of particulate matter that is released via coughing or sneezing.

Over time, exposure of the respiratory system to gaseous and particulate pollution can result in the development of respiratory diseases. Respiratory diseases commonly associated with air pollution include emphysema, asthma, bronchitis, and cancer. Respiratory diseases have implications for other systems in the body, including pulmonary (heart) function, immune system response, and circulation. In pregnant women, these problems can have a devastating impact on the developing fetus. Some air pollutants are known to cause birth defects and even death. Air pollution has also been associated with changes in mental alertness and cognitive functioning.

Although the human health impacts of air pollution are serious issues that must be addressed, the welfare effects of air pollution are often seen long before human health problems manifest. Air pollution has a detrimental impact on the entire ecosystem, shaping the way various parts of the system interact with each other. Examples of the welfare effects of air pollution include the greenhouse gas effect, depletion of the ozone layer, acid rain, and smog.

Primary Pollutants

While air pollution generally has an impact on human health and the environment, each specific source of air pollution can have a different impact. Primary pollutants, noted earlier in this chapter, are pollutants that are directly released into the environment. These substances are not typically found in the air we breathe. For example, hydrogen fluoride is released from coal-fired power plants but is not commonly found in Earth's atmosphere. Primary pollutants can also include substances that are already present in some quantity in the environment. Release of additional amounts of a pollutant increases the amount in the air and brings the total quantity of the pollutant to a level that is considered to be unsafe.

Primary pollution can have both anthropogenic and biogenic sources. Anthropogenic sources of primary pollution include power plants and automobile emissions. Biogenic sources of primary pollution may be events such as volcanic eruptions, or geographical features such as bogs or marshes, which emit gases. Although primary pollutants can have a direct negative impact on environmental health, they

HIGH-RISK GROUPS Groups of individuals who are more likely to be susceptible to injury or harm.

ACUTE Impacts over the short term.

CHRONIC Impacts over the long term.

Trees in Polish mountains destroyed by acid rain

often have a more devastating impact when they are converted into secondary pollutants.

Secondary Pollutants

Secondary pollutants are substances that may have begun as primary pollutants, but reacted with different gases and chemicals in the atmosphere to produce new pollutants. Sulfur dioxide, when released into the air, is a primary pollutant that can cause breathing problems. However, when sulfur dioxide mixes with water in the atmosphere, it forms sulfuric acid, a secondary pollutant that contributes to acid rain. Controlling primary pollutants and their release into the atmosphere therefore affects both the direct impact of these pollutants and their potential to transform into secondary pollutants.

Several secondary pollutants have significant implications for human health. In particular, the formation of low-level ozone as a secondary pollutant from power plant emissions represents a significant health threat to humans. Some ozone is beneficial, particularly the ozone in the high layer of atmosphere, which shields the Earth from harmful ultraviolet (UV) radiation from the Sun. However, hydrocarbons and nitrogen oxides released from power plants can interact with sunlight to form harmful low-level ozone. This type of ozone can exacerbate health problems for individuals with respiratory illnesses. Additionally, this type of ozone can be toxic to plant life and can contribute to global warming.

Smog and Brown Clouds

Smog is a term formed from the combination of the words "smoke" and "fog." Although this suggests that smog is simply a mixture of smoke and fog, in reality smog can be comprised of as many as 100 different chemicals, originating from different sources. Smog is most commonly the result of sunlight reacting with hydrocarbons and nitrogen oxides to create low-level ozone. Particulate matter such as dirt, soot, and dust can become suspended in the ozone, giving it a dark appearance, similar to that of a brown cloud. The hydrocarbons and nitrogen oxides needed to produce smog are commonly emitted from activities that involve burning fossil fuels, such as driving automobiles and operating coal-fired power plants. Smog can reduce visibility and pose significant health threats to human populations. Even individuals without respiratory illnesses may find air containing smog difficult to breathe. Breathing smog has been found to damage the lungs as much as—if not more than—cigarette smoking. Smog can lead to serious health problems, including lung cancer.

Smog is a significant problem in the US. In heavily populated areas such as Los Angeles, control measures put in place by the EPA to reduce emissions of smog-producing pollution have not completely eliminated the problem.

In developing countries such as India, smog is a particular issue of concern. India currently does not enforce strict policies to reduce hydrocarbon and nitrogen oxide emissions from automobiles. Rapid industrialization in developing countries means further increased reliance on fossil fuels. Without strict standards to regulate emissions, the amount of smog in heavily populated areas continues to increase. The health threats posed by smog in India are exacerbated by the continued use of leaded gasoline. Lead released from the combustion of leaded gasoline can become trapped in smog. Individuals breathing this air inhale lead into their bodies. In Mexico City, smog is such a prominent health issue for urban residents that the government has issued warnings advising young children and the elderly not to live in the city. In China, the Ministry of Environmental Protection regulates environmental issues but the pace of rapid development is often over looked by agencies at the national or local level to keep up with the challenges. For example, China has more rigid emissions policy than the US but the number of cars on the roads, with production going from 42,000 cars in 1990 to one million in 2004, contributes significant greenhouse gases as the total number of passenger cars on Chinese roads tops 16 million.

Controlling the pollutants that cause smog is the best method for reducing this type of pollution. Although efforts have been made to reduce pollutants at their source, population growth has made it difficult for existing legislation to effectively reduce smog production. As a result of this situation, smog-prone cities in the US such as Denver and Los Angeles have developed a host of initiatives to reduce pollution. One initiative instituted in Denver requests that all citizens not drive to work one day a week to reduce emissions from automobiles. Another initiative in Los Angeles asks residents to carpool and use public transportation. Population growth will continue to impact the development of smog in cities, even with laws in place to limit pollutants. Innovative solutions such as those developed in Denver and Los Angeles may become mandatory in order to ensure that smog does not substantially harm human and environmental health.

Sunrise over Los Angeles, California

Acid Precipitation and Deposition

Acid precipitation and deposition—more commonly known as acid rain—represents another form of secondary pollution. Compounds such as nitrogen and sulfur oxides released into the atmosphere react with water and other compounds to form acids. Although the term "acid rain" is commonly conceptualized as precipitation (snow or rain) that contains acid compounds and falls to the Earth, acid rain actually refers to two different processes that enable acids suspended in the atmosphere to deposit on the Earth's surface: wet and dry. **Wet acid deposition**, or precipitation, occurs when acids suspended in the atmosphere fall to the Earth's surface via rain, snow, or fog. In this process, moisture of some sort is needed to bring the acid to Earth. **Dry acid deposition** occurs when acid particles suspended in the atmosphere drop to the Earth's surface in gas or particulate form. Solid acidic particles that form in the atmosphere can deposit on buildings and bridges. Over time, these solid particles erode the concrete, requiring repair of these surfaces.

Acid precipitation and deposition represent extensive problems for the environment because of the way in which acid compounds can impact large areas. Nitrogen and sulfur oxides released at a power plant in California, for instance, will not immediately result in wet and dry deposition of acid compounds into the environment. Rather, once these oxide compounds enter the atmosphere, it takes days for them to react and produce acids. By the time this process occurs, the nitrogen and sulfur oxides released in California may be over the East Coast. Based on the amount of the pollution released, the amount of acids formed in the atmosphere, and the atmospheric weather patterns, populations can be impacted by acid rain

WET ACID DEPOSITION Occurs when acids suspended in the atmosphere fall to the Earth's surface via rain, snow, or fog.

DRY ACID DEPOSITION Occurs when acid particles suspended in the atmosphere drop to the Earth's surface in gas or particulate form.

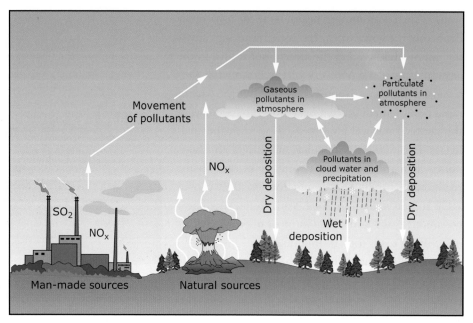

FIGURE 7.1 Acid precipitation and deposition

formed from nitrogen and sulfur oxides released thousands of miles away. Thus, pollution emitted from a specific plant in one state may have environmental implications for several states across the country.

Acid deposition and precipitation are not constrained by international boundaries. Many nations use fossil fuels extensively but do not have legislation in place to limit air pollutants, meaning that they can contribute to acid deposition and precipitation both locally and in other countries. Nations that have not taken action to limit air pollution must consider how their actions and the resulting acid deposition will impact the global environment. These outcomes also highlight the importance of maintaining rigorous standards for air pollution control in developed nations such as the US and those in Europe.

The impact of acid deposition and precipitation on the environment can be extensive. Once acid compounds are released into the environment, they are deposited into soil and water bodies, increasing the acidity of these resources. Acidic water is not potable for humans. Further, increasing levels of acidity in bodies of water can make the aquatic environment unsuitable for some fish and wildlife. Water acidity caused by nitrogen compounds may result in algae blooms that cover bodies of water. These algae blooms consume available oxygen resources, suffocating aquatic life in these areas. Acidic soil impacts vegetation. Forests in Germany have been decimated as a result of acid deposition. Acid precipitation has eroded the external surfaces of the trees while acidification of the soil has resulted in toxic conditions. As a result, thousands of trees in the forests have died. Acid deposition and precipitation also have implications for buildings, roads, and bridges, including the erosion of these structures.

Temperature Changes Affect Growing Seasons

The Midwest region of the US supplies the country with much of its grain—wheat, corn, soybeans—and is one of the most productive agricultural areas in the world. As the planet's climate changes, the location to grow crops, the best time to plant crops, and the production levels will likely change. If our climate cools, the resulting shorter growing seasons may result in limited crop yields and locations of productive farms may have to move or they may have to change crops depending on the weather and environmental conditions. Warmer temperatures mean longer growing seasons, and most farming operations will benefit from the extra production. Studies by organizations like the United Nations (UN) and the US Department of Agriculture indicate crop production could increase by anywhere from 5 to 20 percent during the next few decades if the growing season lengthens.

A warmer climate may have risks as well as benefits. The crops people enjoy could enjoy longer growing seasons if the climate warms a few degrees. When the climate changes cycles, some areas could benefit from the longer growing seasons, but other locations will likely be more vulnerable to droughts. Longer growing seasons could cause some fruit-growing areas that are normally cool, like the upper Midwest, to become more productive and damage crops such as grapes in California wine country, where the climate is already perfectly suited to them. A longer growing season will not necessarily guarantee more crops because the changes in weather patterns also bring other risks. Insects and other pests can become a problem if weather changes and may also be able to migrate to areas that become warmer. Changes in weather patterns could affect an area that experiences additional rain or dry conditions, which can cause both drought and increased flooding. The change in climate can also shift rainfall itself, when and how often it comes, and how much. Put together, the effects of climate change on crop production are hard to predict.

Climate Change

The world weather patterns have changed constantly throughout history. The Earth has cycled through weather patterns many times, with periods when most of it was frozen to times when the ice packs and glaciers have melted and flooded it. Within each major period there have been many maximums, when living organisms flourished due to more favorable environmental conditions, and minimums, when organisms had difficulty surviving due to harsh conditions. The Holocene epoch spanned from the end of the last Ice Age to the present—or the most recent 10,000–12,000 years of the Earth's history. It was the warming period of the previous ice age. Human subspecies including *Homo Sapiens* (current human race), *Homo Habilis*, *Homo Erectus*, and *Archaic Homo Sapiens* appeared and dispersed over most of the world well before the start of the Holocene. During the Holocene, the human population experienced an explosion in population and during all of humanity's recorded history, including the rise and fall of many civilizations. Most atmospheric scientists understand or express that the fundamental contributions of man to our current climate started several millennia ago, with large scale deforestation for farming resulting in large carbon emissions released to the atmosphere, habitat destruction, habitat fragmentation, pollution, and other results. The warming and glacial melt associated with the Holocene period actually began during the epoch period. An example of how the warming during the Holocene affected global areas is when the Norwegian Sea gyre pattern broke down abruptly with massive melting of Arctic ice with this, the Holocene pattern appears to have shifted—even within the last 5,000 years. Holocene vacillations point to the notion that man's impact on climate began thousands of years ago, with the massive deforestation, livestock grazing (including considerable overgrazing), and construction that assisted the rise of humans to dominate the Earth beginning in the early Holocene. The climate of the Holocene is very similar to the Eemian epoch, which was the prior interglacial era.

Currently, we have at least three main views concerning climate change among scientists, the general population, and politicians. One view is that the science is

CLIMATE CHANGE A change in the world's overall climate, sustained for a significant amount of time (usually over decades) due to natural factors and processes or from human activity.

final and no further testing is required concerning global warming and that the present warm period is man-made, caused by burning fuel that releases CO_2 into the atmosphere. This is often called the Anthropogenic Global Warming (AGW) theory. Those who hold this view feel that urgent and expensive action to prevent future disaster is required immediately. The second view asserts that more scientists each day are re-thinking what is causing the change to our environment and are conducting research and testing the many other theories that influence world climate. The second group feels that the science is far from settled and critical data requires further analysis to determine to what extent elements cool the atmosphere and elements warm the atmosphere. Major cooling and major warming elements include the Sun's energy output, which changes constantly; changes to cloud cover; ocean ventilation; transformation of the Earth's surface; negative feedbacks from biological and chemical processes; and human emissions of all greenhouse gases. Unless we include the correct data with our climate models, no one can predict our future climate or if policy is needed throughout the world. The third group feels current climate conditions are the result of man-made pollution and natural processes combined. Most scientist agree that man-made contributions exist that can damage our environment and change climate conditions but disagree on the actual effect from each theory.

Since the end of the mini Ice Age, we have known that the Earth is warming at a slow rate. Only recently have government agencies, the press, politicians, and a few scientists made climate change a highly publicized issue. For example, in order to make the population aware of the current warming period, Sir John Houghton, the first co-chair of The Intergovernmental Panel on Climate Change (IPCC) and lead editor of its first three reports stated, "Unless we announce disasters no one will listen." Sir Houghton is passionate with concern to the environment and promoted scare tactics to promote his views and understanding of the climate. Climate has changed continually throughout history going through many ice ages and warm periods. The current warm period has experienced weather conditions with warmer and colder decades. A few of the warm cycles have been warmer than our current weather patterns and other cycles have been colder.

If the climate continues to warm less than a degree per century (which it well may not) should we really be concerned about the ability to adapt and create policy in attempt to reduce warming? Climate is driven by energy from the Sun. The greenhouse effect stops enough of this energy from escaping back into space, resulting in the Earth having a temperature capable of supporting life as we know it. Without the greenhouse gases, the average temperature on Earth could be $-18°C$, not the current $15°C$ that makes our planet livable. Water vapor and clouds make up about 95 percent of the greenhouse effect, with CO_2 responsible for 3.6 percent. Of this, about 0.12 percent, or $0.039°C$, can be attributed to human activities. CO_2 is essential for all plant and animal life—and thus—some say it is the greenest gas on Earth.

During the onset of the Holocene, the population of humans went through a rapid expansion because the milder temperatures enabled humans to expand their geographic range and dominate the world. The Holocene was a period of transition; humans moved from a hunter-gatherer society to a society that lived in villages and farmed fruits and vegetables and maintained livestock. As agriculture increased, the population increased and people built cities, roads, large scale farms, and mines, and destroyed vast forests to allow for farming and procure wood for building and for fuel. As population increased, so did the need for additional raw materials and food, resulting in the disruption of ecological systems throughout the world; in fact, clearing features of the natural environment for food production likely comprised the largest amount of habitat destruction activity early in the Holocene, long before the Industrial Revolution.

From 1988 until the present, the IPCC has maintained the viewpoint that the Earth is experiencing global warming. Politicians have voiced concerns with regard to climate change (a few use the term "global warming"). During February 2013, Britain's Meteorology Office confirmed that Dr. Rajendra Pachauri, the chairman of the IPCC, acknowledged global temperatures have not increased since 1996 (17 years). This statement is significant because it contradicts the previously stated viewpoint of the IPCC—which uses its vast resources on studies concentrated on proving the anthropogenic (man-made) global warming, also known as the AGW theory—that states CO_2 causes global warming. The following graph provides the predicted temperature in black, the actual level of CO_2 in red, and the actual temperature in blue.

Dr. Pachauri also stated that discussions about controversial science and politically incorrect views are an essential part of climate change science. President Bush said on October 11, 2000, "Some of the scientists, I believe, haven't they been changing their opinion a little bit on global warming? There's a lot of differing opinions and before we react, I think it is best to have the full accounting and full understanding of what's taking place." Scientists continue to study climate change throughout history to gain a better understanding of current and possible future weather patterns.

By studying the environment and weather patterns, we have developed several theories and hypotheses that explain possible outcomes for our climates. The

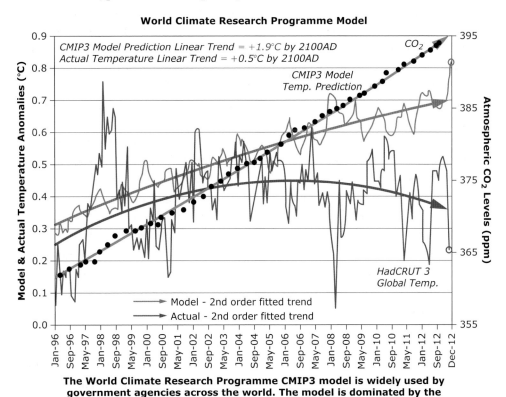

World Climate Research Programme Model

The World Climate Research Programme CMIP3 model is widely used by government agencies across the world. The model is dominated by the influence of atmospheric CO_2 levels. As a result, the model has proven completely unable to predict global temps.

Source: http://c3headlines.typepad.com. 'C3' model source for temperature anomalies: dlmexp.knmi.nl/ and www.metoffice.gov.uk. 'C3' source for CO_2 levels: www.esrl.noaa.gov.

FIGURE 7.2 Temperatures and CO_2 levels

following are believed to be the main theories about climate change that scientists are studying. The first theory of climate change states that human emissions of greenhouse gases—including CO_2, methane, and nitrous oxide—are causing global temperatures to increase. The mechanism causing this to happen is called the enhanced greenhouse effect. This theory is the anthropogenic global warming theory, or AGW for short. The second theory of climate change states that negative feedbacks from biological and chemical processes entirely (or almost entirely) offset whatever positive feedbacks might be caused by rising CO_2. These processes act as a "global bio-thermostat," keeping temperatures in equilibrium. We have evidence of at least eight such feedbacks—not counting cloud formation—which is treated as a separate theory. A third theory of climate change states that changes in the formation and albedo of clouds create negative feedbacks that cancel out all (or nearly all) of the warming effect of higher levels of CO_2. This theory is based largely on observational data reported by a series of researchers, rather than computer models, as in the case of the AGW theory. A fourth theory states that mankind's greatest influence on climate is not its greenhouse gas emissions, but its transformation of Earth's surface by clearing forests, irrigating deserts, and building cities. Roger Pielke, Sr., a climatologist at the University of Colorado in Boulder, phrases the theory as follows: "Although the natural causes of climate variations and changes are undoubtedly important, the human influences are significant and involve a diverse range of first-order climate forcing, including, but not limited to, the human input of CO_2." Advocates of the AGW theory falsely attribute higher temperatures caused by urban heat islands to rising atmospheric CO_2 levels. The fifth theory of climate change contends that global temperature variations over the past century and a half—and particularly the past 30 years—were due to the slow-down of the ocean's Thermohaline Circulation (THC). William "Bill" Gray, professor emeritus of atmospheric science at Colorado State University and head of the Tropical Meteorology Project at the university's Department of Atmospheric Sciences, is the leading proponent of this theory. The following summary is based on his work: ocean water is constantly transferred from the surface mixed layer to the interior ocean through a process called ventilation. The ocean fully ventilates itself every 1,000 to 2,000 years through a polar region (Atlantic and Antarctic) deep ocean subsidence of cold-saline water and a compensating upwelling of warmer less saline water in the tropics. This deep ocean circulation, called the Meridional Overturning Circulation (MOC), has two parts, the primary Atlantic Thermohaline Circulation (THC) and the secondary Surrounding Antarctica Subsidence (SAS). The sixth theory of climate change states that most or all of the warming of the latter part of the twentieth century can be explained by natural gravitational and magnetic oscillations of the solar system induced by the planet's movement through space. The seventh theory of climate change, as described by Joseph L. Bast of the Heartland Institute, is that "solar variability accounts for most or all of the warming in the late twentieth century and will dominate climate in the twenty-first century regardless of man-made greenhouse gas emissions. Changes in the brightness of the sun are caused by sunspots—bursts of energetic particles and radiation—that vary in frequency in cycles of roughly 11, 87, and 210 years. These cycles cause changes in the amount of electromagnetic radiation—also called "solar wind"—that reaches Earth and its atmosphere, which, in turn, affects Earth's climate. Most proponents of the theory that solar variability drives changes in Earth's climate believe positive feedback occurs either by a process involving the influence of the solar wind on cosmic rays, which affects cloud formation, or on the oceans' Thermohaline Circulation (THC), which affects sea surface temperatures and wind patterns."

When using climate models, there are many opportunities for errors in the measurements and averaging techniques to influence the temperature datasets against which data methods are calibrated and verified. Fortunately, when increasing the size of the samples being averaged and tested, random and uncorrelated errors tend to cancel, enhancing the confidence in the variations produced.

There is also the added burden of dealing with new versions of particular datasets. Estimates by research groups of large-scale average temperatures for particular periods have changed somewhat over time. This occurs when the different groups (a) update the primary source data used in the large-scale averages; (b) institute new adjustment procedures; or (c) adopt new spatial or temporal averaging techniques. Thus, a proxy record calibrated or verified using an early version of an instrumental record may be altered slightly if the instrumental data against which the proxy was calibrated changes.

OZONE A reactive gas that consists of molecules with three oxygen atoms (O_3).

STRATOSPHERE Upper level of the atmosphere located between 10 and 50 km (6 and 30 miles) above the Earth's surface.

OZONE-DEPLETING SUBSTANCES Man-made chemicals that destroy the ozone layer.

OZONE LAYER

Ozone is a reactive gas that consists of three oxygen atoms (O_3) and can have different impacts on human and environmental health depending where it is located in the atmosphere. Ozone is found high up in the stratosphere or at ground level (as in the case of smog). Stratospheric ozone is beneficial to human health and is necessary for sustaining life on Earth. Ground level ozone, however, can have a detrimental impact on both human health and the environment.

High-level ozone is naturally made in an upper level of the atmosphere known as the stratosphere. The **stratosphere** is located 10-50 km (6-30 miles) above the Earth's surface. Here, molecular oxygen (O_2) interacts with ultraviolet (UV) radiation from the Sun to form ozone. Ozone in the stratosphere serves as a protective barrier of sorts, limiting the amount of UV radiation from the Sun that reaches the Earth. By limiting the amount of UV radiation that hits the Earth, the ozone layer provides important protections that enable human, animal, and plant life to be sustained. In many respects, the ozone layer represents a filter that allows needed UV light to reach the Earth's surface while protecting the planet from harmful levels of this type of radiation. The human body needs UV light to produce vitamin D. Vitamin D is responsible for strengthening bones and preventing the development of diseases such as Rickets and colon cancer. UV radiation is also important in different ecosystems. For instance, bees use UV light to navigate and guide their pollen collection. Although UV radiation is needed for vital life processes, too much UV radiation can cause changes in cellular metabolism, impacting health.

Although stratospheric ozone does not directly produce any harmful effects for human and environmental health, chemicals developed and used by humans have damaged and continue to damage this ozone layer. When released into the atmosphere, chemicals including CFCs, hydrochlorofluorocarbons (HCFCs), halons, and methyl chloroform, react with and deplete the ozone layer high in the atmosphere. These compounds are known as **ozone-depleting substances** (ODS). ODS can be found in certain types of coolants, solvents, pesticides, and aerosol propellants. Although many of these compounds are no longer used, some continue to be used in limited quantities. When these compounds are released into the environment, it can

take years for them to reach the stratosphere, where they react with and deplete the ozone layer. Once in the stratosphere, ODS react with UV light to form molecules that destroy the ozone layer. One molecule of an ODS has the potential to destroy 100,000 stratospheric ozone molecules.

The impact of ozone depletion can be significant for the environment. Ozone depletion increases the amount of UV radiation that reaches the Earth's surface. Diseases such as skin cancer, cataracts, and impaired immune system function have been associated with increased levels of ultraviolet radiation. Melanoma, a specific type of skin cancer, has been widely associated with increased UV radiation. While it is very hard to draw a cause-and-effect relationship, some studies in parts of the world where the ozone is more depleted—such as Australia—show a link between the depletion and increased risk of developing melanoma, which has doubled since 1990. Increased UV radiation from the sun may also impact crop yields. Crops such as soybeans can be damaged by excess levels of UV radiation. This can have implications for world food supplies.

Because of the importance of stratospheric ozone to environmental and human health, various actions have been taken by developed and developing nations to address the problem. In the US, the EPA has established regulations, starting with the 1997 Ground-Level Ozone Standards, to phase out the use of ozone-depleting chemicals. Phase-out includes the prohibition of some ODS and the replacement of others. New alternatives for ODS are still being developed in some cases. In 1994, the EPA launched the Significant New Alternatives Policy (SNAP) to ensure a smooth transition to practical, safe, and economically feasible alternatives to ozone-depleting materials. Through this program, more than 300 alternatives for more than 60 industrial, commercial, military, and consumer uses have been approved. Additionally, recognition of the problem of stratospheric ozone depletion by the international community resulted in the adoption of the Montreal Protocol in 1987. This agreement is signed by the US and 190 other countries. The specifics of this agreement are reviewed later in this chapter.

Ground Level Ozone

Although stratospheric ozone provides important protections for human and environmental health, low-lying ozone or ground-level ozone can be quite harmful. Ground-level ozone is found in the troposphere—the lowest level of the atmosphere—and is generated when air pollutants including nitrogen oxides and VOCs undergo chemical reactions in the presence of sunlight. The end result is the creation of O_3 similar to that which is found in the stratosphere. Nitrogen oxides and VOCs can be emitted from a host of sources, including power plants, automobile exhaust, and gasoline vapors. Ground-level ozone is most commonly found in the summer months. Increased sunlight during the summer results in more chemical reactions and the production of more ground-level ozone. While urban areas are most prone to the development of ground-level ozone—due to increased traffic and energy use—winds can carry ground-level ozone to surrounding communities and rural areas.

The most notable effect of ground-level ozone is on human health. Healthy individuals who breathe in excess amounts of ozone can experience health problems that include chest pain, coughing, congestion, and irritation of the throat. For individuals with underlying lung problems—such as bronchitis—emphysema, or asthma—breathing ozone can exacerbate these conditions. Repeated exposure to ozone can scar lung tissue and result in permanent damage to the lungs. Individuals in high-risk groups may also be significantly impacted by high levels of ground-level ozone. Children, whose lungs are still developing, may experience difficulty breathing or other lung complications as a result of exposure to ground-level ozone.

AIR QUALITY INDEX A scale that provides daily data regarding air quality.

Ground-level ozone can also have implications for the environment. In particular, vegetation and ecosystems may be negatively impacted by this compound. Ground-level ozone can reduce crop and tree seedling yields. Ozone can also increase plant susceptibility to diseases and pests. Ground-level ozone also damages vegetation and plants, altering the surroundings of parks, cities, and other outdoor areas.

In order to address the problem of ground-level ozone, the EPA has instituted health-based standards for ozone levels under the CAA. The standards are met through a variety of measures aimed at reducing nitrogen oxide and VOC emissions. More specifically, efforts to reduce these air pollutants have focused on reformulating fuels, such as adding ethanol, reducing emissions from vehicles, and reducing emissions from industrial and power plants. Additionally, recommendations for voluntary action have been supported in many communities across the US. In particular, carpooling and using public transportation have been supported as measures that can help reduce air pollutants that lead to the development of ground-level ozone.

While efforts continue to limit the amount of ground-level ozone found in the atmosphere, there are instances in which ground-level ozone levels still reach dangerous levels. In an effort to protect public health and limit health problems that can result from ground-level ozone, the EPA has created the **Air Quality Index (AQI)**. The AQI is a scale that provides data regarding the daily air quality. The information provided in the index indicates how clear or polluted the air is and the specific health effects that are associated with the pollution level. Although ground-level ozone is factored in when determining the AQI, the EPA also determines air quality based on the levels of four other air pollutants: particulate pollution, carbon monoxide, sulfur dioxide, and nitrogen dioxide.

In order to provide information to the public about air quality, the AQI uses a scale that ranges from 0 to 500. The higher the value on the scale, the greater the level of air pollution and the greater health risk posed. Generally speaking, an AQI value of 100 is typical, indicating the national standard set by the EPA for healthy air quality. Values below 100 represent good air quality that represent a minimal threat to human health. Air quality levels above 100 represent different threats to human health. For instance, the range between 101 and 150 corresponds to moderate health risks for some high-risk groups. An AQI between 151 and 200 is considered to be unhealthy for all high-risk groups, and exposure to this air may result in significant health problems for these individuals.

AQI VALUES	LEVELS OF HEALTH CONCERN	COLORS
When the air quality is in this range:	. . . air quality conditions are:	. . . as symbolized by this color:
0–50	Good	Green
51–100	Moderate	Yellow
101–150	Unhealthy for Sensitive Groups	Orange
151–200	Unhealthy	Red
201–300	Very Unhealthy	Purple
301–500	Hazardous	Maroon

FIGURE 7.3 The EPA AQI

Air quality is considered to be very unhealthy when it reaches levels between 201 and 300. When air quality reaches this level, all individuals regardless of their risk status are in danger of being impacted by the quality of the air. Individuals in high-risk groups may experience serious health issues as a result of the air quality.

Air quality levels above 300 are classified as hazardous. A reading this high would trigger emergency procedures, as all individuals in the general population could be negatively impacted by the air quality. Even healthy individuals may experience shortness of breath and fatigue as a result of the poor air quality at this level.

When air quality is forecast to reach unhealthy levels, the state or local government may issue an Air Quality Action Day. On these days, individuals should review recommendations made for citizens based on their health needs. Using this information, individuals can determine their level of outdoor activity to help prevent health problems.

Montreal Protocol

The Montreal Protocol on Substances that Deplete the Ozone Layer, also called the Montreal Protocol, is an international treaty that was developed to help protect the ozone layer by reducing the use of ozone-depleting substances. The treaty was first established in 1987 with the requirement that countries start implementing the phase-out of ODS beginning in 1989. When the treaty was first proposed, 20 countries agreed to participate. Since its inception, more than 191 countries have agreed to adopt the provisions of the treaty. Over the course of the last 24 years, the treaty has been revised seven times. These revisions have been undertaken to improve compliance with the treaty and to reflect the development of new technologies for phasing out ODS. The original goal of the treaty was to help return the ozone level to pre-1980 levels by 2050. Scientists predict that with the support of developing nations, the ozone layer will be returned to the proposed pre-1980 levels between 2060 and 2075.

The impetus for the Montreal Protocol began in 1974 with the work of two Nobel Prize-winning scientists. Sherwood Rowland and Mario Molina noted that CFCs commonly found in aerosol cans were capable of depleting the stratospheric ozone layer. Environmental scientists demonstrated that the ozone layer over Antarctica was, indeed, thinning. This thinning was referred to as the ozone hole. Subsequent reviews of the ozone layer showed holes in the ozone layer over Antarctica and the Arctic. Recognizing the dangers of ozone depletion to the health and well-being of the planet, the Montreal Protocol was developed during the Vienna Convention held in Austria in 1987.

The specific actions required under the Montreal Protocol focus on the phase-out of several chemicals identified as ozone-depleting substances. The specific substances identified under the protocol include CFCs, HCFCs, halons, methyl-chloroform, chlorobromomethane, and methyl bromide. In addition to phasing out these substances, scientists have worked to develop safer alternatives that will not pose a significant risk to the ozone layer or the environment in general. While the reduction of ODS have helped to spur the repair of the ozone layer—because many of the ODS are also greenhouse gases—efforts to reduce the emissions of these substances have also resulted in a reduction of these types of emissions. Specifically, CFCs have greenhouse gas properties that are thousands of times more potent than more common greenhouses gases such as CO_2. Consequently, reductions in the use of these compounds have also contributed to reducing overall greenhouse gas emissions. This suggests that the Montreal Protocol has had broader benefits.

"The EPA estimates that the Montreal Protocol will result in $4.2 trillion in health benefits between 1990 and 2165 and prevent 6.3 million skin cancer deaths during this same time period."

In addition to the general impact that the Montreal Protocol has had on the environment, researchers estimate that the initiative has also had positive implications for society, including economic and health benefits. Although the ozone layer has not been fully restored, thinning of the ozone layer has started to decrease in size and should be fully restored by 2070. Based on these outcomes, the EPA estimates that the Montreal Protocol will result in $4.2 trillion in health benefits between 1990 and 2165 and prevent 6.3 million skin cancer deaths during this same time period. While the impact of reducing greenhouse gas emissions has not been estimated, these general improvements in the environment will have implications for human and environmental health.

MID-CHAPTER QUESTIONS

1. What is the difference between stratospheric ozone and ground-level ozone?

2. What are some of the negative effects of stratospheric ozone depletion?

3. What are the major goals of the Montreal Protocol? What are the biggest benefits to human health that could come out of successful implementation of these goals?

GEOGRAPHIC FACTORS OF AIR CONTROL

In this chapter's discussion of ground-level ozone, it was noted that levels of this secondary pollutant were higher in urban areas during the summer months. Although more common in urban areas, increased levels of ground-level ozone have also been reported in suburban and rural communities. Geographic factors such as weather patterns and the topography of the landscape can contribute to the transport and dispersion of air pollution in the environment. **Topography** refers to the surface features of land, including mountains, plains, and plateaus.

TOPOGRAPHY The surface features of land including mountains, plains, and plateaus.

Weather clearly has an impact on the transport and dispersion of air pollution. One pertinent example of how weather patterns can influence the flow of air pollution can be seen in the way that weather flows from west to east across the US. Thus, air pollution released in California can have environmental impacts in other parts of the country, such as in the case of acid precipitation and deposition (see p. 167).

A common feature of weather is wind. Wind results when warm air rises and cold air moves into a particular area. Cool air is heavier and has a higher air pressure than warm air and is capable of displacing the warm air in an area. Wind is responsible for the transport and dispersal of air pollution. When wind speed increases in an area, the wind transports air pollution farther away from the immediate area of dispersal.

The amount of air pollution in the atmosphere can also be impacted by the amount of turbulence present near the emission source. **Turbulence** refers to the horizontal and vertical motion of air in the atmosphere. The presence of turbulence interrupts typical wind patterns and changes the direction in which air pollution flows. Other weather conditions that can impact the flow of air pollution in the atmosphere include solar radiation, humidity, and precipitation such as rain or snow. Precipitation can help remove pollutants from the air by transferring them to bodies of water and soil. Thus, air pollution becomes water and soil pollution.

Although weather patterns directly influence the transport and dispersion of air pollution, topographic features present in the landscape also impact the way in which air pollution moves. When wind blows across land that is flat, air pollution carried in the wind travels farther. This is due to the fact that wind is not hindered by natural barriers in the land's topography. Similarly, if geographical structures such as mountains are present, air inversion may occur, resulting in concentrated air pollution in these areas. A warm air mass moving over a cooler and denser air mass can trap the cooler layer of air, allowing pollutants to build without the ability to escape. One specific example is the city of Denver, located at the foot of the Rocky Mountains. Air pollution in Denver has resulted in significant problems with smog in this city in recent years.

These general principles of the transport and dispersion of air pollution affect the flow of air pollution across the US. Air pollution produced in the Midwest, for instance, has been shown to have impacts on lakes and forests in the eastern part of the country. As a result of such impacts, the EPA in 2005 enacted the Clean Air Interstate Rule (CAIR) to regulate power plant emissions that cross state lines. In 2011, the EPA replaced the CAIR with the Cross-State Air Pollution Rule (CSAPR), which requires states to reduce emissions from power plants that make their way to other states, specifically small particle and ozone pollution.

Topographic factors that influence air pollution transport and dispersion have implications for the types of pollution that will occur in specific areas. For instance, if polluted air is not able to flow over a mountain, the pollution in the air may react to form secondary pollutants. As a result, the area located before the mountains may be susceptible to the harmful effects of primary and secondary pollution. Changes in wind patterns and the development of weather events such as precipitation or turbulence may change the outcomes for a geographical location. Hence the physical landscape of the environment must be taken into consideration—together with weather patterns—to understand how air pollution is transported and dispersed.

Generally speaking, little can be done to control weather patterns and the landscape of the country. With this in mind, controlling the transport and dispersion of

TURBULENCE The horizontal and vertical motion of air in the atmosphere.

air pollution requires the use of technology to help address the problem. The pertinent method used to control the geographic factors related to air pollution is smokestacks. Smokestacks release pollution into the Earth's atmosphere, well above the surface. This enables the air pollution to disperse before it reaches the ground level. Building higher smokestacks can help to ensure that pollutants are dispersed before they can reach distant locations, but the removal of pollutants by control technologies before the pollutants leave the stack is a better approach than dilution and dispersion alone.

MID-CHAPTER QUESTIONS

1. What types of geographical features impact the transport and dispersion of air pollution?

2. How can turbulence affect the dispersion of air pollution?

3. How can smokestacks reduce the concentration of air pollution in a particular community and what is a better way to control pollution?

CARBON CYCLE

The natural levels of CO_2 in the atmosphere are necessary to support the carbon cycle. The **carbon cycle** is a natural process in which carbon is released and absorbed to sustain life. One example can be seen in human respiration. Humans inhale air that contains oxygen and expel CO_2 as a waste product. The expelled CO_2 can be used by plants in the process of **photosynthesis**. Photosynthesis is the process by which plants, algae, and some bacteria grow. One of the byproducts of plant photosynthesis is oxygen. This oxygen can be used by humans, completing the cycle. The carbon cycle relies on a balance of CO_2 in the atmosphere. Thus, increased levels of CO_2 in the atmosphere that are the result of greenhouse gas emissions can create imbalances in the carbon cycle.

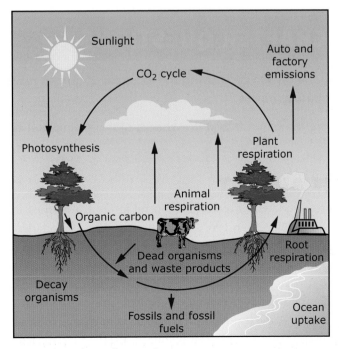

FIGURE 7.4 The carbon cycle

FUEL ECONOMY

50 MPG
40 MPG
30 MPG
20 MPG
10 MPG

CO_2 emissions can result from a host of human activities. Among the most pertinent source of CO_2 emissions is the burning of fossil fuels, such as in the combustion of gasoline in a car engine or the burning of coal to fire a power plant. Increased CO_2 in the atmosphere has created an imbalance in the carbon cycle. CO_2 is one of the principal greenhouses gases that are responsible for trapping heat on the Earth's surface. Because CO_2 levels can be controlled through the use of renewable fuels and a reduction in the use of fossil fuels, reducing carbon emissions can be a viable pathway for addressing some of the issues of air quality.

EPA Regulation of Fuel Economy and Emissions

The EPA has addressed the problem of greenhouse gas emissions as it works to improve fuel economy. Beginning in 1975, the EPA established the **Corporate Average Fuel Economy (CAFE) standards**. CAFE standards refer to the average fuel economy—measured in average miles per gallon (mpg)—that an automobile manufacturer's fleet must meet each year, depending on the vehicle class. By increasing average fuel economy via the CAFE standards, the EPA can reduce the amount of fuel that is burned in car engines and reduce US dependence on the importation of foreign fuel sources. Increased mileage results in the need for less fuel.

Even though the regulation of vehicle emissions through mpg standards appears to have notable benefits for both the consumer and the environment, controversy over the standards continues to be an important area for political debate. In order to achieve better fuel economy, automobile manufacturers must invest in new technologies, which ultimately cost the company money. Many automobile manufacturers do not want to pass these increased costs on to consumers. However, automobile manufacturers argue that improving fuel economy does require some of the costs to be passed to the consumer. As a result, consumers may pay higher prices for more efficient automobiles.

MID-CHAPTER QUESTIONS

1. **Explain the carbon cycle using the example of human respiration and plant photosynthesis.**

2. **What are the benefits and drawbacks of increasing fuel economy?**

CLEAN AIR ACT

Initial efforts to address air pollution control in the US resulted in the passage of the Clean Air Act (CAA) in 1963. This act established a foundation for researching the issue of air pollution and funding cleanup of existing air pollution problems. Although this legislation provided the foundation for the federal government's efforts to control air pollution, it was not until the passage of the CAA amendments in 1970 that the federal government instituted clear rules governing air pollution standards. In 1977, the legislation was expanded to require more action from state and local governments to control air pollution. Via the EPA, the federal government

CAFE STANDARDS The average fuel economy (mpg) that a vehicle manufacturer's fleet must meet each year.

BUSINESSES GOING GREEN: GALAXY PRESS

Going green requires a commitment by an organization to focus on business practices that will reduce harm to the environment and, where possible, contribute to sustainable development. While large-scale changes in operations can have a positive environmental impact, organizations that take small steps to protect the environment can also contribute to environmental sustainability. This point is well-illustrated in the case of Galaxy Press in Concord, California.

Although Galaxy Press has consistently worked to improve its green business practices, the organization has made notable progress in recent years because of its efforts to make its entire operation environmentally sustainable. In order to bring the organization's operations into compliance with all government regulations, the owners of Galaxy Press utilized a number of different practices that clearly have implications for reducing air pollution. Some of these practices include:

- *Computerizing operations:* This practice has led to a reduction in the use of photochemicals. Photochemicals contain VOCs and other air pollutants. In addition, this practice reduced energy and water usage.
- *Establishing a solvent recycling program:* This reduces the amount of chemicals consumed by the company and limits air pollution from chemical waste. Greenhouse gas emissions and VOCs are reduced though this type of program.
- *Using low-VOC inks:* Using inks that contain fewer VOCs reduces the amount of these compounds that are released into the environment. VOCs contribute to problems such as ground-level ozone and smog.

All of these practices, when combined together, have enabled Galaxy Press to become the first printer in Contra Costa County to become a certified green business. In addition to protecting the environment, many of the green practices also provide the added benefits of saving money and time. Thus, "going green" has been a benefit for both Galaxy Press and the environment.

oversees air pollution control, but state and local governments—with EPA support and approval—are primarily responsible for implementing the direct measures that are responsible for air pollution control. The CAA was again amended in 1990, expanding the authority of Congress to implement and enforce air pollution regulations. Additionally, the 1990 amendments focused on the need for more cost effective solutions for pollution control.

The passage of the CAA in 1970 has had a number of benefits for the environment. In particular, data indicate that the amount of the six most common air pollutants has decreased by 50 percent since its regulations were enacted. Air pollutants from industrial operations have been reduced by 70 percent and most ozone-depleting substances have been phased out of use. Additionally, data indicate that since the passage of the law, GDP has tripled and energy consumption and vehicle use have increased by 50 percent and 200 percent, respectively. Based on this data, it is evident that the CAA has created numerous benefits at a time when energy consumption has increased. Further, the legislation has not hindered economic growth as seen by the growth in GDP. The legislation is also estimated to have increased average life expectancy by five to seven years.

A report released following the 1990 amendments to the CAA further demonstrate positive benefits of the legislation. The report indicates that the cost of implementing the amendments to the legislation was $65 billion. While these costs are indeed high, the savings from the amendments were estimated at $2 trillion. Additionally, the amendments are projected to save 230,000 lives by 2020 by preventing premature deaths due to air pollutants. When the costs and benefits of the legislation are weighed, the benefits outweigh the costs by a factor of 30 to 1.

CHAPTER SUMMARY

Air pollution represents a serious threat to human and environmental health. Air pollution has been classified according to a number of different criteria, including primary or secondary pollution, criteria air pollutants or hazardous air pollutants, and particulate or gaseous pollution. Classification of pollution provides insight into the root causes of the pollution and the specific methods that can be used to control or reduce it. While all forms of air pollution must be controlled, specific types—such as ground-level ozone—represent significant threats to human health and require precise action to be controlled. Ground-level ozone must be differentiated from stratospheric ozone. Stratospheric ozone must be protected because of the benefits it provides for sustaining life. The climate changes continuously and in recent years, one group of scientists feels human contribution is the main cause; the second group feels climate change is a natural process; and others feel climate change is due to both natural sources and humans. In February 2013, the head of the IPCC stated that the Earth has not increased in temperature.

Efforts to combat air pollution have focused extensively on policy in both a national and international context. The Montreal Protocol was signed in 1987 and represents an international commitment to reducing the use of ozone depleting substances to repair the stratospheric ozone layer by 2075. On a national level, Congress has passed legislation to increase average fuel economy in automobiles; in 2011, US emissions of energy-related CO_2 were 8.7 percent below 2005 levels. The EPA is responsible for implementing the dozens of provisions in the CAA that protect air quality. Estimates suggest that the CAA has resulted in significant financial savings, as well as benefits to health and the environment.

REFERENCES

Air and Waste Management Association. (2007, April). Air pollution emission control devices [Fact sheet]. Retrieved from http://events.awma.org/files_original/ControlDevicesFactSheet07.pdf

Air Now. (2010). Air quality index. Retrieved from http://airnow.gov/index.cfm?action=aqibasics.aqi

Bast, J. (2010). *The seven theories of climate change.* Chicago, IL: The Heartland Institute.

Berwyn, B. (2011, December 4). NASA satellite confirms air quality improvements. *Summit County Citizens Voice.* Retrieved from http://summitcountyvoice.com/2011/12/04/nasa-satellite-confirms-air-quality-improvements/

Goodstein, E. (2009, October). The trade-off myth. Center for Progressive Reform. Retrieved from http://www.progressivereform.org/perspenviro_regs_jobs.cfm

Lefsrud, L. M., & Meyer, R. E. (2013). Science or science fiction? Professionals' discursive construction of climate change. *Organization Studies, 33,* 1477–1506.

National Oceanic and Atmospheric Administration, Paleoclimatology Program. (2008, August 20). A paleo perspective on abrupt climate change. Retrieved from http://www.ncdc.noaa.gov/paleo/abrupt/

Piers, F., Andrews, T., Good, P., Gregory, J., Jackson, L., & Zelinka, M. (2013). Evaluating adjusted forcing and model spread for historical and future scenarios in the CMIP5 generation of climate models. *Journal of Geophysical Research: Atmospheres, 118*(3), 1139–1150.

Scafetta, N. (2012). Testing an astronomically based decadal-scale empirical harmonic climate model versus the IPCC (2007) general circulation climate models. *Journal of Atmospheric and Solar-Terrestrial Physics, 80,* 124–137.

Thorning, M. (2011, February 9). The impact of EPA regulation of GHGs under the Clean Air Act on U.S. investment and job growth. American Council for Capital Formation. Retrieved from http://accf.org/news/publication/the-impact-of-epa-regulation-of-ghgs-under-the-clean-air-act-on-u-s-investment-and-job-growth

U.S. Environmental Protection Agency. (2010). Control emissions technologies. Retrieved from http://www.epa.gov/apti/course422/ce1.html

U.S. Environmental Protection Agency. (2011). Cross State Air Pollution Rule (CSAPR). http://www.epa.gov/airtransport/

U.S. Environmental Protection Agency. (2007). Montreal Protocol, backgrounder. Retrieved from http://www.epa.gov/ozone/downloads/MP20_Backgrounder.pdf

U.S. Environmental Protection Agency. (n.d.). Montreal Protocol [Fact sheet]. Retrieved from http://www.epa.gov/ozone/downloads/MP20_FactSheet.pdf

U.S. Environmental Protection Agency. (2003, June). *Ozone: Good up high, bad nearby.* Retrieved from http://www.epa.gov/oar/oaqps/gooduphigh/ozone.pdf

U.S. Environmental Protection Agency. (2010). Pollutants in the ambient air. Retrieved from http://www.epa.gov/oar/oaqps/eog/course422/ap2.html

U.S. Environmental Protection Agency. (2011). Second prospective study. Retrieved from http://www.epa.gov/air/sect812/prospective2.html

U.S. Environmental Protection Agency. (2010). Smog. Retrieved from http://www.epa.gov/oar/oaqps/eog/course422/ap7b4.html

U.S. Environmental Protection Agency. (2010). Source control technology. Retrieved from http://www.epa.gov/apti/course422/ce6.html

U.S. Environmental Protection Agency. (2012, March 6). Understanding the Clean Air Act. (2011). Retrieved from http://www.epa.gov/air/caa/peg/understand.html

U.S. Environmental Protection Agency. (2010). Welfare effects—acid rain. Retrieved from http://www.epa.gov/oar/oaqps/eog/course422/ap7b1.html

Vision Los Angeles. (2011). *Clearer roads, clearer skies.* Retrieved from http://www.visionlosangeles.org/pdf/VisionLA_Report.pdf

Wong, E. (2011, December 6). Outrage grows over air pollution and China's response. *New York Times Online.* Retrieved from http://www.nytimes.com/2011/12/07/world/asia/beijing-journal-anger-grows-over-air-pollution-in-china.html?_r=1&scp=1&sq=Outrage%20Grows%20Over%20Air%20Pollution%20and%20Chinas%20Response&st=cse

Yardley, J. (2008, July 7). Cities near Beijing close factories to improve air for Olympics. *New York Times Online.* Retrieved from http://www.nytimes.com/2008/07/07/sports/olympics/07china.html

Zississ, C., & Bajoria, J. (2008, August 4). *China's environmental crisis.* Council on Foreign Relations. Retrieved from http://www.cfr.org/china/chinas-environmental-crisis/p12608

Economics, Politics, and Public Policy

CLEAN AIR RULES AND ECONOMIC COSTS IN SALEM, MASSACHUSETTS

For many years, a large coal- and oil-fired power plant in the city of Salem, Massachusetts provided abundant energy for the community and provided jobs for about 150 local workers. The industry made significant financial property and income tax contributions to the local economy. Despite these benefits to the community, air pollution emissions from the power plant were reportedly linked to many health problems for local residents.

The plant began operations in 1951. Since then, it had been considered one of the least environmentally efficient plants in the region, producing high levels of carbon emissions and pollution. It had consistently been the source of arguments between those who wanted the plant to close and those who wanted it to switch to more efficient processes. Local labor leaders and city officials leery of losing the jobs and revenue the plant brought to Salem needed a solution to the dilemma.

In 2010, before an environmentally safe and efficient operating process could be implemented, Dominion Energy, the company that owned the plant, announced that it would be closing the Salem power plant. New federal regulations limited the amount of air pollution plants could produce. The regulations were designed to keep the air cleaner and safer by limiting the amounts of toxic chemicals that could be emitted from the facilities. Dominion Energy began cutting some of the plant's functions late in 2011, with the goal of closing the entire plant by 2014. At least 30 power plants throughout the United States (US)—including the Salem facility—announced they would cease operations when the new federal regulations went into effect. Owners of the power plants that are closing expressed that the cost required to maintain environmental compliance with the new federal regulations will cost each plant more money than they can generate or charge so closure is their only option presently.

At the time of the announcement, the Salem plant had contributed about $4.75 million annually to the city's tax base, which was about seven percent of the city's total tax revenue. The power plant was the largest contributor to the local tax base. Salem officials expressed concern about how they would replace that money when the plant shut down. When Dominion Energy announced the plant closing, the mayor admitted the city would have to raise taxes or cut city services due to the lost tax revenue from the plant.

MAIN GOVERNMENT AGENCIES

The US government has a number of agencies that enforce environmental safety laws. Congress passes the laws and federal agencies write many of the **regulations** that businesses, industries, and residents must follow. For example, Congress can pass a law that requires vehicles to be more fuel-efficient. Then, the Environmental Protection Agency (EPA) must develop a rating system for exactly how many miles a car should be able to drive on a gallon of gas and create a testing process to certify which companies and cars are meeting that new mileage standard. Besides setting the rules, federal agencies also enforce those rules, which can mean anything from conducting a surprise investigation, to conducting an impact study, to suing a person or company that violates the rules, with the possibility of criminal fines and prison.

In some cases, many agencies work on the same issues and share responsibilities. Some agencies do not actually create regulations, but are in charge of enforcing the specific regulations created by other agencies. Several different US presidential cabinet departments have one or more offices with an environmental focus, each with specific jobs.

US Environmental Protection Agency (EPA)

The EPA—founded in 1970—handles a range of more than 100 environmental laws and issues. It was designed to oversee environmental policies for the nation, combining jobs that had earlier been divided among many government departments. It sets up and enforces specific rules about clean air and water, waste cleanup, recycling, pesticides and other chemicals, and limiting pollution. It oversees everything from certifying which appliances use energy efficiently to making sure polluters clean up waste sites to determining which animals are considered endangered species and therefore must be protected. In addition to its headquarters in Washington, DC, the EPA has ten regional offices that create and enforce more specific rules for different parts of the country.

REGULATION A rule issued by a government agency that has the force of law.

1. Is it worth passing tougher environmental laws if companies threaten to shut down plants, terminate employees, or relocate operations to areas with less expensive environmental regulations?

2. What is the primary responsibility of the US government in a situation like this? Will increasing regulations in the US actually reduce pollution worldwide? Should it be more worried about passing laws to protect the air or about companies being profitable and hiring domestic workers?

The Environmental
Protection Agency in
Washington, DC

US Department of Agriculture (USDA)

The USDA is a cabinet-level department that sets farm policies for the country. The department also regulates and inspects meat, poultry, aquaculture, and dairy. The USDA oversees the Forest Service and the Natural Resource Conservation Service.

US Forest Service (USFS)

The USFS protects more than 150 designated national forests, including fighting forest fires. Forest fire fighting activity accounts for more than 40 percent of the department's budget.

Natural Resource Conservation Service (NRCS)

The NRCS regulates conservation of grazing land, the Great Lakes and many river basins, wildlife habitats, and wetlands. The NRCS also works to limit soil erosion and other damage caused by natural disasters such as floods and hurricanes.

Department of Health and Human Services (HHS)

The Department of HHS studies environmental problems that affect public health. The Agency for Toxic Substances and Disease Registry tracks dangerous pollutants, such as asbestos, lead, and formaldehyde. The Centers for Disease Control (CDC), based in Atlanta, provides information to the public about air pollution, water pollution, and other environmental problems that can affect people's health. The HHS oversees the Food and Drug Administration.

Food and Drug Administration (FDA)

The FDA, part of the HHS, is concerned with protecting the public from diseases, including testing food and medicine for safety and inspecting factories. The FDA sets regulations for seafood, grains, and fruits and vegetables, inspects food imported from other countries, and manages recalls when there are food-related disease outbreaks.

National Parks Service (NPS)

The Department of the Interior oversees the NPS, which operates and preserves about 400 properties around the country, including national parks, forests, monuments, and historic sites. Some of the most well known of these sites include the Grand Canyon, Yellowstone National Park, and Yosemite National Park.

Office of Energy Efficiency and Renewable Energy (EERE)

The US Department of Energy's (DOE) Office of Energy Efficiency and Renewable Energy (EERE) funds projects to develop cleaner, naturally replenished sources of energy, such as solar and wind power, which can reduce the need for high-polluting fossil fuels like oil and coal.

Office of Environmental Management (EM)

The Office of Environmental Management (EM) oversees the cleanup of waste created by the development of nuclear weapons and nuclear energy over the past several decades.

National Oceanographic and Atmospheric Administration (NOAA)

Under the Department of Commerce, the National Oceanographic and Atmospheric Administration (NOAA) operates the National Ocean Service (NOS), which sets aside marine sanctuary environments and coral reefs for protection. The NOS tracks risks to the ocean from rising sea levels and other natural disasters. It also operates the National Marine Fisheries Service (NMFS), which enforces rules about fishing, keeps track of fish populations, and works to protect endangered marine species from overfishing.

US Congress

Both houses of the US Congress have committees that focus on writing and amending environmental laws. In the House of Representatives, the Committee on Natural Resources and the Committee on Agriculture are responsible for writing and updating the laws. In the Senate, the Energy and Natural Resources Committee and the Agriculture, Nutrition, and Forestry Committee are responsible for preparing environmental legislation. These committees contain lawmakers from both the Democratic and the Republican parties, with a chairperson chosen by whichever party has more members in that chamber at the time.

MID-CHAPTER QUESTIONS

1. **Name three government agencies that have a role in regulating how people and businesses use the environment.**

2. **Give two examples of how a federal agency might enforce its regulations.**

EFFECTS OF REGULATION

The bald eagle has been America's national symbol for more than two centuries, but by the 1960s, this species had a very good chance of becoming extinct in most of the US. These majestic birds were once plentiful, filling the skies with an estimated 25,000 to 75,000 eagles living in the lower 48 states. Around 1963, a study found only 417 breeding pairs left in the wild. Hunters were a big part of the problem. They shot many eagles for trophies. Also, because eagles scavenge, they often ate dead animals that had been shot with lead bullets; many birds died from lead poisoning. But another big factor was dichlorodiphenyltrichloroethane (DDT), a powerful pesticide that was widely used by farmers. In 1962, biologist and author Rachel Carson published the book *Silent Spring*, which reported how dangerous

DDT and other pesticides were to wildlife, to the environment, and to people's health.

DDT was inexpensive and extremely effective for insect pest control on farms and mosquito control in suburban communities. The primary problem with DDT was its persistence. The chemical was not easily broken down in the environment or by metabolic functions if it was ingested. The pesticide was passed up the food chain—DDT was sprayed on plants; plants were eaten by insects; insects were eaten by birds, mammals, reptiles, amphibians, and fish; and bald eagles ate many of these species. Since the DDT was not broken down earlier in the food chain, the eagles received a concentrated dose of it. Eventually, DDT was detected in eagle eggs and eaglets. DDT also reduced egg viability.

While some farmers and agricultural businesses stopped using DDT voluntarily, others ignored the risk and continued to use it. The bald eagle became a symbol of the problem, and the government took steps to save the bird with new regulations. In 1972, the EPA announced that DDT would be banned nationwide for most uses (however, it is still in use for malaria control in Africa and other areas). The next year, Congress passed the Endangered Species Act (ESA), giving the EPA the authority to protect at-risk wildlife. When the bald eagle was placed on the endangered species list in 1978, the EPA was able to regulate the protection of the birds' habitat and nesting grounds, and to institute restrictions that made it illegal to hunt them. This combined effort saved the national bird from extinction. In 1995, the bald eagle was doing well enough that its status was downgraded from "endangered" to "threatened," as scientists found bald eagles were using ten times as many nests as they had been in 1963. In 2007, the population had recovered enough for the bald eagle to no longer be considered at risk of disappearing. However, population recovery does not mean that bald eagle hunting should be allowed to resume.

Brown pelicans also experienced a decline in population in the 1940s as a result of heavy DDT use in the US. By the 1960s, populations along the Gulf Coast and in California were gone or no longer able to reproduce as a result of consuming contaminated fish. The pelican's diet of fish contaminated with DDT resulted in their eggs having very thin shells that were unable to support incubation. In 1970, the US Fish and Wildlife Service (USFWS) placed the bird on its endangered list. This protection, combined with the 1972 ban of DDT, allowed for the recovery of the population and it was removed from the endangered species list in 1985. The birds are now found along the Gulf Coast, Atlantic Coast, and in California.

The publication of *Silent Spring* is often credited with inspiring the modern environmental movement, which led to the creation of many government agencies and federal regulations the US. The environmental movement prompted more Americans to become concerned about the effects of chemicals and other pollutants on the environment and human health. Congress and President Richard Nixon established the EPA in 1970, and soon passed the Clean Air Act (CAA), the first major law that gave the EPA the power to establish regulations for air pollution. Under the CAA, the EPA set target emission levels for factories, vehicles, and other sources of pollution to meet within five years. It set up a compliance process in which EPA officials would monitor and inspect factories, test new sources of energy to make sure they obeyed the law, and fine or even close companies that routinely violated the new rules.

Prior to the CAA, air pollution control systems were not required, and many companies did not even consider them. At the time the CAA was implemented, many factories were using old and outdated manufacturing technologies. The mindset of the time was that if a factory was emitting smoke, people were employed, which was viewed as positive. Once CAA regulations were enacted, many companies could not afford to install air pollution control devices and technologies, so they ceased operations. The CAA was partly responsible for expanding the "Rust Belt" (abandoned and defunct factories) across the US from the East Coast to the Great Lakes and Midwest regions. Many plants closed or shifted operations overseas to reduce labor and manufacturing costs.

Over time, enforcement of the CAA and the regulations it created played a major part in reducing air pollution. For example, CAA regulations reduced the amount of lead allowed in gasoline, making unleaded gas the new standard. This improvement in the safety of automobile fuel happened because lead in the atmosphere had been linked to reduced intelligence in children exposed to it, and to adult health problems such as hypertension and heart disease.

The EPA estimates that between 1970 and 1990, more than 200,000 Americans died from air pollution-related illnesses. If the CAA regulations had not been created, millions more would have suffered from those illnesses. The law saved trillions of dollars in medical bills and other health costs. Over time, Congress passed a series of amendments to the CAA, further limiting the amount of pollution in the atmosphere.

The CAA also became a model for many 1970s environmental laws, including the Clean Water Act (WA), the ESA, the Safe Drinking Water Act (SDWA), the Hazardous Materials Transportation Act (HMTA), and the Toxic Substances Control Act (TSCA). Another federal program developed to identify and clean hazardous sites is the Comprehensive Environmental Response, Compensation, and Liability Act (CERCLA)—commonly known as Superfund—which was enacted by Congress on December 11, 1980. This law created a tax on the chemical and petroleum industries and provided broad federal authority to respond directly to releases or threatened releases of hazardous substances that may endanger public health or the environment. The EPA uses Superfund guidelines and regulations to identify and clean up hazardous waste sites. As of September 2012, the EPA included 1,304 sites on its national priority list, with 360 listed as removed due to cleanup efforts. This list was created in response to the disaster at Love Canal, a neighborhood in upstate New York where the Hooker Chemical Company had illegally dumped more than 20,000 tons of toxic chemical waste. After journalists uncovered the dump and publicized the effects the waste had on the people living near it—including birth defects, leukemia, and severe chromosome damage—the federal government declared Love Canal a disaster area and began the remediation process.

The establishment of Superfund gave the government the authority to make Hooker Chemical and future polluters pay for the cleanup efforts required because of their behavior.

Superfund also prompted industries to be more environmentally responsible and cognizant of their operating procedures. The goal was to make them think twice before dumping dangerous chemicals and making sure taxpayers did not have to pay for the needed cleanups. The polluters were now legally responsible for any accidental or intentional environmental hazards or pollution released from their facilities. They were liable for all remediation and damage costs. By the time the EPA filed suit against Hooker Chemical to make it cover the cleanup of Love Canal and other costs of the disaster, the EPA had already compiled a list of 3,913 other potential hazardous-waste disaster sites around the country and were inspecting those sites.

Even in cases like these, where the benefits of regulation to the public might seem obvious, there were those who considered the regulations unnecessary. In the Love Canal case, Hooker Chemical fought the EPA in court, arguing that it had the right to dump its waste. It argued that it was dumping on land it had paid for and legally owned, even though that dumping posed a huge risk to the nearby people who could not protect themselves from the health problems the waste caused. Similarly, many farm interests argued against the DDT ban, because it meant they would lose some crops to the insects that the DDT had been killing. As a result, they would therefore lose the money they would have made from those additional crops. Now farmers can plant genetically modified crops resistant to pests, reducing the need for such pesticide use.

The Issue of Responsibility

Environmental regulations attempt to solve what ecologist and Professor Garrett Hardin called "the tragedy of the commons" in a famous 1968 article by that name published in the magazine *Science*. Hardin's phrase is based on the following scenario:

> Consider a pasture, where everyone in the community is allowed to let their cows graze. If everybody uses the land fairly, without putting too many cows in the pasture, it can work well for everybody. But without rules and regulations, one farmer can bring in more animals and use up more than his share of the land. Of course, that is done at the expense of the other farmers, who then have less land than they need for their cows.

As Hardin explained in his article, pollution is a good example of the same problem. Natural resources such as air and water are considered common property, which are required and used by everyone. But when companies pollute the air or dump poison in the water, even if they do so on their private property, they are not only using more than their share of the "commons," but they are doing so at the expense of everyone else who needs to use them. Regulations are the government's attempt at solving that problem by trying to balance the needs of the public and the environment against the needs of businesses.

Conflict Between Business and Regulators

As with the DDT ban, businesses often argue that existing or additional government regulation regarding the environment limits their ability to run their businesses the way they want and costs them revenue. For example, in 2011 the EPA decided to make national regulations about **hydraulic fracturing (fracking)**.

Fracking is a relatively inexpensive and efficient natural gas and petroleum extraction process. The process uses large amounts of water, sometimes as much as one to five million gallons per well—depending on the type—plus relatively small amounts of sand and chemicals under very high pressure to break rock formations deep underground. Even though the percentage of chemicals is relatively small compared to the volume of water used in the process, the actual amount of chemicals used is large. The rock formations contain trapped petroleum and natural gas. The formations are fractured (fracked) by the high-pressure fluid, which releases the resources. The resources are forced to the surface, where they are recovered.

Typical drinking water wells are only a few hundred feet deep. Rock fracture occurs at much deeper depths, somewhere around 7,000–8,000 feet below the surface in oil shale formations, far below the drinking water supply. Fracking could become problematic if the fluid being held in retention containers is allowed to escape. If care is not taken to ensure safe waste water handling to and from the retention containers, it could leak into the soil, drinking water supply, and waterways. Some operations dispose of the wastewater by injecting it in the ground at depths greater than 9,000 feet below the surface. Some of the chemicals used in fracking operations have health and safety issues.

The wastewater and pollution created from fracking started to get more public attention in 2011, as companies began to drill for newly discovered deposits of natural gas deep in shale rock. Environmental activist groups worried that—unless the EPA set national regulations—the different rules in different states would make businesses shift to those states with fewer restrictions on drilling. Several states have enacted state regulations and additional policies that energy companies must follow. Colorado and Wyoming have laws mandating the use of equipment that separates chemicals from the wastewater. Other states, such as Pennsylvania, have state regulations based on federal regulations and do not require drillers to use the same equipment. As a result, some energy companies have started or increased operations in those states. Currently the EPA is considering making a decision to consider new rules for a consistent, national standard.

Sometimes, government officials and businesses conflict regarding federal regulations, as in the case of the Arctic National Wildlife Refuge (ANWR) in northern Alaska. ANWR is the largest protected wildlife reserve in the US, covering more than 19 million acres. It is home to large wild animal species such as musk oxen, grizzly bears, and caribou. In 1980, Congress declared ANWR a federally protected area with a law that included a regulation that anyone planning to drill for oil in ANWR could not do so unless they got specific approval from Congress. Developers have wanted to drill in part of the reserve, in a plains area near the coast. They lobbied for Congress to lift the ban, which came close to happening a few times.

In 1996, the House of Representatives approved drilling in ANWR, but President Bill Clinton vetoed the bill, and Congress did not have enough votes to override his veto. In the 2000s, with the US becoming concerned about the effect of unrest in the Middle East on oil prices and supply, a combination of energy companies, the state government of Alaska (which saw drilling as a way to create more jobs in the state) and President George W. Bush urged Congress to allow drilling in ANWR. People more concerned with protecting the ANWR ecosystem, including environmental organizations like the Natural Resources Defense Council (NRDC) and a group of more than 200 native Alaskan tribes, fought against opening ANWR to drilling. These groups argued that even if the largest estimates for how much oil was actually under ANWR were correct—and the estimates ranged widely—drilling would only slightly decrease the amount of oil from overseas that the country needed, and would permanently destroy part of the refuge where caribou gave birth and raised their young. Despite the combined work of Alaska state officials, President Bush, and the oil companies, enough members of Congress opposed lifting the ban, and the reserve remained protected.

Business Incentives

In situations like ANWR protection, some businesses consider environmental regulations harmful to their businesses and the economic benefits of job creation. The fracking example illustrates how some businesses choose one state rather than another based on how environmental regulations impact their operating costs. One of the most common arguments against the government creating environmental regulations is the idea that they hurt the profitability of businesses or give them a reason to go somewhere else.

However, the government agencies tasked with regulating the environment also have many programs that give businesses and individuals financial incentives to use environmentally friendly, "green" practices and materials. For example, the EPA and the Department of Energy (DOE) run a joint program called Energy Star, a labeling program that lets companies voluntarily put a sticker with the Energy Star seal on products proven to use energy efficiently and limit the amount of greenhouse gasses they produce. This branding program started with computers, but now includes the certification of more than 60 types of products, including battery chargers, light bulbs, and vending machines. Manufacturers try to get the sticker and certification so that their products stand out in stores, giving them an advantage when trying to attract customers who are concerned about energy costs. There is also a tax incentive part of the program, in which customers who buy energy-efficient appliances can write off part of the cost on their income taxes. Many homeowners and businesses take advantage of this program when choosing office equipment and supplies. There are many other federal and state tax credits and incentives that reward businesses that make energy-efficient products, recycle, or invest in new kinds of energy.

Some environmentally friendly and energy-saving tax reduction incentives include:

- Many state governments give tax credits to companies that recycle, giving them a way to save money while increasing the environmental sustainability of their operations. In Nevada, for example, manufacturing companies that follow state recycling guidelines can write off three-quarters of their state property taxes for up to 10 years. Georgia allows manufacturing companies that invest in recycling programs to write off part of the cost on their income taxes, with three levels of tax incentives they can use.

- As part of a 2009 federal act designed to stimulate the economy, the federal government made a major commitment to investing in energy efficiency, with more than $27 billion dedicated to that goal. The incentive money included tax breaks for companies' research and development of wind, hydroelectric, solar, geothermal, and other renewable forms of energy. It funded a Department of Labor (DOL) program to train out-of-work people for jobs in green technology, provide millions of dollars in rebates for consumers who bought energy-efficient appliances, and provide money for the development of electric cars, new kinds of fuel cells, and other green technology.

Trans-Alaska pipeline

■ The EPA offers homebuilders tax credits for making use of energy efficient design. Skylights, metal roofs, exterior windows, central air conditioning, insulation, and certain kinds of high-efficiency heat pumps and water heaters all carry tax incentives.

BUSINESSES GOING GREEN: BROWNFIELD DEVELOPMENT AND GREEN BUILDING

Besides making rules about what businesses can and can't do when it comes to the environment, the EPA also provides money for companies that follow environmentally friendly guidelines. When the city of Dallas needed a new, larger police headquarters, it used EPA grants and other funding to build the new headquarters on a **brownfield** site—an abandoned commercial area in need of environmental cleanup and redevelopment.

Not only did the Jack Evans Police Building project revitalize a parcel of contaminated land, but the six-floor structure, which opened in 2003 and stays open all day year-round, was built using some very advanced architectural techniques designed to minimize the waste of building materials, energy, and natural resources. All the water used to maintain the grounds comes from collected storm water, while the bathrooms use "low-flow" showers and toilets (which use less water) and waterless urinals (which don't constantly fill with water and then flush it, a process that wastes water). The building itself was constructed to use less energy. Windows and reflecting surfaces were placed for maximum "daylighting," which refers to using natural light in the offices instead of electricity. The walls were insulated to keep heating costs down, and a natural gas (rather than electric) generator was installed to help with cooling the building during the summer. City officials say the efficient design of the new police station saves Dallas taxpayers hundreds of thousands of dollars in energy costs, while at the same time conserving environmental resources. Other sustainable features of this high-profile municipal building include reserved parking spaces for carpoolers and the headquarters' downtown location near public transportation.

The Dallas City Council set a goal that the new police station achieve LEED (Leadership in Energy and Environmental Design) Silver certification from the US Green Building Council, a program that publicly recognizes buildings that employ sustainability best practices in their design, construction, and operation. The City Council used the success of the police station project to pass a law requiring all future new buildings constructed by the City of Dallas to achieve the same LEED Silver certification.

MID-CHAPTER QUESTIONS

1. Briefly explain the idea of "the tragedy of the commons." What role does regulation play in avoiding this type of situation?

2. What are some of the ways the government rewards companies for being environmentally responsible?

OPPORTUNITY COSTS The loss of potential gain from other alternatives when one alternative is chosen.

COSTS AND BENEFITS OF REGULATION

Think about the situation in the chapter opener. Federal regulators were worried about asthma and other medical problems linked to pollution from factories like the Salem power plant. City officials worried about the money and jobs Salem would lose when the plant owners announced they would close the facility because of tougher regulations. Measuring the potential good such laws create against the potential harm that could result from them is a form of cost-benefit analysis. In an ideal situation, the plant would be able to employ people in the town and function in a way that made a substantial profit without producing pollution that causes medical problems.

In this particular case, the potential costs from rules that required the plant to produce less pollution would include:

- The financial costs paid by the company that owns the plant in order to comply with new government regulations
- The loss of jobs and tax revenue if the plant owner decided to close or to move to another state (or country) with less-stringent, if any, environmental laws
- The loss of the goods or services provided by the operation of the plant—in this case, relatively low-cost electricity

In the same scenario, the potential benefits if the plant produced less pollution would include:

- The improved health of the local community and the associated quality-of-life improvements enjoyed by those people living longer, healthier lives
- The lower health care costs that would result from fewer cases of asthma and other health problems associated with higher pollution levels
- Potentially cleaner air and water, leading to higher-quality environmental amenities that could be enjoyed by the public; this benefit can also be understood as lowering the **opportunity costs** imposed by the current pollution levels (i.e., a lack of opportunity for the general public to use the aspects of the environment damaged by the pollution)
- The potential new jobs that could be created by building projects to upgrade and modernize the plant to meet higher health and safety standards

In this scenario, as in many scenarios concerning environmental regulation, the costs and benefits can contradict each other. The goal of regulation is to maximize the benefits while minimizing the costs.

A similar scenario happened in 2010, when American Electric Power (AEP), one of the country's largest coal companies, announced it would close five of its coal power plants by 2014. At the time, the head of AEP blamed the timeline imposed by the Environmental Protection Agency to upgrade older plants or to close the power plants. The executive called the EPA's tougher air-pollution regulations a "war on coal."

Before enacting the regulation, the EPA did an impact study to look at the benefits of the rule, most of them focusing on public health. According to that study, upon full implementation in 2014, the Cross-State Air Pollution Rule (CSAPR) would prevent between 13,000 and 34,000 premature deaths, 1.8 million missed days of school or work due to illness, and more than 19,000 hospital or emergency room visits. The EPA estimated that the Rule's benefits, both to public health and to the environment, would be worth between $120 billion and $280 billion per year by 2014, with financial costs of about only $800 million per year. Impact studies like the one the EPA used in this case are a common way for federal agencies to determine both the costs and benefits of a regulation before it becomes official policy. When a law or regulation comes directly from Congress, the Government Accountability Office (GAO, formerly the Government Accounting Office) prepares a detailed report about the impact of the regulation. The GAO is an independent, non-partisan agency. Its director, selected by the President from a list created by Congress, serves a 15-year term so that he or she can remain independent from elections and politics once in office.

In the case of American Electric Power closing five of its plants rather than alter them to adapt to the lower emission standards created by the CSAPR, the company itself saw both costs and benefits from regulation. In 2010, AEP closed its coal plant in Ohio near the Muskingum River—one of the five it decided to close. According to the EPA, it was the third-worst plant in terms of pollution emissions in the US. The pollution issues created an undesirable environmental cost to go with its energy-production benefit. Closing the plant would cost more than 150 workers their jobs, which would be a negative impact on the community.

However, even while closing those coal plants, the company started construction on a natural gas-fueled power plant elsewhere in Ohio. The new plant would not employ as many people, but would still create jobs. Complying with the new EPA regulations will reduce carbon dioxide (CO_2), sulfur, particulates, and other pollution. In another of its existing Ohio plants, the company built a "scrubber"—a device that uses limestone to remove most of the sulfur dioxide emissions from coal-fueled power plants. Not only will that scrubber greatly reduce air pollution, to the benefit of the public and environment, but the company hired 40 new permanent employees to operate it in addition to more than a thousand temporary workers to build and install it. So in this case, while the company's reaction to the new regulation did cost some jobs, it also created others. Of course, the towns with the closing plants felt more of the costs, and the towns where AEP chose to upgrade its plants or build new ones felt more of the benefits.

While increased government regulations will cause some unemployment, some studies indicate that a few companies tend to overstate the impact of regulations on job loss. As evidenced by the coal plant example, regulation can lead to the creation and elimination of jobs. In 2009, the federal government set aside funds specifically to train unemployed workers in new, environmentally friendly technologies. While regulations on pollution, for example, might diminish the number of jobs in heavily polluting industries like coal and oil, similar regulations pay for worker training and give companies tax incentives to hire workers in cleaner technology industries like wind power and solar power. Researchers have estimated that changing from coal to natural gas and alternative green fuels (wind, solar, hydroelectric) could generate as many as half a million jobs in the US in the next ten years, and companies like AEP have the option of taking their existing expertise in creating energy and opening plants that use natural gas or other cleaner forms.

Individual consumers also face a cost-benefit analysis when it comes to their own energy consumption. The effects of regulation can influence their decisions. For example, a person purchasing a car could select a fuel-efficient hybrid model that was built after recent regulations and is better for the environment. Hybrid technology is still fairly new, so even a used hybrid would cost more money upfront than buying a less

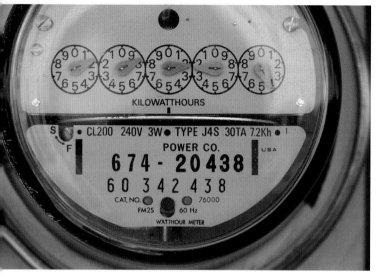

efficient car from the 1990s, which could be purchased fairly cheaply. However, the hybrid would get better gas mileage, meaning the cost of driving it would be lower. The person buying the car would have to consider not only the costs and benefits to the environment and their community's air quality, but how the difference in the cost of gas over time would compare to the difference in upfront costs.

When it comes to energy at home, customers have for several years been able to buy energy-efficient, compact fluorescent light bulbs (CFLs). The bulbs cost slightly more upfront than the traditional incandescent light bulbs Americans have used for most of the past century, but use less electricity and may last longer. The savings from the cheaper monthly bills could make up for the higher upfront cost, and in 2007 the government passed a regulation phasing out the less-efficient, incandescent bulbs. However, despite the energy savings costs, CFLs contain small amounts of mercury, which pose extreme environmental and health risks. If you break or drop a CFL, you are at risk of mercury poisoning. (Before you clean up the glass, vacate the enclosure and ventilate the area for a minimum of 15 minutes and wash any exposed skin with running water for several minutes. Also, take proper precautions when you dispose of burned-out CFLs.) Light bulbs made with light-emitting diodes (LED) are a safer alternative to CFLs, but currently they cost significantly more.

One of the concerns for alternative power sources is to find ways to make them inexpensive enough that their costs do not outweigh their environmental benefits. Solar power, for example, is a clean technology that could dramatically cut pollution if it became popular enough. However, solar panels can run hundreds of dollars each, making them a difficult sell for many homeowners, even if they would benefit from long-term energy savings by supplying their own solar power instead of buying electricity from the municipal grid. Most forms of technology—from music players to flat-screen televisions to electric cars—start out expensive, because fewer companies are make them and not enough people buy them for companies to sell enough volume. As with many consumer goods, the price of solar panels would come down

if they became popular enough, with different companies competing for consumers. But, at this point solar panels are still too expensive upfront for many homeowners to consider buying them. Some of the EPA incentive programs discussed earlier encourage homeowners and businesses to buy solar panels through tax incentives, but these initiatives have not yet been enough to dramatically lower costs.

All these kinds of costs and benefits—not just the financial costs and benefits, but also the harder-to-quantify opportunity costs—play roles in the regulations the government institutes. By regulating in favor of efficient light bulbs and more-efficient hybrid cars, Congress created rules that save the public money while protecting the environment with lower emissions. In regulating pollution emissions, it prompted the creation of cleaner plants that produce less pollution, though that did have some negative impact on jobs. In other cases, as in food inspections to verify safety for human consumption (which will be discussed more in the next section), the government takes preventative steps to reduce food contamination and public health care costs of the related illnesses.

When enforcing regulations setting aside public lands or preventing drilling in national parks, the government chooses not to realize an immediate financial benefit in exchange for longer-term benefits. How the government weighs the costs and benefits of each proposed regulation, and how those costs and benefits affect the general public and the nation's economy, are key factors in decisions regarding nearly all regulations, including those affecting the environment.

MID-CHAPTER QUESTIONS

1. In the coal power plant example above, name two costs that were the result of the new EPA regulations. Name two benefits. Were the benefits or the costs more important in this case?

2. Using one example from the chapter, explain the conflict between business and government regulation. What did the government hope to achieve by the regulation, and why did the business or businesses oppose it?

REGULATION METHODS

History of Environmental Regulation

In 1848, the City of Chicago engineered the Chicago River to flow upstream, to keep the city's sewage from flowing out into Lake Michigan and contaminating the city's drinking water. This is an early example of local pollution control and environmental regulation.

The Rivers and Harbors Act (RHA) of 1899 is usually considered the first federal environmental regulation in the US, though some individual states passed their own environmental laws before that. There had been previous versions of the RHA, but they did not specifically address environmental issues. The 1899 act made it illegal for anyone to dump any kind of waste in rivers, lakes, or other bodies of water without a permit. It also made it illegal for anyone to build dams or reverse the flow of rivers without government permission. The RHA also created penalties for anyone who violated the new restrictions.

Human Health and Safety Regulations

The first big wave of regulation in the US was focused less on the health of the environment itself but on the safety of food and drugs—mainly the health of both those making them and those using them. In 1862, the USDA created what would eventually become the FDA with a lab to test and analyze food and soil

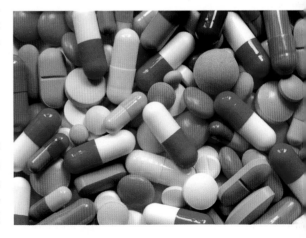

samples (grapes used in wine were the first crops tested). The FDA became an official agency in 1906. Before that, the federal Customs Office was in charge of inspecting drugs imported from other countries, but there was basically no serious oversight of food or drugs produced inside the US. It was common at the time for people to sell dangerous drugs—including now-illegal narcotics such as opium and cocaine—as cure-all medications. Salesmen put on popular, touring "medicine shows" with music and circus animals, where they sold tonics and other medicines with no regulations about whether the products did what the salesmen claimed, what ingredients they contained, or even if they were safe to use. Chemist and college professor Dr. Harvey Wiley, who was then heading the USDA's chemistry lab, was among the activists who helped bring public attention to the dangers of contaminated food and drugs. He tested chemicals commonly used as food preservatives on a team of volunteers who came to be known as the "poison squad," and revealed the dangerous effects of the chemicals on his volunteers. Wiley and others pushed for a federal law to regulate food and medicine.

Along with the public reaction to Upton Sinclair's novel *The Jungle* (see case study below) those efforts resulted in a 1906 law that empowered the government to create rules requiring that labels about what was in food or drugs be truthful, and giving the government the power to sue companies or individuals who broke that law. The original act was weak, but over time it was strengthened by amendments and, in 1938, the government passed the far more powerful Federal Food, Drug, and Cosmetic Act (FD&C Act). It required drug makers to prove that their products were safe before they were allowed to sell them to the public. It also gave the FDA the power to inspect factories and punish those that broke the law. It banned a number of poisons in food, and set limits on the amounts of pesticides and other chemicals that could be used in growing or making food. It also gave the government new ways to stop companies that broke the law, including court injunctions and prosecutions.

As discussed earlier in this chapter, a large number of environmental regulations were passed in the 1960s and 1970s, after the public grew concerned about the dangers of herbicides and pesticides, such as DDT, and other threats to the air and water. April 22, 1970, marked the creation of Earth Day, which drew more than 20 million people to public events and demonstrations around the country, and helped advance the grassroots environmental movement that pushed for the creation of the EPA and for legislation like the CAA and the CWA. Most of the major regulations have been updated several times since their passage, in order to adapt to the changing nature of environmental issues, advanced technology, and our scientific understanding of them. Using a number of different types of regulation, some described below, the government has also tried to address new threats to the environment.

Taxes

Federal and state governments often use the tax code to encourage or discourage certain behaviors, from high cigarette taxes to discourage people from smoking to tax breaks for people who donate money to charity or invest their money in a retirement account. They do the same to influence how people treat the environment.

As discussed earlier, companies can get tax breaks by designing green technology, and customers may qualify for a federal tax credit claim when filing personal and corporate taxes, saving money by purchasing hybrid cars or efficient appliances. In some cases, the government uses taxes to encourage companies to avoid using certain pollutants. For example, by the 1980s, scientists were warning about the dangers of chlorofluorocarbons (CFCs), chemical compounds used often in refrigerators, air conditioners, and aerosol cans. CFCs that entered the atmosphere were depleting the Earth's ozone layer. The ozone layer is an important part of the atmosphere that blocks harmful ultraviolet (UV) radiation from the sun. Ozone depletion was linked to documented increases in skin cancer, cataracts, and other health problems. While the US took part in an international agreement to phase out CFCs, signing the 1987 Montreal Protocol, it also used the tax system to urge companies to stop manufacturing CFCs and to use substitutes that will not harm the ozone layer. In 1990, Congress raised taxes on eight complex CFC chemicals, such as trichlorofluoromethane, linked to ozone destruction and regularly used in aerosol cans and refrigerators. The first year, CFCs were subjected to a tax of $1.37 per pound. As a result, many companies chose to reduce their production of CFCs to save money. CFC emissions fell dramatically; the tax did what the emission cap included in the Montreal Protocol did not—it gave a concrete financial incentive for companies to stop producing CFCs. The federal tax later went up to more than $3 per pound of CFCs. Companies continued to cut their use of the chemical compounds that were having negative impacts on their profit margins, as well for the ozone layer and public health.

Trading Schemes

Besides taxing emissions, governments have proposed dealing with emissions through trading schemes, sometimes referred to as **"cap and trade"** programs. These specifically were used to reduce CFCs and were proposed by several nations to limit CO_2 emissions. These are considered by proponents to be a more business-friendly approach than an outright carbon tax. The point of a trading scheme is to "cap" the total maximum allowable greenhouse gas emissions. If world governments agree to a carbon tax, companies and nations that remain below their maximum emission level may have the ability to sell "credits" to other companies or nations that pollute more than their proposed capped limit. The system rewards companies financially for staying below the emission caps, since they can sell their credits, and penalizes companies for producing above the limit by making them purchase credits for the right to do so.

The emission caps would be lowered gradually over a period of years, giving high-polluting facilities time to reduce their impact while buying credits in the meantime. In the European Union (EU), a trading scheme is mandatory, with each member nation setting its own emission caps. Businesses that use less than their allotted emissions are permitted to sell credits. The US does not have a mandatory trading program for CO_2. However, there are voluntary trading programs that use the same basic format.

Since 2003, a number of cities, companies, and universities have taken part in trading emission credits through the voluntary Chicago Climate Exchange (CCE), which lowered its initial cap in 2007. In 2005, mayors of more than 100 American cities pledged to meet emission caps even if the federal government did not set any.

Another voluntary program is the sale of **carbon offsets,** in which firms or individuals contribute to green projects as a way of making up for the emissions they create. Some common offsets include money invested in efficient public transit, or

CARBON OFFSET An action undertaken to reduce the emissions of greenhouse gases in response to an action that created emissions.

in planting forests to soak up carbon. Critics of carbon trading programs (and of offsets) argue that reducing carbon is a worldwide necessity, that the caps are too high, or that richer companies are able to buy their way out of compliance. Supporters see trading schemes as a market-based way to financially encourage companies to get below the caps without creating a universal tax on carbon emissions.

The cap and trade program is all about perspective. Purchasing carbon credits is paying for the "right" to produce additional CO_2, which is basically a type of fine. Carbon offset purchases aim to reduce or neutralize greenhouse gas emissions. Facilities can still produce emissions, but the offset costs can be used to fund environmental programs, such as tropical rainforest conservation and reforestation programs. Reforestation aims to have more trees available to absorb atmospheric CO_2, thus theoretically reducing greenhouse gas levels.

CASE STUDY: UPTON SINCLAIR AND *THE JUNGLE*

Before government regulation, there were a number of potential dangers people did not know about when they sat down to eat a hamburger. And when they found out what was really in their food, it caused a sensation and spurred the government to try cleaning up the food industry.

In 1906, journalist Upton Sinclair published *The Jungle*, a disturbing account of the filthy and unsafe conditions in a Chicago meatpacking plant. While the book was technically a novel, Sinclair worked undercover for weeks in meatpacking plants in the Chicago Stockyards to research the behind-the-scenes reality. He used real details in the fictionalized story of a poor Lithuanian immigrant family forced to work in the dangerous and corrupt world of the American meatpacking industry.

Sinclair's goal was to expose the ways that poor workers were being exploited—including children being forced to work dangerous jobs. Workers were made to live in dilapidated slums they could not afford and risked getting kicked out of if they complained. Many workers were dying or getting horribly injured in the factories. But when The Jungle was published—first as an article series in the left-wing magazine Appeal to Reason, then as a shorter version in book form—readers reacted as much or more to Sinclair's descriptions of tainted food.

He described workers falling to their deaths in rendering vats in the packing plants, their bodies becoming part of the processed fat. Work areas were infested with insects and rats. The meat was full of diseases like tuberculosis. President Theodore Roosevelt responded to public concern by sending inspectors to the Chicago packing plants. Even though plant bosses were tipped off before the inspections and rushed to clean them up in time, the inspectors still found the plants dirty, dangerous, and in need of regulation. They published their findings as the influential Neill-Reynolds Report. The report inspired the 1906 Federal Meat Inspection Act (FMIA), which regulated cleaner conditions for how animals were slaughtered and how the meat was processed. The Act gave the USDA the power to inspect factories to enforce animal and meat processing regulations. Along with the other efforts discussed in this section, the intense response to *The Jungle* helped urge the federal government to create the modern Food and Drug Administration and give it the power to regulate the industry.

Legislation

The most traditional form of regulation is legislation. Congress or state legislatures pass specific laws to deal with anything from banning the use of particular toxic pollutants to creating public parks to creating the kinds of taxes or incentive plans detailed above. Many of the most important environmental regulations in the US—from the RHA to the creation of the EPA to the increased taxes on CFCs that led to their elimination—came about through legislation.

As explained at the beginning of this chapter, regulatory agencies like the EPA, USFS, and FDA are in charge of enforcing many of those laws. Sometimes these agencies craft specific rules for their operations. But the laws that give force to those regulations usually come through acts of Congress, or in the case of individual states, their state legislatures.

Major EPA Regulations

Since its creation in 1970, the EPA and other federal agencies have enforced major environmental regulations.

Clean Air Act (CAA) and Clean Water Act (CWA)

Passed in 1970 to replace a far weaker act of the same name, the CAA was the first of the major regulations created in response to the growing environmental movement that also prompted the EPA's creation. It gives the agency the authority to reduce emissions that cause air pollution, and damagedthe environment. In addition to the powers described earlier in the chapter, the law ensures any state or local government cannot allow any air quality standards weaker than those enforced by the EPA (though they can be stronger), and gives the EPA authority to enforce those standards at all levels. The CAA was also updated in 1990 to enforce standards against acid rain, require large polluters to get operating permits and track their emission levels, and add more pollutants to those the EPA could regulate. The 1972, the CWA took a similar approach, giving the EPA the power to regulate water pollution by setting pollution standards for wastewater, helping towns set up effective sewage treatment plants, punishing illegal dumping, and testing water quality.

Resource Conservation and Recovery Act (RCRA)

Passed in 1976, the RCRA gave the EPA full authority for regulating hazardous waste, doing for pollution of land what the CAA and CWA did for those parts of the environment. Under RCRA, the EPA identifies which waste is hazardous, and also sets rules for how it is handled, how to dispose of it, and how to safely transport hazardous waste to the disposal site. It also sets standards for the condition of dumps and helps communities improve existing dumpsites. The Act gave the EPA the power to issue daily fines against anyone violating those safety standards, and also oversight for the disposal of non-hazardous waste. The EPA's Office of Resource Conservation and Recovery is in charge of enforcing the Act, and later amendments to RCRA gave it the power to regulate smaller amounts of waste, to ban the dumping of liquids without containers, and to make sure hazardous waste dumps are not set up in places where the hazardous waste can contaminate drinking water.

National Environmental Policy Act (NEPA)

The NEPA went into effect in 1970 as part of a wave of environmental legislation. Rather than setting up regulations for fighting specific environmental problems, NEPA outlined the concept of a national environmental policy for the first time. It created the procedures for when and how the federal government evaluates the impact of federal programs on the environment. The first part of the Act names the overall goals of all national environmental policy—making "enjoyable harmony" between people and nature an official goal, along with making the environment safe and useful for the public, promoting recycling and renewable resources, and generally protecting natural resources for future generations. The rest of the act lays out the "NEPA process" for the documents a governmental organization must prepare before going forward with a proposed project that could affect the environment. It created three kinds of documents:

- Environmental Impact Statement (EIS);
- Environmental Assessment (EA), and;
- Categorical Exemption (CE)

The NEPA outlined when agencies must prepare and submit these documents. The EIS requires an agency to explain all the possible environmental impacts of a project, which cannot be avoided and which will have long-term and short-term impacts. It also requires an examination of realistic alternatives to the project or action in the proposal. The EA is a shorter document that determines if there will be an impact at all, which then leads to an EIS. The CE documents when an agency doesn't need to do an impact study because previous, similar assessments show there is minimal risk to the environment.

Endangered Species Act (ESA)

Since taking effect in 1973, the ESA has allowed the federal government—through the USFWS and National Oceanographic and Atmospheric Administration (NOAA)—to declare species of animals or plants endangered and take steps to conserve their numbers and the ecosystems in which they live. NOAA handles species in marine environments. USFWS handles freshwater species. The ESA gave the government the ability to place at-risk species on the newly created Endangered Species List, with statuses ranging from "endangered" to "threatened" and with species at greatest risk getting highest priority. The agencies in charge of enforcement can ban hunting, trade, or other "taking" of endangered species, with large fines and prison time for violations. Because the loss of habitat is one of the main causes of species' extinction, agencies can identify "critical habitats" and set them aside as protected land. The ESA also gave the agencies the ability to create endangered lists for individual states, for when a species is endangered in certain parts of the country but its overall numbers are not critical. More than 1,200 species have gone on the Endangered Species List since its creation and more than 50—including the bald eagle, brown pelican, and black-footed ferret—have come back from the brink of extinction in part because of government action under the ESA. However, some of the many native species still on the Endangered Species List include the bison, Hawaiian bat, caribou, polar bear, and California condor. Parts of the ESA, dealing with pesticides and their effects on at-risk plants and animals, are regulated by the EPA through its Office of Pesticide Programs.

Comprehensive Environmental Response, Compliance, and Liability Act (CERCLA)

CERCLA—the Superfund program—was created in 1980 in response to the hazardous waste disaster at Love Canal. Detailed earlier in this chapter, people living near this dumpsite suffered serious health problems after Hooker Chemical buried thousands of tons of toxic waste. The government used the Superfund program to sue the company to make it pay for the cleanup of the site it destroyed. The law also included taxes on hazardous chemicals and petroleum products, raising $1.6 billion dollars for the program in the first five years. Through CERCLA, the EPA identifies potentially hazardous sites, sends inspectors to assess the sites, and decides which are the most important for cleanup. The agency can order preventative cleanups (before a disaster) or emergency cleanups after people or land are affected. The agency also creates a National Priority List for which cleanups will go first. Through Superfund, the EPA can oversee cleanups itself if companies do not comply, then sue them to recover the cost. (Assets in the existing Superfund trust, collected from tax revenues, are used to pay for cleanup in the meantime, when necessary.) CERCLA created the regulations for both that trust fund and the legal liability on the part of polluters. About 70 percent of Superfund cleanups were eventually funded by the polluters, and the National Priority List usually has the EPA considering at least a thousand waste sites potentially dangerous at any time.

Oil Pollution Act (OPA)

Congress passed the OPA in 1990 to give the EPA more authority over the cleanup of oil spills and—as CERCLA did for other hazardous waste polluters—to hold oil companies legally liable for their spills. Like CERCLA, the OPA was partly a response to an environmental disaster. On March 24, 1989, the *Exxon Valdez* oil tanker spilled hundreds of thousands of barrels of oil—more than 11 million gallons—while on its way from Alaska to California. Until the 2010 Deepwater Horizon BP oil rig leak in the Gulf of Mexico, the *Exxon Valdez* incident was considered the worst oil spill in American history, covering more than 11,000 square miles of ocean and killing untold numbers fish and marine wildlife, including sea otters, migrating birds, and whales. The federal government, including EPA specialists, public university experts, and the Coast Guard, took part in the cleanup effort. As with the Love Canal disaster, the government had to sue the polluter in court to get money for the cleanup. Exxon lost the lawsuit, but started an appeals process that continued into the 2000s. Still, Exxon wound up paying some seafood producers for the damage caused to their businesses by the spill, and spent millions of dollars directly on the cleanup. The *Exxon Valdez* disaster helped urge Congress within a year to pass the OPA, which made sure the responsible companies were liable for cleanup costs, set financial liability amounts for vessels of different sizes, created fines for companies that do not report spills, gave individual states the power to add additional liability costs to companies that spill, and set up daily fines for polluters that do not comply with cleanup orders from the government. The OPA was later amended to require companies using offshore oil platforms or oil vessels to submit response plans to the government detailing how they would respond to an oil spill. In the case of the 2010 BP spill, caused by an accident on an offshore oil platform, OPA was used to hold the company financially liable for damage it caused to the Gulf region.

Toxic Substances Control Act (TSCA)

Passed in 1976, the TSCA gave the EPA the job of regulating all chemicals that are potentially dangerous to the environment or to public health. Instead of dealing with the effects of pollution, it covered the manufacture of chemicals themselves to limit the damage of the pollution they could create. Under the TSCA, the EPA keeps a list of chemicals being manufactured, and tests any new chemicals to make sure they are safe. Sections added over time to the 1976 act also require the EPA to regulate specific dangerous chemicals, including polychlorinated biphenyl (known as PCB), asbestos, indoor radon, and lead contamination—all of which have been proven to cause serious health problems, including cancer, as well as damage to the environment. In 1978, for example, the EPA banned the manufacture of lead-based paint, which had been linked to learning disabilities and seizures in children. Asbestos—a kind of strong silicate fiber—was commonly used in construction for many years because it worked well as insulation. It was later proven to cause cancer and other serious problems when airborne asbestos particles were inhaled, so the EPA created regulations to limit its release into the atmosphere when buildings are renovated or demolished. Critics have long noted that while the TSCA gives the EPA authority to test chemicals, only a tiny percentage of those already in use by 1976 have been tested under the act. TSCA has many exceptions, including chemicals already regulated by other government agencies, including the FDA.

Supreme Court Decisions

While the Supreme Court does not make laws, it provides a way for states, companies, or others affected by regulations to challenge laws. As mentioned earlier, the Court sided with Massachusetts and other states when they sued the EPA to make sure it enforced standards on greenhouse-gas emissions, and backed the CERCLA program when companies tried to challenge its ability to make them pay for environmental cleanup. The Court has also ruled on cases in which two states differed on how to treat shared resources. The Supreme Court consistently supports the EPA's authority to enforce regulations when businesses and states have challenged the agency's rulings.

State Regulations

Each of the 50 states also passes its own environmental laws. As discussed in the fracking example earlier in this chapter, the strictness of state regulations can vary dramatically. However, each state must meet federal standards. Along with a state legislature passing laws, each state also has departments set up to enforce state regulations. California, for example, has six specific environmental agencies, while most others have one or two departments that handle environmental regulations.

PRESERVATION: AIR POLLUTION REGULATION IN CALIFORNIA

When the CAA went into effect in 1970, one of the ways the federal government enforced the rules was to cut federal funding for highway and other building projects in states that failed to meet the national standards for air quality. At the time, California was unable to meet those standards, and cities like Los Angeles had become famous for their smog—thick air pollution caused by a combination of automobile emissions, emissions from coal-burning plants, and other pollutants that reacted with sunlight to create a fog-like chemical mist. Smog was linked to health problems, including asthma, and California's state government started a series of programs to reduce the amount of pollution in the air.

In 1982, the California legislature created the California Smog Check, which requires drivers to have their vehicles tested every two years to make sure their emissions are within state standards and make necessary repairs if the vehicle fails the test. (This improved on a California program started in 1966 by requiring more frequent testing and setting higher standards for vehicles to pass.) Tougher emission standards for Smog Check were created in 1996, and the program has some of the strictest standards of any emissions check program in the country.

California's state government also passed the Children's Environmental Health Protection Act (CEHPA) in 1999, which requires the state's Air Resources Board (ARB) to conduct studies on a number of different air pollutants and set new standards for the ones ranked as most dangerous—including ozone and nitrogen dioxide. Starting in 1998, the ARB also required a "smog index label" on all new cars sold in California, and in 2007 it added an "Environmental Performance Label" that gives every new car a smog score and another score for emissions that contribute to air pollution.

California has not always met its ambitious goals for reducing emissions, but these programs have helped the state cut its ozone pollution by more than half over the past 30 years, with the result of visibly cleaner air in cities and reduced health problems linked to the smog.

MID-CHAPTER QUESTIONS

1. Give two examples of ways government can regulate environmental activity. What are the costs and benefits of each?

2. Explain how an emissions trading scheme works. What are the pros and cons of such a program?

3. Name two pieces of environmental legislation enforced by the EPA. What problems were those regulations created to address?

PRIVATIZATION AND NATIONALIZATION OF RESOURCES

Because natural resources are both limited and valuable, there will always be some conflict between preserving them and using them for profit. The question of whether the public, represented by the government, or private businesses should be permitted to manage or use the resources as they see fit is an issue Americans have wrestled with for a long time.

The idea of **public lands**—land protected by the government for the use of all Americans—and the idea of privatizing them date back to the late 1700s, when the federal government started creating regulations for who could buy or use land purchased or conquered by the US. Preserving public lands for national parks, national wilderness areas, and similar projects became a popular idea in the last half of the 1800s, after the US had expanded to cover most of the land that now makes up the lower 48 states. Not all public lands are operated by the federal government, as every state owns and operates its own public lands, including state parks, forests, and other set-aside areas. The federal government also owns public land that has nothing to do with preserving the environment, such as military bases, government offices, and much of Washington, DC.

Some public areas—while set aside from development—are still used by many people. Every year, millions of Americans visit national parks like the Grand Canyon in Arizona, Yellowstone National Park in Wyoming, and Yosemite National Park in California. Most national parks have some basic facilities for visitors (information centers, parking lots, restaurants, restrooms, payphones, and others) and employ people ranging from tour guides to cleaning crews. Also, the areas around popular parks attract a lot of local businesses that want to cater to the large numbers of tourists, including hotels, restaurants, and shopping centers, and other private businesses benefitting by opening near the parks. Those private businesses directly benefit from the government operating the public lands.

Even within public lands, there are often private sections. In Alaska, for example, many private cabins and other residences exist inside state and national parks. Usually, that happened because, while the government created the outline for the park, it did not buy all the land inside. That is true even of some of the country's oldest public lands. Ten percent of the national park at Valley Forge, Pennsylvania—where George Washington and his Revolutionary War troops famously camped during a difficult winter—is private land. While the federal government owns most of the Petrified Forest National Park in Arizona, more than 100,000 acres of the park is not owned by the government. The US also contains almost 56 million acres of land managed by the Bureau of Indian Affairs, under the Department of the Interior, set aside in trust for American Indian tribes. These lands are sovereign territories and often contain a mix of tribal and individual property.

Such situations, in which both public and private land exists within the same boundary, often prompt calls for **privatization** or **nationalization**. While some public lands generate significant revenue through tourism, business interests regularly lobby for the government to sell land that holds large amounts of natural resources—privatization—or to allow private businesses to operate inside public lands. Nationalization occurs when the government buys previously private land, such as private parcels within national parks.

The desire of oil and gas companies to drill inside the ANWR, discussed earlier in this chapter, is an example of private business wanting to operate on public land. In other cases, privatization would mean the government selling the land outright to private enterprises, usually by auction. People who support privatization argue

PUBLIC LANDS Land held by the federal government or state governments.

PRIVATIZATION To change from government or public control to private ownership.

NATIONALIZATION To change from private ownership to government or public control.

that the current system of protecting public lands charges taxpayers for the preservation and upkeep of land that they might not ever use. Similar arguments have been made against public schools, with opponents arguing that taxpayers without children should not have to pay for a service they do not use. Instead, they argue, private businesses should be able to operate the land and charge those people who choose to use it. While the federal government usually tends to favor protecting public lands rather than privatizing them, there have been exceptions. President Ronald Reagan and President George W. Bush, as well as several members of Congress, proposed auctioning off public lands to raise money. In 2006, Bush proposed selling about

300,000 acres of national forest in 41 states to developers. Congress did not support the plan, with opponents arguing that the money the auction would create in the short term was not worth the permanent loss of those forest areas.

More often, the federal government and environmental organizations urge nationalization, in which the government buys up private land, either to preserve it or to open it to the public. Supporters of nationalization argue it gives all Americans the right of equal access to the land, and that it is important to keep lands preserved in the long term. In cases like Valley Forge and other public lands with private land inside their boundaries, supporters of nationalization point out that development on the private portion can damage the public land around it, and urge the government to buy more of the private portion of those lands. In 1964, Congress created a Land and Water Conservation Fund (LWC), which pays for the federal government to purchase private land on behalf of departments like the USFS and the USFWS. Also, state organizations and environmental groups sometimes raise money independently to purchase land and then donate it to national parks or other public entities. For example, in 2003, a group called the Peninsula Open Space Trust spent about $30 million to buy thousands of acres of private land that was inside the public Golden Gate National Recreation Area in and near San Francisco, California, with the goal of keeping it protected from development, and the trust planned to sell the land to the NPS.

The same debates regarding privatization and nationalization take place over other natural resources. Oil is one of the most obvious of these resources, with private companies drilling for a valuable resource they can sell for profit, but often doing so in territory they do not own. The 2010 disaster in the Gulf of Mexico, when the explosion of BP's Deepwater Horizon drilling rig released more than 200 million gallons of oil in the worst spill in American history, was a worst-case scenario for environmental fears, as the company's mistakes had a major negative impact on everything from fish stocks to tourism in several states along the Gulf Coast. In some other countries—including Canada and Mexico—the oil industry is nationalized, run by the federal government rather than private companies.

Water supplies are another example. In the US, about half of all water was owned privately until local governments started taking over that role after World War I, and now only about 15 percent of American water is private. Most American privatization of water has occurred at the local, rather than state or national level, with towns, villages, or neighborhoods contracting private companies to supply their water. When

ENVIRONMENTAL MISCONCEPTIONS: THE POTENTIAL OF DOMESTIC OIL RESERVES

One of the many problems faced by environmental regulators is that many of the resources they're trying to protect are limited, while the demand to use them keeps growing. Oil is a good example, because there is only a finite amount in the ground, and nations continue to increase the amount of oil they use. As of 2010, almost half of the oil used by Americans had to be imported from other countries. While more imported oil comes to the US from Canada and Mexico than from any other nations, a series of presidents and other leaders have argued for years that the country needs to reduce its dependence on oil from overseas, usually citing political problems in some of the countries from which the US imports oil.

In the 1970s, an embargo by the Organization of Petroleum Exporting Countries (OPEC) cut off imports to America and greatly limited the US oil supply, making gas prices increase dramatically. More recent tensions in the Middle East, and political differences between the US and nations like Venezuela, have been seen as reasons to diminish the use of foreign oil. Many of the programs mentioned earlier in this chapter were designed to do that by developing other sources of energy to replace some of the oil, including solar, wind, and hydroelectric power.

Many companies and people feel that increased drilling within the US is a route to greater energy independence. America's combined energy resources are, according to a report from the Congressional Research Service (CRS) dated November 30, 2010, the largest on Earth, or 23 percent of total world reserves. US reserves eclipse Saudi Arabia (3rd), China (4th), and Canada (6th) combined and that's without including America's shale oil deposits and, in the future, the potentially astronomic impact of methane hydrates.

privatization works, companies are able to supply water to municipalities efficiently and at a reasonable profit. However, there have been problems with private companies selling contaminated water or overcharging customers for the service. Sometimes, towns even buy back control of their water supplies, as Indianapolis did in 2003, when it bought back control of the city's water from the company that had operated it since the 1870s.

In other countries, water privatization has become a much bigger concern, with a few large water companies from wealthier countries contracting with governments in the developing world. In some poorer countries, that privatization has meant better piping that gets water to more people and a more modern process that cuts down on disease. However, it also means companies can bottle and sell the water they now own, taking it out of the developing country and creating a potential shortage prob-

MID-CHAPTER QUESTION

1. What is one benefit of privatizing natural resources? What is one benefit of nationalizing them?

FOSSIL FUEL RESERVES AND RESOURCES			
	Country	**Fossil Fuel Native Units–BOE**	**BOE = Barrels of oil equivalent (in billions)**
Technically recoverable oil	United States	162.9	162.9
	Saudi Arabia	262.4	262.4
	Canada	175.2	175.2
	Iran	137.6	137.6
	Iraq	115.0	115.0
	Kuwait	104.0	104.0
	Venezuela	99.4	99.4
	Total	1056.5	1056.5
		Fossil Fuel Native Units–trillion cubic feet	**BOE = Barrels of oil equivalent (in billions)**
Technically recoverable natural gas	United States	1420.9	251.8
	Saudi Arabia	263.5	46.7
	Canada	62.0	11.0
	Iran	1045.7	185.3
	Iraq	111.9	19.8
	Kuwait	63.5	11.3
	Venezuela	176.0	31.2
	Total	3143.5	557.1
		Fossil Fuel Native units–billion short tons	**BOE = Barrels of oil equivalent (in billions)**
Recoverable reserve base of coal	United States	261.0	900.5
	Saudi Arabia	0.0	0.0
	Canada	7.3	25.2
	Iran	1.5	5.2
	Iraq	0.0	0.0
	Kuwait	0.0	0.0
	Venezuela	0.5	1.8
	Total	270.3	932.7

Source: Congressional Research Service as of November 30, 2010.

Figure 8.1 Fossil fuel reserves and resources

lem in the future. As of 2005, almost 10 percent of people worldwide were getting their water from private companies.

POLITICS AND THE ENVIRONMENT

Naturally, the same conflicts that drive the privatization versus nationalization debate also play out in the politics of the US. Businesses that want to operate without regulations, or at least with fewer and weaker regulations, routinely spend large sums of money lobbying the government and funding candidates who are less supportive of regulation.

Until the past few decades, environmental protection was not seen as a particularly partisan issue, as presidents of both major political parties took steps toward better regulation. In the case of the conditions highlighted by *The Jungle*, Republican President Theodore Roosevelt responded by making improved food safety part of his reform agenda. Democratic President Franklin Roosevelt did the same in greatly expanding the FDA's powers. In response to the environmental movement gaining popularity in the 1960s, the Democratic-controlled Congress and Republican President Richard Nixon set up the EPA, the CAA, and other landmark changes in regulation.

CHAPTER SUMMARY

Environmental regulation often comes down to a question of rights and responsibilities. What rights does the public have to use the land, water, and other resources? What rights do businesses have to use the same resources, and whose rights are more important? Whose responsibility is it to make sure the air is clean, or that endangered species and wilderness areas continue to exist? What responsibilities do businesses or the government have when it comes to how their actions affect the environment, and what should happen when those actions damage other people's health or livelihoods? The increase in US government regulations on environmental activity over the past century—from the establishment of the FDA to test the safety of what the public eats to the creation of the EPA to regulate air and water quality—can be seen as an attempt to clarify and enforce the rights and responsibilities of different users of the environment through public policy. At times, environmental regulation achieves the goal of balancing the economic costs of regulation with the benefits that the regulation is meant to create. Other times, regulation is less successful at achieving this balance, either because it does not go far enough to protect the public from harm, is selectively enforced, or goes too far and imposes economic burdens seen by some as more costly than beneficial. As the American people, through their elected leaders, have responded to environmental problems over the last century—whether it was chemical or pathogen-contaminated food, toxic pollution emitted from factories, or garbage dumped in water people used for drinking—government's role in preserving the environment has expanded to create the complex federal regulatory system in place today.

REFERENCES

Associated Press. (2004, March 16). *Study: ANWR oil would have little impact.* Retrieved from http://www.msnbc.msn.com/id/4542853/ns/us_news-environment/t/study-anwr-oil-would-have-little-impact/#.TweN6WCatCp

Broder, J. (2007, May 23).. California wants strict auto emission rules. *The New York Times.* Retrieved from http://www.nytimes.com/2007/05/23/us/23climate.html

California Environmental Protection Agency. (2009, November 24). *California Ambient Air Quality Standards.* Retrieved from http://www.arb.ca.gov/research/aaqs/caaqs/caaqs.htm

Centers for Disease Control and Prevention. (n.d.). *About CDC.* Retrieved from http://www.cdc.gov/

Centers for Disease Control and Prevention. (2013, May 7). *Agency for Toxic Substances and Disease Registry.* Retrieved from http://www.atsdr.cdc.gov/

Clifford, C. (2011, August 23). BP oil spill fund: $5 billion in claims paid out. *CNN Money.* Retrieved from http://money.cnn.com/2011/08/23/smallbusiness/BP_oil_spill_claims/index.htm

Cufone, M. (2008, November 21). Ocean fish farms and public-resource privatization. *The American Prospect.* Retrieved from http://prospect.org/article/ocean-fish-farms-and-public-resource-privatization

Dallas City Hall. (n.d.). *Jack Evans Police Headquarters: Green building design.* Retrieved from http://www.dallascityhall.com/pdf/ehs/JackEvansPoliceBldg.pdf

Dallas Police Department. (n.d.). *Jack Evans Police Headquarters.* Retrieved from http://dallaspolice.net/index.cfm?page_ID=4658&subnav=51&openid=1

Dalton, T. (2010, November 18). Dominion to close Salem plant. *The Salem News.* Retrieved from http://www.salemnews.com/local/x852123427/Dominion-to-close-Salem-plant

Dowie, M. (2005, July/August). In law we trust. *Orion Magazine.* Retrieved from http://www .orionmagazine.org/index.php/articles/article/122/

Energy Star. (n.d.). Federal Tax Credits for Consumer Energy Efficiency. Retrieved from http://www .energystar.gov/index.cfm?c=tax_credits.tx_index

Goldstein, A. (2006, June 18). Privatization backlash in Indiana. *The Washington Post.* Retrieved from http://www.post-gazette.com/pg/06169/698927-84.stm

Hardin, G. (1968). The tragedy of the commons. *Science, 162*(2859), 1242–1248. Retrieved from http://www.garretthardinsociety.org/articles/art_tragedy_of_the_commons.html

Howe, P. (2011, May 12). Salem, Mass. power plant to close. *New England Cable News.* Retrieved from http://www.necn.com/05/12/11/Salem-Mass-power-plant-to-close/landing_business .html?blockID=521746&feedID=4209

Ifill, G. (2003, May 21). Being green? *The NewsHour with Jim Lehrer.* Retrieved from http://www .pbs.org/newshour/bb/environment/jan-june03/bush_5-21.html

Janssen, W. (1981, June). The story of the laws behind the labels. Retrieved from http://www.fda .gov/AboutFDA/WhatWeDo/History/Overviews/ucm056044.htm

Krupp, F. (2009, March 24). Carbon caps are the best policy. *The Wall Street Journal.* Retrieved from http://online.wsj.com/article/SB123785178691219381.html

Kusnetz, N. (2011, October 21). EPA plans to issue rules for hydraulic fracturing wastewater. *Scientific American.* Retrieved from http://www.scientificamerican.com/article.cfm?id=epa-plans-issue-rules-hydraulic fracturing –wastewater

Library of Congress. (n.d.). *America's story: The first Earth Day.* Retrieved from http://www .americaslibrary.gov/jb/modern/jb_modern_earthday_1.html

McLaughlin, D. (1995). *Silent Spring* revisited. *PBS: Frontline.* Retrieved from http://www.pbs.org/ wgbh/pages/frontline/shows/nature/disrupt/sspring.html

Mihelich, P. (2007, June 28). Bald eagle soars off endangered species list. *CNN.* Retrieved from http://articles.cnn.com/2007-06-28/tech/bald.eagle.delisting_1_bald-eagle-golden-eagle-protection-act-eagle-habitat?_s=PM:TECH

More, T. A. (2006). The privatization of public lands. *Proceedings of the 2006 Northeastern Recreation Research Symposium* (GTR-NRS-P-14, pp. 135–141). Retrieved from http://nrs.fs.fed.us/pubs/ gtr/gtr_nrs-p-14/18-more-p-14.pdf

National Atlas. (2013, January 14). The Public Land Survey System. Retrieved from http://nationalatlas.gov/articles/boundaries/a_plss.html

National Oceanic and Atmospheric Administration. (n.d.). About NOAA. Retrieved from http://www.noaa.gov/about-noaa.html

National Oceanic and Atmospheric Administration. (n.d.). Fisheries service. Retrieved from http://www.nmfs.noaa.gov/

National Oceanic and Atmospheric Administration. (n.d.). National ocean service. Retrieved from http://oceanservice.noaa.gov/

National Parks Conservation Service. (n.d.). *About us.* Retrieved from: http://www.npca.org/about-us/

Ngowi, R. (2011, December 19). Federal pollution regs threaten Salem power plant. *The Boston Globe.* Retrieved from http://www.boston.com/news/local/massachusetts/articles/2011/12/19/ ap_survey_epa_rules_threatens_salem_power_plant/

Schoen, J. (2004, October 25). How long will the world's oil last? *MSNBC.* Retrieved from http://www.msnbc.msn.com/id/5945678/ns/business-oil_and_energy/t/how-long-will-worlds-oil-last/#.TweSh2CatCp

Sinclair, U. (1906). *The Jungle.* Retrieved from http://www.online-literature.com/upton_sinclair/jungle/

Smithsonian National Zoological Park. (n.d.). *Bald eagle* [Fact sheet]. Retrieved from http://nationalzoo.si.edu/animals/birds/facts/factsheets/fact-baldeagle.cfm

Solomon, D. (2011, July 29). EPA unveils air-quality rules for natural-gas hydraulic fracturing *The Wall Street Journal.* Retrieved from http://online.wsj.com/article/SB100014240531119048 00304576474462644360884.html

U.S. Department of Agriculture. (n.d.). Animal and Plant Health Inspection Service. Retrieved from http://www.aphis.usda.gov/

U.S. Department of Agriculture. (n.d.). Food Safety and Inspection Service. Retrieved from http://www.fsis.usda.gov/

U.S. Department of Agriculture. (n.d.). Natural Resources Conservation Service. Retrieved from http://www.nrcs.usda.gov/wps/portal/nrcs/main/national/home

U.S. Department of Energy. (2011, November 29). Crude oil and total petroleum imports top 15 countries. Retrieved from http://ftp.eia.doe.gov/pub/oil_gas/petroleum/data_publications/company_level_imports/current/import.html

U.S. Department of Energy. (n.d.). DOE environmental management. Retrieved from http://www .em.doe.gov/Pages/EMHome.aspx

U.S. Department of Energy. (n.d.). Energy efficiency and renewable energy. Retrieved from http://www.eere.energy.gov/

U.S. Department of Energy. (n.d.). The National Environmental Policy Act of 1969. Retrieved from http://ceq.hss.doe.gov/nepa/regs/nepa/nepaeqia.htm

U.S. Department of Labor, Bureau of Labor Statistics. (2013, May 13). Table 2: Reason for layoff:; Extended mass layoff events, separations, and initial claimants for unemployment insurance, private nonfarm sector, selected quarters, 2012 and 2013. [Press release: Economic News Release]. Retrieved from http://www.bls.gov/news.release/mslo.t02.htm

U.S. Department of the Interior. (n.d.). Bureau of Land Management. Retrieved from http://www .blm.gov/wo/st/en.html

U.S. Energy Information Administration. (n.d.). EIA: Frequently asked questions. Retrieved from http://205.254.135.24/tools/faqs/

U.S. Environmental Protection Agency. (2002, December). *Brownfields redevelopment efforts are big in the heart of Dallas* (EPA Report No. 500-F-02-155). Retrieved from http://nepis.epa.gov

U.S. Environmental Protection Agency. (2011, December 12). CERCLA overview. Retrieved from http://www.epa.gov/superfund/policy/cercla.htm

U.S. Environmental Protection Agency. (2012, February 17). Clean Air Act. Retrieved from http://www.epa.gov/air/caa/

U.S. Environmental Protection Agency. (2013, April 25). Cleaning up the nation's hazardous waste sites. Retrieved from http://www.epa.gov/superfund

U.S. Environmental Protection Agency. (2013, March 28). Exxon Valdez. Retrieved from http://www.epa.gov/osweroe1/content/learning/exxon.htm

U.S. Environmental Protection Agency. (2012, June 25). National Environmental Policy Act. Retrieved from http://www.epa.gov/compliance/basics/nepa.html

U.S. Environmental Protection Agency. (2011, January 28). Oil Pollution Act overview. Retrieved from http://www.epa.gov/osweroe1/content/lawsregs/opaover.htm

U.S. Environmental Protection Agency. (2011, January 27). Oil Spill Liability Trust Fund. Retrieved from http://www.epa.gov/osweroe1/content/learning/oilfund.htm

U.S. Environmental Protection Agency. (2012, March 6). The plain English guide to the Clean Air Act. Retrieved from http://www.epa.gov/air/peg/index.html

U.S. Environmental Protection Agency. (n.d.).Summary of the Clean Water Act. Retrieved from http://www.epa.gov/lawsregs/laws/cwa.html

U.S. Environmental Protection Agency. (n.d.). Summary of the Endangered Species Act. Retrieved from http://www.epa.gov/lawsregs/laws/esa.html

U.S. Environmental Protection Agency. (n.d.). Summary of the Resource Conservation and Recovery Act. Retrieved from http://www.epa.gov/lawsregs/laws/rcra.html

U.S. Environmental Protection Agency. (2012, June 27). Toxic Substances Control Act. Retrieved from http://www.epa.gov/agriculture/lsca.html#Summary%20of%20Toxics%20Substances%20Control%20Act%20(TSCA)

U.S. Fish and Wildlife Service. (n.d.). Arctic National Wildlife Refuge. Retrieved from http://arctic .fws.gov/November

U.S. Fish and Wildlife Service. (2009). Brown pelican: *Pelicanus occidentalis*. Retrieved from http://www.fws.gov/contaminants/pdf/brown_pelicanfactsheet09.pdf

U.S. Fish and Wildlife Service. (n.d.). Endangered Species Act of 1973. Retrieved from http://www .fws.gov/laws/lawsdigest/ESACT.HTML

U.S. Fish and Wildlife Service. (n.d.). Endangered Species Program. Retrieved from http://www.fws .gov/endangered/

U.S. Fish and Wildlife Service. (n.d.). Rivers and Harbors Appropriation Act of 1899. Retrieved from http://www.fws.gov/laws/lawsdigest/RIV1899.HTML

U.S. Fish and Wildlife Service. (2013, May 13). Species reports. Retrieved from http://ecos.fws.gov/tess_public/pub/listedAnimals.jsp

U.S. Food and Drug Administration. (n.d.). About FDA. Retrieved from http:// www.fda.gov

U.S. Forest Service. (n.d.). About the Forest Service. Retrieved from http://www.fs.fed.us/

U.S. Geological Survey World Energy Assessment Team. (2001). *World petroleum assessment 2000*. Retrieved from http://pubs.usgs.gov/dds/dds-060/

Walsh, B. (2011, November 14). On coal, jobs and regulations. *Time Magazine*. Retrieved from http://ecocentric.blogs.time.com/2011/11/14/on-coal-jobs-and-regulations/

Wayne, A. (2012, January 4). Health effects of hydraulic fracturing for natural gas needs study, says CDC scientist. *Bloomberg.com*. Retrieved from http://www.bloomberg.com/news/2012-01-04/health-effects-of-hydraulic fracturing -for-natural-gas-need-study-says-cdc-scientist.html

Whitney, G., Beherns, C., & Glover, C. (2010, November 30). U.S. fossil fuel resources: Terminology, reporting, and summary (Congressional Research Service Report No. 7-5700). Retrieved from http://epw.senate.gov/public/index.cfm?FuseAction=Files.View&FileStore_id=04212e22-c1b3-41f2-b0ba-0da5eaead952

Williams, T. (2004). For a week's worth of gas. *Mother Jones*. Retrieved from http://motherjones .com/politics/2004/09/weeks-worth-gas

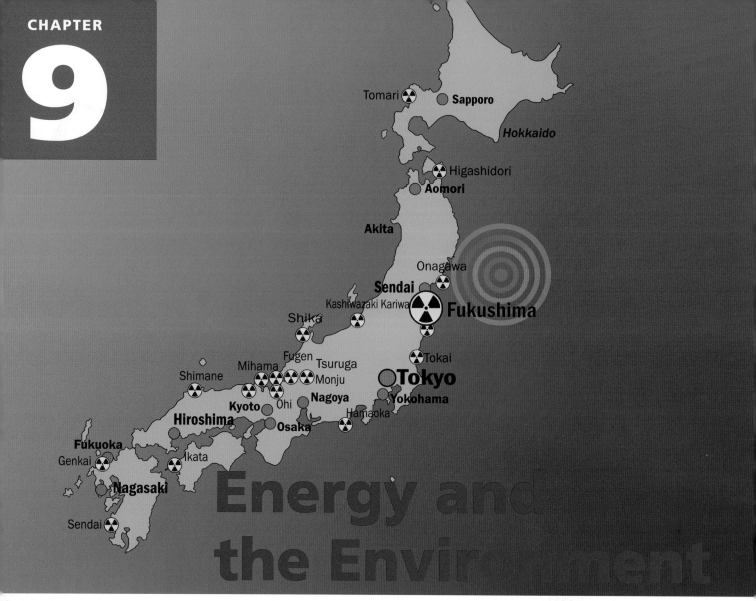

Tomari
Sapporo
Hokkaido
Higashidori
Aomori
Akita
Onagawa
Sendai
Kashiwazaki Kariwa
Shika
Fukushima
Fugen
Tsuruga
Tokai
Mihama
Monju
Tokyo
Shimane
Nagoya
Yokohama
Kyoto
Ohi
Hamaoka
Hiroshima
Osaka
Fukuoka
Ikata
Genkai
Nagasaki
Sendai

Energy and the Environment

NUCLEAR ENERGY AFTER FUKUSHIMA

In March 2011, Japan faced one of the world's most catastrophic nuclear crises at the Fukushima Daiichi power plant, owned by the Tokyo Electric Power Company (TEPCO). A 9.0 magnitude earthquake generated a tsunami in the Pacific Ocean that caused flooding and power outages at the nuclear power plant, overwhelming the plant's backup resources. As a result, the reactor cores came close to a meltdown, which caused explosions and radiation seepage within the first three days of the incident. This incident was rated a "7" on the International Nuclear and Radiological Event Scale (NES), the highest possible rating, where there are "widespread harmful health and environmental effects." For comparison, the Chernobyl Disaster also had a "7" rating.

Recent studies by the World Health Organization (WHO) and the United Nations (UN) show that while the disaster caused radiation background levels to increase worldwide, they have not increased to levels of serious concern to date. However, to continually assess the health risks to the local population, the Japanese government conducts regular tests on agriculture, livestock, seafood, drinking water, and soil in the regions surrounding the Fukushima plant to monitor the levels of radioactive contamination.

This disaster has focused attention on the evaluation of safety procedures at nuclear plants around the world. For example, the United States and France have ordered safety inspections on their nuclear reactors as a result of the disaster. Germany, Switzerland, and Italy are now terminating their nuclear power programs. Because of a loss of public confidence in the safety of nuclear power in Japan, the country is now looking at alternative sources of energy to replace the roughly 30 percent of the country's electricity formerly provided by the nation's 50 main nuclear reactors. Alternatives under consideration include taking advantage of Japan's extensive Pacific coast to build wind farms and the use of the country's 120 active volcanoes and 28,000 hot springs to generate geothermal power.

GEOGRAPHIC DETERMINATIONS AND APPROPRIATE POWER SOURCES

Eighty percent of US energy consumed comes from fossil fuels. This energy is used for a wide range of purposes—transportation, heating and cooling buildings, industrial processes, and household needs, such as cooking and laundering clothes. Fossil fuels, however, are in limited supply, and produce greenhouse gases when used. A resolution to this dilemma would be to use alternative sources of energy that are readily available, cost effective, and do not cause pollution.

Energy sources differ in cost based on their availability, transportability, and renewability. These characteristics are largely dependent on whether the energy source is remote or localized. Remote energy sources are mainly non-renewable sources, such as fossil fuels, that have to be transported for use. A localized energy source is one that can be found close to where the energy is used.

Local energy sources are often determined by the geomorphology—or physical features—of a region. For example, geothermal energy, (discussed in detail later in the chapter) can be produced in volcanically active regions, where the Earth's crust is thin and the high temperature of the magma, or molten rock, inside the Earth can be used for energy generation. In these places, water above magma produces hot springs and geysers, and their steam can be used to power turbines to produce electricity.

Most geothermal activity in the world occurs around the Pacific Basin in an area called the Ring of Fire. Other regions that may be able to take advantage of geothermal energy production include New Zealand, Turkey, Iran, northern India, the Aleutian Islands of Alaska, and south along the coast of North and South America.

Other examples of localized energy sources include the mechanical energies of tides in coastal regions and rivers near these bodies of water. Geographic regions where the weather produces an abundance of wind can use its power for energy production. Similarly, regions near the equator can turn abundant solar radiation into solar power. Additionally, **biofuels** such as ethanol, butanol, methanol, and biomethane can be produced in agricultural regions. Biofuels are produced from renewable biomass, the organic material made from wood, crops, and waste. According

BIOFUELS A source of energy produced from renewable biomass, such as wood, crops, and waste.

1. How did the 2011 nuclear crisis in Fukushima impact the environment?

2. What did the Fukushima crisis show about the effectiveness of disaster preparedness and safety procedures before the earthquake?

3. Do you think the risks inherent in the production of nuclear energy are enough to justify shutting these plants down?

URANIUM A heavy silvery-white metallic element, radioactive and toxic, easily oxidized, and having 14 known isotopes, of which U238 is the most abundant in nature.

FISSION A nuclear reaction in which a massive nucleus splits into smaller nuclei with the simultaneous release of energy.

FUSION A nuclear reaction in which two nuclei combine to form a nucleus with the release of energy.

to the Environmental Protection Agency (EPA), biofuels require less energy input to produce than traditional fuels. However, sources for biofuel, such as corn, are subject to environmental conditions, such as the drought of 2012. Demand for corn for livestock feed, human consumption, and biofuel creates competition. We must be careful to ensure crops are available for human consumption during times of need, such as droughts or floods. Currently, about 40 percent of corn crops are required by federal regulations to be used for the manufacture of ethanol to fuel automobiles.

A localized source of energy does not always pertain to a large-scale energy system. Small, decentralized energy sources can also be used locally. Solar panels used to power individual homes are an example of a small, decentralized energy source. Another example is heating a home with a fireplace that burns wood as an alternative to a furnace run on oil or natural gas.

Remote coal and petroleum energy sources often require the use of ocean vessels to transport these fuels from one country to another. These vessels are prone to oil spills, one hazard of remote energy sources. Another disadvantage of remote energy sources is that they often result in a country's dependency on other oil-producing nations for their energy, which means political instability can interrupt supply.

MID-CHAPTER QUESTIONS

1. **Identify the difference between localized and remote energy sources.**

2. **What are the benefits and drawbacks of using remote energy sources?**

NUCLEAR ENERGY

Nuclear energy is a non-renewable energy source because it relies on a radioactive element called **uranium** for its production and this element is available in limited amounts. Nuclear power is produced in reactors where the unstable atom of uranium is split in a process called **fission**, which generates massive amounts of heat to boil water to create steam that powers turbines to create electricity. Another form of nuclear power can be produced when hydrogen atoms are forced together to form helium in a process known as **fusion**. This process is still being researched to develop

and optimize safe and sustainable energy because, while hydrogen is abundant in the atmosphere in the form of water vapor and might be considered a renewable source of energy, it has to be extracted from water by adding chemical substances in the process of electrolysis. Atmospheric hydrogen gas (H_2) exists in extremely minute concentrations, for which extraction is not yet cost-effective and practical for commercial purposes.

The heat energy generated from fusion or fission heats water to produce steam that powers turbines in an electric generator. As these turbines spin, a magnetic field is created, producing electricity. After the steam cools and condenses as water, the water is recycled and the process repeats.

Nuclear power is controversial, and, as seen in Fukushima, when something goes wrong, the results can be disastrous. Another example is the 1986 disaster at the Chernobyl Nuclear Power Plant in the Ukraine. When the reactor core melted down, enough radiation was released to adversely impact the lives of many thousands of people. The Chernobyl disaster resulted in an estimated 4,000–25,000 deaths from radiation exposure and over 6,000 thyroid cancer cases in children.

In 2008, 20 percent of the electricity produced in the US came from nuclear power. In that year, 104 reactors in 31 states produced up to 806.2 billion kilowatt-hours (kWh) of electricity. For reference, in simplest terms, one (1) kWh of electricity powers ten (10) 100-watt lights for one hour. France gets 80 percent of its total energy from nuclear power, while in the rest of the world, an average of 16 percent of electricity used is produced by nuclear power plants.

Nuclear Power as an Efficient Energy Source

Energy efficiency is the percentage of the energy output compared to its input. In the power industry, nuclear plants operate at an average of 98 percent efficiency, determined by the amount of energy the plant generates with uninterrupted operation. Nuclear power is an efficient energy source because the costs to generate extensive amounts of electricity by operating and maintaining the plant, purchasing fuel, and paying for the management of used fuel are relatively low. According to Global Energy Decisions (GED), in 2006, nuclear power cost consumers on average, 1.87 cents/kWh. By comparison, coal-fired power plants produced electricity at 2.37 cents/kWh and natural gas-fired power plants had average production costs of 6.75 cents/kWh.

Benefits of Nuclear Energy

Nuclear power meets the goals of the Clean Air Act (CAA) of 1970. Nuclear power plants do not emit criteria pollutants (such as ozone, nitrogen oxides, sulfur oxides, particulate matter, or lead) or the greenhouse gases that are produced from the combustion of fossil fuels. In this sense, nuclear power can be considered to be a clean source of energy. It is also highly efficient, as discussed above.

Disadvantages of Nuclear Energy

Nuclear power plants, when operating properly, do not emit hazardous, radioactive, or toxic gases into the atmosphere. However, they do leave artifacts behind as a permanent legacy from their operations.

Spent fuel (uranium rods depleted of usable power) is a byproduct from nuclear reactors. Spent fuel is radioactive waste that needs to be isolated to minimize risks of radiation exposure. Burying the depleted fuel rods underground has been considered the best way to dispose of the used fuel and byproducts, rather than securing them onsite in steel and concrete vaults. The highly radioactive, spent fuel poses a hazard to all living organisms if not handled and stored properly. Radioactive waste must be stored for hundreds of years in sealed environmental casks that are approved for storage of spent fuel under the conditions specified in the operator's certificate of compliance.

The risk of accidents during the operation of a nuclear power plant is a significant drawback to nuclear energy. Chernobyl and Fukushima stand out as examples of the potential for harm when the chain reactions in reactors slip beyond human control, but these are by no means the only accidents in the historical record. In Pennsylvania,

Three Mile Island experienced the worst nuclear accident in US history. On March 28, 1979, a partial meltdown occurred as a result of the malfunction of equipment and the design of the plant. As a result, radioactive waste was dumped into the nearby Susquehanna River, causing potential health risks to the local population.

Another notable drawback to nuclear power is that building new plants now will not reduce fossil fuel dependency in the short term because of the length of time it takes to construct a fully operational plant, anywhere from 25 to 40 years. Also, since nuclear power plants use large quantities of water for steam production and cooling, diverting water from a lake or river can affect fish and other aquatic life. Extremely hot, cooling-tower water from reactors is continuously discharged into waterways. As a result, the heated water raises the ambient waterway temperature, which can alter biological life-cycles and ecological balances.

Growth in nuclear energy in recent decades is a result of an increase in energy demand, the need for security of energy supply, concerns about environmental damage, and the economics of energy. Another important aspect of this growth has been the increase in safety standards of nuclear power plants, which have significantly improved as a result of lessons learned from past mistakes. Some critics of nuclear energy argue that uranium is scarce, questioning whether nuclear energy has a dependable long-term supply.

MID-CHAPTER QUESTIONS

1. What advantage does nuclear energy have over fossil fuels?

2. What impacts does nuclear energy have on the environment?

3. What is the chemical process that occurs to make nuclear energy?

FOSSIL FUELS

Fossil fuels were formed millions of years ago from the organic remains of prehistoric organisms whose main component was carbon. Natural gas, coal, and oil are the three major forms of fossil fuel.

Natural Gas

Natural gas is considered the cleanest of all fossil fuels. Like coal and oil production, natural gas plants produce carbon dioxide (CO_2) and nitrogen oxides, and they do so in much smaller amounts. In comparison, coal production produces twice as much CO_2 and two-thirds the amount of nitrogen oxide. The US has an abundant supply of natural gas, but there are challenges associated with its production. These include challenges related to exploration, drilling, water resources, hydraulic fracturing, wastewater management, and radioactivity.

Production Challenges

Seismic surveys are used to generate the geologic structures of a subsurface and produce images to locate underground natural gas reservoirs. After examining the surveys, site preparation is the next step to facilitate the drilling process in a given area. This site preparation—which includes the construction of roads to access the well and the installation of pipelines to transport natural gas—can destroy any existing flora and fauna. Mining process failures can result in natural gas blowouts, which release harmful chemicals into the atmosphere. Another challenge is ground subsidence, or the motion of the surface of the Earth caused by mining. This motion is geologically hazardous because it can cause roads to collapse and flooding in areas affected by the interference. Sometimes, small-scale earthquakes can occur.

Hydraulic fracturing, also known as "fracking," involves a fracture made through rock using high-pressure fluids to create a well to extract gas. The fluids have the potential to contaminate both the gas and surrounding environment. The EPA, at the request of Congress, in 2011 began to study potential environmental impacts of large amounts of water for hydraulic fracturing, potential contamination from chemical mixing, well injection, and the water produced by hydraulic fracturing, in addition to wastewater treatment and removal strategies. Currently, measures are taken to recycle the water and use biodegradable hydraulic fluid derived from vegetable oil, which lessens any environmental impact. In addition to reducing the potential for groundwater and drinking water contamination, it is also essential to prevent methane gas contamination by injecting fluid into the well. In early 2012, the EPA and the Obama Administration released new air pollution regulations related to the handling of wastewater from the hydraulic fracturing process.

The Clean Water Act (CWA) effluent guidelines program sets national standards for industrial wastewater discharges based on best available technologies that are economically achievable. Effluent guidelines for oil and gas extraction prohibit the onsite direct discharge of wastewater from shale gas extraction into waters of the US. While some of the wastewater from shale gas extraction is reused or re-injected, a significant amount still requires disposal. However, no comprehensive set of national standards exists at this time for the disposal of wastewater discharged from natural gas extraction activities. As a result, some shale gas wastewater is transported to treatment plants (publicly owned treatment works [POTWs] or private centralized waste treatment facilities [CWTs])—many of which are not properly equipped to treat this type of wastewater.

Other changes to natural gas extraction outlined in the new regulations state that, starting in 2015, wells will need to capture the volatile organic compounds (VOCs) produced by the wells. This is called **green completion**. Colorado and Wyoming already require green completion and companies in areas where they will need to begin this practice are allowed to burn off these harmful gases using a completion combustion device—a process called flaring—between now and 2015. After 2015, natural gas producers much capture the gases and make them available for sale, reducing VOCs and methane and nitrous oxide emissions.

Aside from the technical challenges of drilling for natural gas, the financial aspect is also a factor. The drill bits are placed in a horizontal position as opposed to a vertical position, which escalates the cost. Seismic surveys are conducted to ensure safe and effective drilling, since details of reservoir structure, faulting, and pore system heterogeneity must be clearly defined. To reduce costs, multilateral (many horizontal directions) drilling that can be more cost-effective as a result of

GREEN COMPLETION A process used to eliminate or collect the VOC emissions produced from natural gas wells with a completion combustion device or a collection procedure that allows for the resource to be used for energy production.

technological advancements may be used. For example, a horizontal drill bit coupled with a multi-lateral drill bit has increased productivity and the rate of return is profitable.

Natural gas is a reliable energy source in the US, due to the availability of infrastructure for delivery and funding for new developments. Natural gas is found in shale rock, primarily Marcellus Shale, which is black and rich in organic sediments. Even though the projected range of this natural gas supply is between 90 and 116 years, there are many financial, regulatory, and technological challenges involved with extracting this resource.

Advantages and Disadvantages of Natural Gas

The development of natural gas has become a priority in recent years because of its many advantages compared to other fossil fuels, including the relative ease of transportation, the vast infrastructure of transportation pipelines available within the US, and lower greenhouse gas emissions as compared to other fossil fuel sources. Natural gas power plants are easier to build than nuclear power plants and pose fewer environmental risks. Regional regulations on the extraction of natural gas may reduce production in some locations, resulting in the need to develop additional delivery methods to maintain supply.

Coal

Coal is a fossil fuel formed from the compressed plant matter of swamplands that existed over 300 million years ago. Coal is primarily composed of carbon atoms. In simple chemical terms, the carbon atoms in coal are bonded together in long chains and complex matrices. The strong bonds that connect the atoms together contain a massive amount of energy. When coal is burned, the bonds are broken and the energy is released as heat.

The four types of coal are anthracite, bituminous, subbituminous, and lignite.

Anthracite coal is 86–97 percent carbon. Its heating value is higher than that of bituminous coal, which is 45–86 percent carbon. Bituminous coal is the most abundant coal in the US and is used as the main fuel in the steel and iron industries. Subbituminous coal has a heating value less than bituminous coal and is 35–45 percent carbon. Subbituminous coal accounts for 47 percent of US production. Lignite coal is 25–35 percent carbon and has the lowest energy content and highest moisture content. It amounts for 7 percent of US production. It is used in power plants to generate electricity. The US has coal reserves of up to 270 billion tons.

Over 90 percent of the coal produced in the US is used for generating electricity, with industrial uses comprising most of the remainder. The exploration of coal is very similar to that of oil, since the exploration process uses the same equipment. Coal is found in a distinct type of sedimentary rock, in geological

COAL TYPE	PRIMARY LOCATION
Anthracite	Northeastern Pennsylvania
Bituminous	Kentucky, Pennsylvania, and West Virginia
Lignite	North Dakota and Texas
Subbituminous	Wyoming

Figure 9.1 U.S. coal type and primary source locations

formations of ancient swamps rather than oceans, and it can be found roughly a mile beneath the Earth's surface. The production of energy from coal begins with coal mining.

Coal Extraction and Production

Coal is harvested by either surface mining, such as strip mining, or underground mining. Strip mining is the removal of all sediment and rock found above the coal. After the coal is extracted, the material that was removed is replaced. After energy organizations remediate a mine, it may take years before the wilderness areas are fully restored to their original state.

Underground mining involves cutting shafts using tunneling equipment and hydraulic cutting machinery. The coal is removed through the mine shaft to the surface, where it can be shipped throughout the world. Safety hazards involved with this type of coal mining include the potential for explosions from the underground build-up of methane gas and coal dust and the potential collapse of mines, trapping miners underground.

Overall, coal is a major contributor to global energy production, despite the potential environmental challenges it poses. These issues have been a problem for many years due to the need to heat homes and produce electricity. With current environmental regulations, mining operations do impact the environment. Coal production is led by six countries: the United States, Russia, India, China, Australia, and South Africa. These nations accounted for 82 percent of the total coal extracted throughout the world in 2006 and they have about 90 percent of the coal reserves on Earth.

In China, 75 percent of all energy used comes from coal, which has had an enormous impact on the country socially and economically. In China, where regulations are not as strict, environmental problems associated with coal mining include coal **gangue**, coal ash, exhaust emission, wastewater, noise, and surface subsidence. Gangue is the material from an ore deposit as a result of mining and has no commercial value and is removed during processing as waste.

As a result of these large reserves, energy generation from coal can be used to strengthen the economies of the developing world, as seen in China. However, the environmental impacts need to be considered. For example, coal mines use millions of gallons of water per day to cool the drill bits and they produce an equivalent amount of water discharge. They also exhaust gas. In China, coal production can produce up to an average of 6 billion tons of gas, 300 million tons of coal ash, and about 3.3 billion tons of sulfur dioxide (SO_2) annually. While coal production in China is growing, it is small in comparison to US operations. In China, the Shendong Coal Mining Company produced 20 million tons of coal in 2007. By comparison, total coal production in the state of Wyoming was 443 million tons in 2010, while West Virginia produced 136 million tons.

In addition to energy production, coal is extensively used as the heat source in the steel industry. Based on estimates from the World Bank, coal production is expected to quadruple by 2020. There is an estimated 270 years worth of coal reserves available worldwide.

Advantages and Disadvantages of Coal

Coal is an abundant but non-renewable resource and an efficient source of energy for electricity production and industrial activities in many parts of the world. Its availability and affordability are its main advantages, but the mining and production processes present environmental problems that are major disadvantages to coal as an

GANGUE The material from an ore deposit as a result of mining. It has no commercial value and is removed during processing as waste.

energy source. Extracting and converting coal to energy produces wastewater, exhaust, ash, and SO_2 contributing to air pollution in coal producing areas. The mining process can be dangerous for miners and damaging to the surrounding ecosystem.

MID-CHAPTER QUESTIONS

1. Where is coal found in the US?

2. What is the primary use for coal?

3. What environmental problems are associated with coal?

Oil

Oil, or petroleum, is formed from microscopic phytoplankton and zooplankton that has undergone immense stresses of temperature and pressure over geological time. Liquid petroleum, also known as crude oil, is found in geological deposits throughout the world as a mixture of hydrocarbons that can exist as black and thick or lighter in color and thinner in consistency. Crude oil is used to create a wide variety of energy products—including gasoline, diesel fuel, jet fuel, and heavy fuel oil—through the process of refining. Other products produced from oil include liquefied gases, coke, asphalt, lubricants, and kerosene.

Crude oil is composed of hydrocarbon chain molecules of various sizes, each of which boil at different temperatures. Fractional distillation is a refining process where the crude oil is heated gradually to a very high temperature and separated into many different products. As the oil is heated, the components vaporize at different temperatures. They are then condensed to a liquid form and collected. The fractions (separated components) can be processed further by breaking large chain molecules into shorter chains or by mixing them in various combinations to create new petroleum-based products. Gasoline is manufactured by fractional distillation.

When oil is refined, it is heated until it evaporates. The vapor is then channeled into a tower separated by horizontal trays. A fractionator is the cylinder in which the distillation takes place. After condensation, the vapor settles into the appropriate trays based on density. Each tray has its own valve where the vapor can bubble. The components that are the products of fractional distillation are not always ready for consumption, since further processing needs to take place to produce diesel fuel, furnace fuels, kerosene, gasoline, and petrochemicals (see Figure 9.2).

PRODUCT	GALLONS PER BARREL
Gasoline	19.36
Diesel	10.02
Jet fuel	3.91
Other Products	6.80
Heavy Fuel Oil	1.68
Liquefied Petroleum Gases (LPG)	1.72

Note: A 42-U.S. gallon barrel of crude oil yields about 45 gallons of petroleum products.

Figure 9.2 Products made from one barrel of crude oil

Source: Energy Information Administration, "Oil: Crude Oil and Petroleum Products Explained" and Annual Energy Outlook 2009 (Updated February 2010).

Oil is a non-renewable but highly valued energy source because it has a high energy density, meaning that the amount of energy that can be extracted from oil is large when compared to other energy sources. Two other characteristics of oil that have led to its wide use is that it is transported easily and is relatively abundant, even though limited in supply. Oil has been the primary source of energy in the US since the 1950s. Oil production paved the way for major advancements in transportation in the twentieth century.

Historical records show that humans extracted petroleum as early as 347 AD, when oil wells were drilled in China with the use of bits attached to bamboo poles. In 1264, the Persians began to mine oil. In 1858 the first oil well was drilled in North America in Ontario, Canada. In the US, the first well was drilled in 1859 in Pennsylvania. The Seneca Indians also became familiar with the seeping of the thick black crude oil in their streams. They used the substance as a mosquito repellent, purge, and tonic. In that region, now Western New York, the settlers called it Seneca Oil and used it for medicinal purposes.

In 1861, the first commercial oil well was drilled in Humboldt County, California. The 1890s to 1920s brought about the use of gushers and cable tools to speed the rate of extraction. The 1930s to 1950s saw further advances in drilling technology with the use of well logs, seismic exploration, and rotary drilling. From the 1960s to today, oil exploration technology incorporates steam, horizontal wells, and computers.

The Organization of the Petroleum Exporting Countries (OPEC) is a permanent intergovernmental organization, currently consisting of 12 oil-producing and oil-exporting countries spread across the continents of Asia, Africa, and South America. The members are Algeria, Angola, Ecuador, Iran, Iraq, Kuwait, Libya, Nigeria, Qatar, Saudi Arabia, United Arab Emirates (UAE), and Venezuela. Saudi Arabia holds the world's largest crude oil reserves, with about 26 percent of the global supply.

Oil fills 37 percent of the total energy demand in the US. Of this oil consumption, 70 percent is used for transportation in the form of gasoline, diesel, and jet fuel. Industrial processes and manufacturing consume 23 percent, 6 percent goes into commercial and residential uses, and the remaining 1 percent is used to generate electricity. It has been estimated that the US has oil reserves of about 21 billion barrels. The top oil-producing states are Texas, Alaska, California, North Dakota, Oklahoma, and Louisiana, though offshore drilling produces more than all the states combined. However, the US must depend on imported oil from Canada, Mexico, and the Persian Gulf to meet its needs.

Production Challenges

Due to environmental and safety concerns, offshore drilling has been a politically controversial topic. In 2008, the US Congress placed restrictions on offshore drilling. In 2010, in response to the BP "Deepwater Horizon" oil spill in the Gulf of Mexico, offshore drilling activities were halted. Applying for drilling permits, which are required by the Department of Interior (DOI), has usually been a lengthy process.

Proponents of expanded oil drilling in the US claim that Alaska's Arctic National Wildlife Refuge (ANWR) has the potential to produce billions of barrels of oil. Benefits to increased domestic oil production would be to reduce dependency on foreign petroleum imports and possibly lower consumer costs. Drilling opponents warn of the potential and possibly permanent ecological and environmental damages to the drilling sites and surrounding areas. This topic continues to be fiercely debated.

Advantages and Disadvantages of Oil

Oil is a non-renewable fossil fuel and a highly efficient source of energy used for transportation, industry, and commercial products. Its high energy density makes it a desirable source of fuel. It is also relatively easy to transport. Supplies are limited but many reserves are not currently being used. Balancing the environmental impact and economic gain of drilling in some of these protected or offshore areas creates heated debates among policymakers.

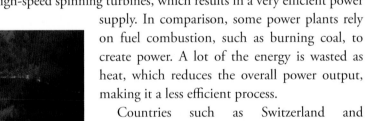

MID-CHAPTER QUESTIONS

1. **Oil is considered a non-renewable energy source. Explain why.**

2. **What are the challenges associated with the production of oil?**

3. **What are the major oil producing countries in the world?**

HYDROELECTRIC POWER

Hydroelectric power, or hydropower, is the use of flowing water to generate energy. In a hydroelectric power plant, the transfer of energy from kinetic to mechanical energy enables large turbines within generators to spin and produce electricity. It is a renewable source of energy because water in the form of precipitation such as rain, snow, or sleet continuously resupplies streams and lakes as part of the natural water cycle. The gravitational force of the water flowing downhill from mountainous regions to sea level provides the force to turn hydroelectric generators, which operate at 90 percent efficiency.

Some of this efficiency is due to the fact that hydroelectric power is a passive process, using falling water to generate electricity. Energy inputs (fuel sources) are not required in the process. A comparatively minimal amount of heat is generated and lost by the high-speed spinning turbines, which results in a very efficient power supply. In comparison, some power plants rely on fuel combustion, such as burning coal, to create power. A lot of the energy is wasted as heat, which reduces the overall power output, making it a less efficient process.

Countries such as Switzerland and New Zealand can take advantage of their mountainous regions, and in these countries hydroelectric power provides more than half of the population's energy needs. Regions at low elevations are not able to produce hydroelectric power.

The power of water has been used for millennia. Over 2,000 years ago, the Greeks used water power to grind wheat into flour. By the 1700s, this energy was used to mill lumber

and grain and pump water for irrigation. The first operational hydroelectric power plant was built in 1882 in Appleton, Wisconsin, producing 12.5 kW of power. By today's standards, where power in generated and measured in millions of watts (megawatts, MW), 12.5 kW is an extremely small amount of power.

Eventually, 300 hydroelectric plants began operating worldwide as a result of the invention of hydraulic turbines. In the early 1900s, 40 percent of electricity in the US was provided by hydroelectric power. Between the years 1905 to 1911, the US Bureau of Reclamation built the Roosevelt Dam in Arizona. This engineering marvel stands as the last and largest masonry dam ever built, with the capacity to produce up to 36,000 kW of power. The dam is primarily used to provide irrigation water and flood control to areas of the desert southwest. In the US, hydropower generates over 90,000 MW, which is enough to supply power to about 28 million people.

Niagara Falls is also used to create large amounts of electricity. The power-generating stations in Niagara provide a quarter of all the power used in the state of New York and the Canadian province of Ontario. Overall, the US obtains 7.1 percent of its electricity from hydropower.

In order of magnitude, China, Canada, Brazil, and the United States produce the most hydroelectric energy. However, there is also potential for hydroelectric power in areas such as Latin America, Central Africa, and India. The world largest hydroelectric power plant is Itaipu Dam, in Paraguay and Brazil. It was built from 1975 to 1991 and has the capacity to generate 14,000 MW of power.

Advantages and Disadvantages of Hydropower

Since water is the primary source of hydroelectric energy, no fuel is burned and no pollution is created. The water cycle is driven by heat energy from the Sun, and thus is completely renewable. Hydroelectric power is more reliable than other renewable energy sources such as wind, solar, or wave power. Once a dam is built, hydropower can be generated continuously and safely at little cost. The energy can be stored and reserves can be accessed when there is high demand. Hydroelectric installations can be also used to breed fish and other aquatic organisms.

One major obstacle to expanding the use of hydroelectricity is that it is expensive to build the plants. Not only is the construction costly, but agricultural, residential, and recreational lands are lost when dams are built. The construction of large hydroelectric power plants results in ecosystem destruction, and the function of the river that remains is also permanently affected. For example, in the Pacific Northwest, where hydropower creates about two-thirds of the area's electricity, salmon populations depend on rivers to complete their spawning activities. Hydroelectric power plants disrupt these rivers. Solutions such as fish ladders or alternate channels have been constructed with dams to help the fish complete their life cycle.

Even though hydroelectric power does not emit greenhouse gases or toxic pollutants into the atmosphere, hydropower generation can greatly alter wildlife habitats by changing the temperature of river water. Also, the quality of water in reservoirs or streams can be affected; areas upstream from hydroelectric plants can suffer from flooding. Droughts can also reduce the output of hydroelectric power stations because a reduction in rainfall will result in a lowering of electricity production. And if a dam is ever destroyed in a natural disaster such as an earthquake, catastrophic damage may be caused downstream.

Countries involved in large-scale hydroelectric development programs are China, India, Iran, and Turkey. Nations that are in progress of investing in hydropower are Sudan, Rwanda, Mali, Costa Rica, and Guyana.

MID-CHAPTER QUESTIONS

1. Explain why hydroelectric energy is a renewable source of energy.

2. How does the use of hydroelectric power impact the environment?

3. How does hydroelectric power affect aquatic life?

BIOFUELS

The term *biofuel* refers to a number of renewable energy sources in which biomass, or biological material, is converted into liquid fuel. Vegetable oils, waste cooking oils, algae, animal fats, or tall oil can be used to manufacture biofuels. Tall oil is the American adaptation of the Swedish word "tallolja," associated with the kraft pulping process of pulp/pine wood.

One of the most common forms of biofuel is biodiesel, which is created in a chemical process called transesterification. This process combines oil (vegetable or animal fats) plus alcohol (typically ethanol or methanol) with sodium hydroxide as a catalyst to produce biofuel and glycerin.

Biodiesel cannot be used in areas where temperatures are very low because the fuel becomes viscous when cold, preventing it from flowing through fuel lines. However, blending biodiesel with conventional petroleum-based fuel lowers the viscosity of the fuel, allowing the fuel to reach lower temperatures before it congeals.

For example, a 50 percent blend of biodiesel is used in France. Of the 85 biodiesel refineries around the world, most are located in France, Germany, Italy, and the United States.

Researchers are continually searching for more economical and efficient fuel sources and blends. Automotive technologies improve continually. For example, in the 1980s, leaded gasoline was phased out due to the introduction of more efficient and cleaner burning unleaded gasoline engines. Stricter air pollution controls as a result of health concerns with leaded gasoline were a primary driver in prompting the engine technology advancements. The US government has been working with the airline industry on biomass-derived jet fuel. In 2011, United Airlines flew a commercial plane in a test from Houston to Chicago with a mix of 40 percent biofuel from algal oil and 60 percent conventional jet fuel.

Advantages and Disadvantages to Biofuels

An advantage of using biofuels is the reduction in the amount of crude oil needed to fuel vehicles. Food and animal waste products that would otherwise be discarded can be recycled for biofuel production, thus reducing disposal costs.

There are some disadvantages to using biofuels. Renewable, biofuels are not a clean source of energy. Nitrous oxide and CO_2 are released into the atmosphere when biofuels burn and the machinery used in the manufacturing process produce waste. The sources of biofuels also require farmland for production, fuel, and water for irrigation. Conversion costs can initially be high. Early durability tests on older vehicles indicated that engines would fail prematurely when operating on fuel blends containing vegetable oil. Engines burning vegetable oil that had been transesterified with alcohols, however, exhibited no such problems and even performed better by some measures than engines using petroleum diesel. The formulation of what is now called biodiesel came out of those early experiments.

Ethanol

Ethanol is an alcohol used as a fuel. Ethanol is made by a similar process to the one that produces wine or beer: a biomass high in carbohydrates (such as corn) is fermented. Another process that produces ethanol is gasification, which uses high temperatures in a low oxygen environment to make synthesis gas or "syngas," which is eventually converted into ethanol. Syngas is a mixture of hydrogen and carbon monoxide, and sometimes CO_2, and needs to be cleaned and processed for further use. Ethanol added to gasoline increases the octane rating and is a form of alternative fuel.

Market Implications of Using Ethanol

Corn is used in two markets, both as a food source (for animals and humans) and for ethanol production. This is a problem because the demand for the crop is greater, which can become an economic and production issue. An increase in the use of corn to produce ethanol causes the price of corn overall to increase, which affects the price for animal feed and corn-related products at the supermarket. Indirectly, the price of other commodities can be affected. Soybeans, meat, poultry, and dairy products are some of the retail foods that can be affected by an increase in corn prices. These issues are further complicated with faced with conditions like the drought of 2012, where the overall supply is affected. In the end, this can also have a spiraling effect on food expenditures and an increase in the cost of the federal government's food assistance programs.

Additional public education and awareness of ethanol as an alternative fuel source is needed for it to gain popularity and acceptance. In addition, the technology to construct engines that can use this alternative fuel needs to be developed on a widespread basis. With regards to the environment, using ethanol may lower emissions of greenhouse gas emissions as well as improve the quality of air and water resources.

Switchgrass

Panicum virgatum, better known as "switchgrass", is a crop that can be used to make ethanol and other biofuels. It grows quickly and is a great alternative to corn for the production of ethanol because the ratio of energy output to energy input is considerable. Switchgrass is an efficient source of biomass because it can withstand drought and flooding and thus has a good range of climatic tolerance. It does not require herbicides or much fertilizer. Another advantage to switchgrass is that it is a perennial and does not have to be replanted every year. An added environmental benefit is that the root structure of the plant binds soil and prevents erosion. Ironically, switchgrass is also known to be a very problematic weed in the Corn Belt in the US Midwest.

Co-Firing

Biomass, such as wood, can be burned as fuel in combination with coal in a process known as "co-firing," which results in lower CO_2, sulfur, and mercury emissions to produce energy. Scrap wood materials can be collected from timber harvesting and processing activities and used for beneficial and productive power generation purposes. Co-firing is economical because no modifications are required to existing coal burning facilities for this process.

MID-CHAPTER QUESTIONS

1. What are the benefits of using biofuels?

2. Why is switchgrass suitable for the production of ethanol?

3. Corn is used as a food source and a fuel. Is this an advantage or a disadvantage? Explain why.

SOLAR ENERGY

Our Sun radiates heat energy—called solar radiation—and could be considered the world's largest power plant. It is the largest star in our solar system and the energy it produces is a form of **electromagnetic energy**. This is a form of energy that is either reflected or emitted in the form of electrical and magnetic waves; it has the ability to travel through space. Other types of electromagnetic energy include gamma rays, x-rays, ultraviolet (UV) rays, visible light, infrared radiation, microwaves, and radio waves. Nuclear fusion occurs at the core of the Sun and releases energy that travels outward to its surface. The Sun warms the Earth and provides power for biological organisms. Via photosynthesis, plants obtain energy that is stored in plant tissues. Humans and animals consume plants and other animals that feed on plants. The stored plant energy is then converted into metabolic energy.

The Earth's magnetic field and atmosphere protect us from most of the solar radiation and reflect some solar energy back into space. The greenhouse effect also affects the rate of solar transmission to earth and reflection into space. Of all the incoming solar radiation, or insolation, 30 percent is reflected back into space, while the rest is absorbed by clouds, oceans, and land masses.

The Sun is responsible for the creation of petroleum, coal, and natural gas. Through billions of years of the Sun delivering power to our planet, ancient plants and algae captured the solar rays and conducted photosynthesis. An enormous amount of solar power was harnessed over the eons. As the plants passed through countless generations, the organic plant remnants seeped down through the soil profile and remained embedded in the Earth. Excessive heat and pressure converted the organic matter into the fossil fuels we rely on today. We are using solar power that was captured and stored billions of years ago.

Even though every part of the Earth receives sunlight, the geographic location, time of day, season, local landscape, and local weather play roles in determining the amount. There is a decrease in intensity of solar energy the further away from the equatorial belt one travels. This directly impacts the number of sunny days through-out the year. Zones closer to the equator have a greater solar potential. Therefore, sunlight throughout the globe is unequal.

ELECTROMAGNETIC ENERGY Energy reflected or emitted in the form of electrical and magnetic waves with the ability to travel through space.

For example, we can compare the daylight sun in Alaska to that of Florida. In Alaska, specifically in the regions above the Arctic Circle, the Sun may shine continuously for 24 hours during the Summer Solstice. At slightly lower latitudes, such as Anchorage, during the summer solstice, the Sun may shine for only up to 19.5 hours each day. Conversely, during the winter, these areas are dark nearly the entire day. Florida, on the other hand, has an average of seven hours of sunlight per day from September to February and an average of nine hours of sunlight from March to August. Florida is susceptible to daily heavy rainfall, which can reduce the daily average hours of sunlight.

Solar energy is an alternative energy source to fossil fuels, such as oil and coal. Two major sources of energy from the Sun are heat and light. Heat can be captured and used in solar powered utility systems while light energy can be transformed into electrical energy.

History of Solar Power

Humans have relied on the Sun as a source of biological and spiritual power and time keeping for thousands of years. Reliance on the Sun—our only local star—is critical for our survival. Early astronomers used the position of the Sun and stars to indicate planting and harvesting cycles. It was not until a few hundred years ago that scientists began to slowly harness and unravel some unknown mysteries of the invisible power of the Sun as solar power.

Solar Power

Electric energy can be produced from a solar energy generator, which is made of two components; a collector and a storage unit. The collector gathers energy from the Sun while the storage unit stores excess energy. There are three types of collectors: flat-plate, focusing, and passive.

Flat-plate Collectors

Flat-plate collectors are automated solar panels that face the Sun. Solar panels work by collecting solar thermal energy. A solar panel is essentially a closed box with a top made of a transparent material such as glass or plastic. When the Sun shines through the glass, the inside of the box, which is painted black, heats up. The heat collected inside the box is used to heat either air or water. The box also contains an inlet through which cool air or water enters and an outlet through which the heated air or water leaves the box and enters the house.

Across the US, more than 10,000 homes have solar energy systems. Solar panels are expensive to install (about $20,000 for an average home) but the return on investment can be over $30,000, since they can increase the value of the home. Many states and the federal government have incentive programs that reward homeowners who choose to go solar. In some parts of the country, solar panel systems are tied to the power grid.

Focus Collectors

In focus collectors, optical devices are positioned to maximize the intake of solar radiation depending on the focus of the collectors. An example of a focus collector is a solar furnace. In a solar furnace, the collectors consist of an inflated cylinder of plastic film. The cylinder has two segments; the first segment is the portion exposed to the Sun. It is made of clear plastic to permit radiation to enter. The radiation shines on the second segment, which is made of an aluminized plastic that acts as a mirror. This is a portable energy production system because it can be deflated for transport. The estimated cost for a focus collector is about $20 per square meter of solar reception.

A trough system is a focus collector made up of a large field of solar panels arranged in rows. A north-south orientation of these fields is characteristic of their alignment for maximum sunlight capture. Receiver tubes, which are part of the trough system, collect the heat absorbed by the panels and transfer it to turbines, which generate electricity. This system produces on an average of 100 kWh/year of energy.

A third focus collector, a Power Tower System, is located on a tower with a transmitter and a receiver. The transmitter is a field of mirrors that reflect the energy to the receiver, which is connected to fluid that heats rapidly because of all the reflected energy. Similar to the trough system, steam is used to turn the turbines to generate electricity. The thermal energy can be stored for future use.

Passive Collectors

There are many examples of passive collection of solar energy. Simple heat from the Sun, that requires no conversion into energy, is used to heat swimming pools and solar ponds. Solar ponds can be used to heat buildings. They are placed near the building or on the rooftop to enable maximum energy absorption. Excess heat can be stored in the pool for later use. Thermosyphoning, a passive method of collection, is used in walls, roofs, and pipes, usually to heat water.

Solar Energy Uses

Solar energy is used in transportation, heating, cooling, and electricity generation. Ships, which move at a slower speed than other vehicles, can operate on solar power. An excellent example of solar power for marine navigation is the *MS TÛRANOR PlanetSolar* ship. It is a completely solar powered vessel that made an approximately 600-day trip around the world, the first solar powered circumnavigation of the world. The ship stopped in many major port cities during the journey to promote the benefits of solar power. Unlike large ships, small vehicles such as cars are not currently equipped to be powered solely by solar energy. However, solar energy stored in the form of a battery makes it possible for a car to be partially solar powered.

Solar energy can also be used for cooling. However, it is expensive and less popular in private homes than solar heating. The process involves changing the state of a liquid to a gas and containing it in a low pressure chamber at a low temperature. Cooling occurs when the gas is moved to the exterior of this container.

Solar Energy Production

Solar energy is produced in a variety of ways, such as by heating water or by using solar photovoltaic (PV) cells. Solar energy may be either active or passive. Active energy includes energy that is captured and converted into electricity by panels and thermal

BUSINESSES GOING GREEN: GOOGLE

The technology company Google reported that in 2010, it consumed two billion kWh of energy. One of the company's missions is to support the environment by finding alternative sources of energy to power its centers and to also sell the excess power it generates from these alternative sources. In order to encourage use of these alternative sources of power, Google's effort involves attempting to lower the costs to produce solar and wind energy. They plan to produce one GW of power at a lower rate than the same electricity produced from coal.

To promote wind power, the company has invested in wind farms in North Dakota, California, and Oregon, and most of the energy it uses comes from wind power. However, their investment in solar energy is even more significant. The company is in the process of spending $75 million to fund the creation of 3,000 residential solar electricity systems throughout the country. Users would not own the panels but would pay Google a monthly fee. Local solar system companies will offer financing plans for the installation.

In Sacramento, California, Google plans to spend $94 million to fund solar panel construction along with Recurrent Energy, a solar developer, and KKR, an investment firm. This infrastructure would enable them to generate energy for the US electric grid and sell it to the Sacramento Municipal Utility District. For Google, this means that clean energy projects would attract new capital while keeping to their mission to foster growth of sustainable energy.

collectors, while passive energy is not. Passive solar energy relies on energy efficient architectural design where maximum energy can be captured from the Sun by placing windows and sunrooms in optimal places.

Solar-Hydrogen Power

The combination of solar energy and water for hydrogen gas production is called solar-hydrogen energy. The need for this type of fuel production came from concerns in environmental issues and the exploitation of fossil fuel reserves. Solar-hydrogen systems separate water into its components, hydrogen and oxygen. The hydrogen is used as fuel to power electric generators and the hydrogen and oxygen can also be stored for use during times of the day or year where abundant sunlight is not available.

Photovoltaic Power

Solar photovoltaic (PV) technology has been in existence for over 50 years. The first photovoltaic component was built by Bell Laboratories in 1954. PV cells are based on photonic technology, which converts light into electricity. Contemporary PV energy systems transmit power via fiber-optic cables.

Thermal Power

Solar thermal energy is produced when rays are collected by pipes filled with water, which is circulated by a pump or convection currents. The heated water can be directed through coiled pipes to heat household water or home heating systems. Solar electric and heating systems capture and convert only a small portion of the solar energy delivered to Earth.

Advantages and Disadvantages of Solar Energy

There are many environmental and other benefits to using solar energy. One of the biggest benefits is that there is no pollution in the form of greenhouse gases produced in the production of energy from the Sun. One kW of power generated from the Sun is equivalent to 150 lbs of coal combustion power. This translates to a reduction of greenhouse gas emissions by 300 lbs of CO_2 released into the atmosphere and 105 gallons of water consumed by coal extraction. In addition to the benefits to the environment, solar energy can be harnessed in remote areas that are not typically on the energy grid

Trough system for collecting solar power

of a major urban center, so it is ideal for people living in remote areas. Even in space, satellites get power from solar efficient cells. Solar energy can be installed on rooftops of existing buildings and do not need special land allocations. Using solar energy also decreases our dependence on fossil fuels.

There are some distinct disadvantages to using solar energy. The first is its initial cost for set-up. Solar cells are very costly and installation can be cost-prohibitive. Energy from the Sun can only be captured during daylight hours and the efficiency of solar cells is affected by the weather. Batteries—made of either nickel cadmium, nickel iron, lead-acid, or lithium—are used to store solar energy. The batteries are expensive and the chemicals in the batteries, such as cadmium and sulfuric acid, create issues for safe disposal. The minerals used, like lithium, are a scarce resource that must be mined from the earth. Mining for material to manufacture long-lasting batteries poses similar environmental issues as coal mining.

Solar Energy in Practice

Solar energy is distinctive among other local and clean energy sources due to its availability. There are some places in the world where it is used to generate power on a large scale. The largest PV power plant is located in Sarnia, Canada with a capacity of 97 MW. In the US, the Solar Energy Generating System (SEGS), developed in the 1980s in the Mojave Desert, is the world's largest energy station, a collection of nine power plants. It has the capacity to produce 354 MW of power. Nevertheless, less than one percent of energy used in America comes from solar power. Other power plants include Spain's Solnova plant, which has three, 50 MW towers that produce a total of 150 MW; and the Andasol plant, which has five, 50 MW towers that produce a total of 250 MW.

Innovations in Solar Energy

Innovations in the use of solar power come from many sources. Products and companies are increasingly using solar energy. For example, the Biblio Leaf, an e-reader created by two Japanese companies, Toshiba and KDDI, uses a mini solar panel to help power the device. To stay competitive with other e-reader options, the Biblio Leaf SP02 has a 6-inch monochrome screen in 16 shades, has 800x600 resolution, 3G and Wi-Fi connectivity, and supports SMDF/PDF/EPUB files. The solar panel creates enough energy that when the device is at full battery power, users can read up to 7,500 pages before recharging.

In a study conducted by Robert A. Freling, the executive director of Solar Electric Light Fund (SELF), a project was launched in the Kalale District of Benin in Africa to promote the use of solar energy to improve the lives of the 44 villages without electricity in 2007. Freling previously determined that countries with a low gross national product (GNP) often had the highest levels of sun exposure, but these countries are unable to provide the infrastructure for power grids for basic necessities such as cooking, space heating, and lighting. In this case study, the major problems faced were food security and lack of water either caused by six months of dry season each year. As a result, a solar-powered drip irrigation system was implemented to generate energy for local water pumps to bring water to the fields and villages year-round.

The outcome of access to solar-powered water pumps was that the villagers began to earn $7.50 more per week because they could grow fruits and vegetables during the dry season. The villages also now have access to clean drinking water. The next step in the project is to provide power to the schools, health centers, and households in the area.

Solar Energy Applications in the Developing World

In some areas of the globe, as in Kalale District of Africa, it can be cost-prohibitive to build the infrastruture needed for power grids or to connect to the local utility grids. In these cases, solar off-grid devices provide an excellent solution where solar energy is abundant. Many of these devices are also inexpensive, clean, and have little-to-no maintenance. Here are a few examples:

Vaccine Refrigerator

Solar-powered vaccine refrigerators use a combination of PV panels to power the refrigerator and lead-acid batteries as a backup source of power. In Nigeria, the company KXN Nigeria Ltd. was able to reduce the use of expensive and flammable kerosene, which was previously used to power electric generators. They installed 189, solar-powered vaccine refrigerators, which provided a place to store vaccines safely and provide better health care to local people.

Water Disinfection

Solar water disinfection or (SODIS) is used by 1.4 million people in Asia; 360,000 in Latin America; and 340,000 in Africa to reduce winterbourne (a dry stream or river during the summer months) diseases. In this process, UV light from the Sun naturally kills bacteria and pathogens in water stored in plastic PET (polyethylene terephthalate) bottles.

Water Pasteurization

In Tanzania, approximately 100,000 people rely on a solar water heater provided by Adventures in Health, Education & Agriculture Development (AHEAD) to pasteurize and disinfect their water supply.

Water Pumps

Solar water pumps have been used in Benin for drip irrigation systems. The solar energy is captured from the PV panels.

Food Dehydrators/Preservers

Solar food dehydrators preservers consist of a ventilated box with open-grid racks; they are used to dry food for future use. Dehydration creates a dry and unsuitable environment for bacteria to live, which reduces contamination and preserves food after harvest. In Uganda, a company called Fruits of the Nile sells dried fruit prepared in these simple boxes in international markets. Fruits of the Nile instructs local farmers in organic farming practices. Excess harvested fresh fruit is purchased by the company, and it is then dried, packaged, and sold around the world.

Electric Fencing

Solar-powered electric fencing is used by Community Markets for Conservation (COMACO) in Zambia to protect crops for over 1,500 families. Solar energy charges the "live" wires in the fence to prevent unwanted animal raids.

Wi-Fi

Solar Wi-Fi is powered by solar panels that are connected to an antenna and router that provide Internet access from broadband. In countries such as Panama and Senegal, Green Wi-Fi has used this efficiently to increase access to information and communication.

Phones

Solar-powered mobile phones improve rural communications by using PV cells to charge the battery within mobile phones. Many companies use this technology to provide access to cellular phones in developing countries. For example, Digicel sells solar phones in Haiti and Papua New Guinea and a company called Safaricom sells solar phones in Kenya.

Radio

Solar radios improve rural communications by using solar energy to power radio transceivers. For example, in rural areas of Peru, The Madrid Association of Engineers Without Borders has used solar radios to support health services for over 50,000 people.

Cooking Devices

In Chad, Ethiopia, Kenya, and Haiti, the company Slow Cookers International has donated its products that run on solar thermal devices to families in refugee camps so that they can reduce their reliance on wood and charcoal and reduce indoor pollution, a cause of asthma and other respiratory illnesses.

Water Heating

Solar water heating is used by 99 percent of the homes in Rizhao, China. The solar thermal collectors heat the fluid and store it in a water tank, thus reducing carbon emissions and pollution.

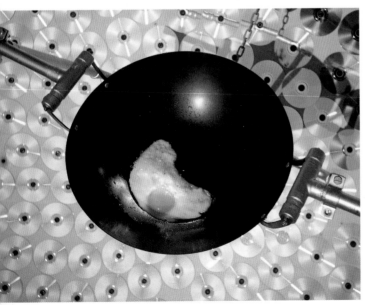

Solar energy is predicted to become more economical than fossil fuels in the next decade. Proponents of solar power point out that the sunlight provides 10,000 more times the total energy we require. With a suitable investment in infrastructure and acceptance in communities, solar power could provide all of our energy needs within the next 20 years.

MID-CHAPTER QUESTIONS

1. Give a description of how solar panels capture energy from the Sun.

2. What are the advantages and the disadvantages of using solar energy?

3. Describe the innovations in the use of solar power. Which would be of most interest to you?

WIND ENERGY

Wind is produced by the uneven heating of the atmosphere coinciding with the rotation of the Earth. Air moves from areas of high pressure to areas of low pressure; the greater the pressure differential, the faster the wind speed. Barometric (atmospheric) pressure is basically a measurement of the weight of air in a given location or region. We cannot feel the weight of the air because our internal body forces are in equilibrium with the external air pressure.

Humans have used the power of wind over the centuries. Ancient sailors powered sailboats by wind. Farmers took advantage of automation of wind energy, using a windmill in Persia about 500–900 AD to grind grain and pump water. The first use of a large windmill to generate electricity was a system built in Cleveland, Ohio, in 1888 by Charles F. Brush. It is estimated that wind energy could generate enough electricity to power 25 million homes in the US by 2020.

Wind energy is a renewable source of energy. The energy from the wind turns wind turbines that generate electricity. A wind turbine is made up of a rotor, a nacelle, and a tower. The nacelle contains a gearbox, a generator, as well as control and monitoring equipment. Modern turbines have three, bladed rotors, and range from 42 to 80 m in diameter. The towers are between 40 and 100 m tall. These structures generate between 600 kW and 2 MW power.

Advantages and Disadvantages of Wind Power

Wind energy has many advantages. It does not cause air or water pollution or emit greenhouses gases. Its supply is unlimited. Wind energy works well in tandem with other forms of energy such as solar panels and geothermal heating. If you have the space to do so, producing your own electricity through wind energy is possible due to advancements in technology and energy kits that are now on the market. As an added economic benefit to users, energy generated by wind can be stored and sold to local electric companies.

ENVIRONMENTAL MISCONCEPTIONS: RENEWABLE ENERGY SOURCES

With fossil fuels in limited supply and the negative impact they have on our environment, alternative energy sources are increasingly looked to as less expensive and cleaner solutions. However, they are not always cheaper than non-renewable sources. Sources of renewable energy can provide savings but initial investment may be high. An 8-kW solar panel system can cost about $70,000, but the excess amount of energy generated from this system per month can either be sold to the grid for revenue or banked for future usage.

Some people also assume that renewable energy sources produce no pollution. A certain amount of pollution is always produced, even if the source itself is pollution-free, there are likely some pollutants created in the manufacturing or transportation. For example, fossil fuels are needed to create solar cells for solar panels even though the solar cells themselves do not emit pollution. The transportation and manufacturing of solar panels produces greenhouse gases. Solar cells also contain mercury, which, if not disposed of properly can be hazardous. Once the renewable sources of energy are in operation, they produce less pollution than non-renewable sources.

Creating energy from wind power also has its challenges. Wind, while in unlimited supply, is not continuous or predictable. It is not a reliable way to produce an expansive amount of energy. Wind turbines are relatively new and costly. They can cause noise pollution and harm birds who fly into the turbines. Wind farms require a large amount of land or water surface area. The wind turbines are often damaged by bad weather and regular maintenance is costly. Wind turbines often fall into the NIMBY (not in my backyard) category, as some believe that the large windmills affect the aesthetics of an area. Excess energy must be stored in batteries that contain harmful chemicals.

The Future of Wind Power

Wind power generation has support from some local and state governments. Several US states have established what is known as the Public Benefit Fund (PBF) to fund renewable energy, energy efficiency, and research and development programs. Electric customers in their states are charged a small amount on their bills to fund these investments. The PBFs help promote wind energy development. In one example, a wind project that creates 10 MW of energy would be eligible to receive 10 percent of its funding from the PBF, equivalent to $2.75 million. States such as Connecticut and California have also participated in the development and maintenance of wind power plants.

Wind energy has a great potential for growth because offshore wind farms have proven to capture 50 percent more wind energy than onshore turbines. This also means that offshore towers do not have to be as tall and can be driven or built into the seabed. Even though offshore farms are currently limited to shallow areas, mounting platforms in the future could be in deeper waters to take advantage of stronger ocean winds. It is necessary to discuss the impact such structures would have on the environment. Both the construction and the operation of turbines will affect local sea life, mammals, fish, plants, and birds.

Wind power generation is widespread in Germany, Spain, Denmark, and India. By 2020, the US Department of Energy (DOE) plans to increase total energy drawn from wind power to five percent of overall power production, but regulatory reforms and well designed incentives are necessary to drive this.

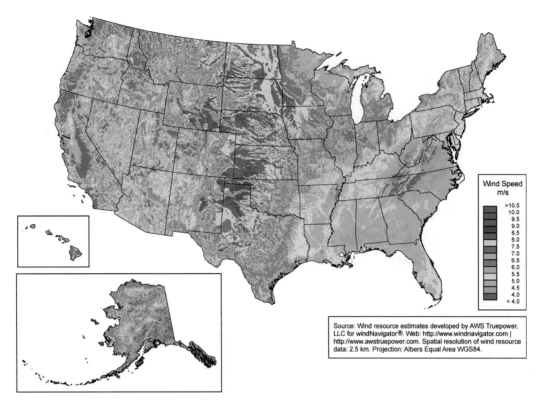

FIGURE 9.3 Average annual wind speeds at 80 meters above ground

MID-CHAPTER QUESTIONS

1. How is wind captured for production of wind energy?

2. What are the disadvantages of wind power?

3. How does wind power affect the environment?

GEOTHERMAL ENERGY

Geothermal energy comes from the natural heat generated from the Earth and is a renewable source of energy in the form of volcanoes, hot springs, and geysers. This heat is derived from either magma or lava coming directly from the Earth's core (where the temperature is 13,000°F). Water in pipes constructed close to these areas produce steam or hot water (hydrothermal resources) used to generate electricity in a geothermal power plant. The temperature of a geothermal reservoir can be greater than 450°F.

In the US, geothermal systems are found in the Geysers Region in Northern California, the Imperial Valley in Southern California, and the Yellowstone Region in Idaho, Montana, and Wyoming. Other countries that use this energy are Iceland, New Zealand, Japan, Italy, and the Philippines. Iceland is noted for its

extreme geothermal activity. In 2009, 66 percent of the island's power was produced by geothermal sources.

The three main types of geothermal power stations are:

- Dry-steam power plants are the simplest and oldest technological design. The steam comes from ground fractures at 300°F and is used to turn the turbines to generate power.
- Flash-steam power plants use deeper hot water found in high-pressure areas that are channeled into tanks of low pressure. The flash steam (355°F) generates the energy to turn the turbines to generate power.
- Binary steam power plants use a primary source of geothermal water with a secondary fluid source that has a lower temperature. The flash of steam created is used to turn the turbines to generate power. This is the most common method to generate geothermal power.

Geothermal heat pumps are used to heat and cool buildings, to heat greenhouses, to dry crops, to heat water at fish farms, and in several industrial processes, such as milk pasteurization. Geothermal power stations are small in comparison to hydroelectric plants and have a limited detrimental impact on the environment. These plants can run continuously with an efficiency of 100 percent. The downside of geothermal energy is that it is not easily accessible in every region of the world and tapping into geothermal energy sources releases hydrogen sulfide in small concentrations into the atmosphere. The waste fluids from geothermal energy production also release toxic substances into the environment.

MID-CHAPTER QUESTIONS

1. Describe how geothermal energy is a renewable source of energy.

2. What are the three main types of geothermal power stations?

OCEANIC ENERGY SOURCES

The potential for ocean energy is vast considering that 70 percent of the surface of the Earth is covered by water. There are two types of energy derived from the ocean: mechanical energy from waves and tides and thermal energy from solar radiation on the surface of the ocean (it acts as a solar collector). Oceanic energy has advantages over even hydroelectric power because it does not depend heavily on stream flow and river supply. Along with hydroelectric power, technological advances in oceanic energy production can have a significant impact on meeting the world's growing energy needs.

Tides and Waves

The ocean produces tides and waves that can be used to produce electrical power. This power has similarities to hydroelectric energy since the primary component of a hydroelectric plant is a dam—sometimes known as a barrage—which traps the water from the tides flowing through the dam. It is used to convert the tidal energy into electricity by forcing the water through the turbines to activate the generator. The turbines are turned as a result of the ebb and flow motion of the tide. In early 1966, tidal barrages were built in France at a plant called La Rance, which is still in operation.

The three main types of wave energy systems are:

- Buoys or floats: motion from the buoys is used to generate energy.
- Oscillating water columns: columns are placed in the ocean; the movement of the water within them generates energy.
- Focusing devices: the ebb and flow of water into channels near the shore drives turbines that produce electricity.

Although it is estimated that there are around one billion watts of worldwide of tidal energy, less than three percent is located in areas suitable for power generation. Wave energy, on the other hand, has an estimated potential of around 1,000–10,000 gigawatts (GW). However, one advantage of tidal currents over waves (or wind) is its predictability, as tides can be accurately predicted weeks or even years in advance.

Electricity can be generated from the ocean by trapping the kinetic energy used in waves and currents, and thermal (heat) osmotic (gradient movements) energy. The first wave farm began operating in Portugal in 2008 and new wave-energy projects—while sometimes slow to come to full operation—are in development.

Benefits of Wave Energy

There are several reasons wave energy is a viable alternative for generating power in the future. It causes little or no pollution. The systems have little impact on shorelines and can actually protect them from erosion by diverting waves. It is cost effective, at less than $0.05/kWh.

Disadvantages of Wave Energy

Widespread use of wave energy is met with challenges because it is limited to coastal areas and, even then, not all coastal areas provide the wave power necessary for such power generation. We do not yet know the impact on the environment or marine and aquatic life. Onshore generators use extended lengths of coastline. Either offshore or onshore, wave system generators affect the aesthetics of the area. In the event of storms, there is the danger of ocean wave generators being damaged or moved from their current location, causing navigation hazards for ships.

Ocean Thermal Energy

The large surfaces on the Earth covered with water act as huge solar collectors. Thermal energy is created as a result of the heat the surface water retains. Ocean Thermal Energy Conversion (OTEC) systems use the energy from the ocean to generate power. These facilities take advantage of the difference in temperature between the warm water on the sea surface and the cool water at greater depths to produce electricity.

This technology also uses the cooler water from beneath the surface to facilitate condensation of the vapors that evolve from the turbines. In ocean thermal energy generation, the three types of electricity conversion systems are known as closed cycle, open cycle, and hybrid.

- A closed cycle system takes advantage of the heat from the surface water on the ocean to vaporize a fluid such as ammonia with a low boiling point. The expanding vapor turns the turbines.
- The open cycle system boils the seawater and operates at low pressures, producing steam to turn the turbines in the generator.
- Hybrid systems use elements of both the closed cycle and open cycle systems to generate power.

MID-CHAPTER QUESTIONS

1. How is power generated from the ocean?

2. Describe different aspects of the ocean that have potential for energy creation.

3. What role do oceanic energy sources play in the environment?

PRESERVATION: OIL INDUSTRY

For over a century, the oil industry has operated in every environment throughout the world, including deserts, mangroves, coral reefs, wetlands, rainforests, and even the frozen tundra. The impact that oil exploration has on the environment creates a need for prevention, mitigation, and control of industrial processes. For example, industry and governments act in collaboration to prevent oil spills and handle emergencies. In some cases, oil spills cause immediate and long-term environmental damage to beaches, marshlands, and marine ecosystems. Spills can kill birds, marine mammals, and fish and destroy the wildlife habitat and breeding grounds of various species.

Regulators and oil companies both monitor the environment to prevent undesirable impacts. In the oil and gas industry, many preventative equipment maintenance programs are in place, such as those that control end-of-pipe emissions. In offshore wells, these measures protect the health of the seabed and bird and mammal populations.

Since oil and gas are limited natural resources, there is also a need to restore sites that have been decommissioned. When extraction activities are complete at a site, oil and gas companies attempt to return the site to its natural state. To plan for this, they pay attention to habitat dynamics. This includes pre-development assessments and studies of long-term impacts of oil and gas exploration and extraction. The benefits of such care are not limited to one company or government but can extend to the global community.

CHAPTER SUMMARY

Humans use energy for a wide range of purposes—transportation, heating and cooling buildings, industrial processes, and household needs, such as cooking and laundering clothes. The source of power available for use is tied to the local geography or the local infrastructure. Energy sources are renewable or non-renewable and each has its benefits and disadvantages.

Eighty percent of US energy consumed comes from fossil fuels: oil, natural gas, and coal. Fossil fuels, while readily available and efficient, are non-renewable, are being depleted quickly, and produce greenhouse gases when burned. Nuclear power is often looked to as a cleaner alternative to fossil fuels, but it is not renewable—because it relies on supplies of uranium—and, as shown with the example from Fukushima, problems can be disastrous.

There are other sources of energy that are renewable—meaning, their supply will not deplete over time. These include hydroelectric power, biofuels, solar power, wind power, geothermal power, and oceanic sources from tide and wave energy. Some of these sources, such as geothermal and oceanic sources, can only be produced in specific locations on Earth where these resources exist naturally. Biofuels are renewable as they can be made from waste materials or plants that can be continually sourced. Solar and wind power are more readily available around the globe, but the initial investment in equipment to produce large amounts of power from these sources can be cost-prohibitive.

REFERENCES

Allaby, A., & Allaby, M. (1999). A dictionary of earth sciences. New York, NY: Oxford University Press. Retrieved from http://www.encyclopedia.com/doc/1O13-gangue.html

Bian, Z., Inyang, H. I., Daniels, J. L., Otto, F., & Struthers, S. (2010). Environmental issues from coal mining and their solutions. *Mining Science and Technology (China)*, *20*(2), 215–223.

Biodiesel: A painless transition from fossil fuels. (2005, October 26). *Biodiesel Times.* Retrieved from http://biodiesel.rain-barrel.net/biodiesel/

ESA21: Environmental science activities for the 21st century: Fossil fuels, coal. (n.d.). Retrieved from http://esa21.kennesaw.edu/activities/coal/coalactivity.pdf

Etemadi, A., Emdadi, A., AsefAfshar, O., & Emami, Y. (2011). Electricity generation by the ocean thermal energy. *Energy Procedia*, *12*, 936–943.

Fahey, J. (2011, September 28). Google wants to help homeowners add solar power panels. *BostonGlobe.com*. Retrieved from http://articles.boston.com/2011-09-28/business/30213497_1_solarcity-green-business-operations-rick-needham

Geothermal energy facts. (2008, March 20). Retrieved from http://interestingenergyfacts.blogspot.com/2008/03/geothermal-energy-facts.html

International Atomic Energy Agency. (2008). Looking back to go forward: Proceedings of an international conference. Vienna, Austria, September 6–7, 2005 (Proceedings series, ISSN 0074–1884). Retrieved from http://www-pub.iaea.org/MTCD/publications/PDF/Pub1312_web.pdf

Kargbo, D. M., Wilhelm, R. G., Campbell, D. J., & Al-Abed, S.R. (2010). Natural gas plays in the Marcellus shale: Challenges and potential opportunities. *Environmental Science & Technology*, *44*(15), 5679–5684.

King, R. S. (2011). The post-Fukushima world. *IEEE Spectrum*, *48*(11), 44–45. doi: 10.1109/MSPEC.2011.6056622

Patel, P. (2011, October 31). Three Mile Island, Chernobyl, and Fukushima: A comparison of three nuclear reactor calamities reveals some key differences. *IEEE Spectrum*, *48*(11). Retrieved from http://spectrum.ieee.org/energy/nuclear/three-mile-island-chernobyl-and-fukushima

Ragheb, M. (2012, May 28). *Fukushima earthquake and tsunami station blackout accident.* Retrieved from http://mragheb.com/NPRE%20402%20ME%20405%20Nuclear%20Power%20Engineering/Fukushima%20Earthquake%20and%20Tsunami%20Station%20Blackout%20Accident.pdf

Schmitt, G. J. (2006, April 13). Energy security, national security, and natural gas. *AEI Online*. Retrieved from http://www.aei.org/article/foreign-and-defense-policy/regional/europe/energy-security-national-security-and-natural-gas/

Si, H., Bi, H., Li, X., & Yang, C. (2010). Environmental evaluation for sustainable development of coal mining in Qijiang, Western China. *International Journal of Coal Geology*, *81*(3), 163–168.

Singh, T. (2011, May 19). Wind power could be the best alternative energy source for Japan. Retrieved from http://inhabitat.com/wind-power-could-be-the-best-alternative-energy-source-for-japan/

Solar Energy Industries Association. (2010). The history of solar energy. Retrieved from http://www.seia.org/galleries/FactSheets/Factsheet_solar%20history.pdf

STM. (2003, May 27). BIOBUS project cuts Montreal CO2 emissions by roughly 1,300 tons [Press release]. Retrieved from http://www.stm.info/English/info/comm-03/a-co030527.htm

Strickland, E. (2011). 24 hours at Fukushima. *IEEE Spectrum, 48*(11), 35–42. doi: 10.1109/MSPEC.2011.6056620

Tabor, H., & Zeimer, H. (1962). Low-cost focussing collector for solar power units. *Solar Energy, 6*(2), 55–59. doi: 10.1016/0038-092X(62)90004-X

U.S. Department of the Interior, Bureau of Reclamation, Power Resources Office. (2005, July). Hydroelectric power: Reclamation – Managing water in the West. Retrieved from http://www.usbr.gov/power/edu/pamphlet.pdf

U.S. Department of the Interior, Bureau of Land Management. (2008, December 19). Wind Energy Development Programmatic environmental impact statement (Instructional Memorandum No. IM 2009-043). Retrieved from http://windeis.anl.gov/documents/docs/IM_2009-043_BLMWindEnergyDevelopmentPolicy.pdf

U.S. Geological Survey, the USGS Summer School. (2012). Hydroelectric power water use. Retrieved from http://ga.water.usgs.gov/edu/wuhy.html

Wind Energy Development Programmatic EIS. (n.d.). Wind energy development environmental concerns. Retrieved from http://windeis.anl.gov/guide/index.cfm

World Health Organization. (2012). *Preliminary dose estimation from the nuclear accident after the 2011 Great East Japan Earthquake and Tsunami.* Retrieved from http://whqlibdoc.who.int/publications/2012/9789241503662_eng.pdf

World Nuclear Association. (2013, April 2). Fukushima accident 2011. Retrieved from http://www.world-nuclear.org/info/fukushima_accident_inf129.html

World Nuclear News. (2011, September 28). WHO warns on urban air pollution. Retrieved from http://www.world-nuclear-news.org/EE-WHO_warns_on_urban_air_pollution-2809116.html

Yokayo Biofuels. (2006). Yokayo biofuels: Biodiesel. Retrieved from http://ybiofuels.org/bio_fuels/history_biofuels.html

Zekai, S. (2004). Solar energy in progress and future research trends. *Progress in Energy and Combustion Science, 30*(4), 367–416.

CHAPTER 10

Land Use

THE DUST BOWL

The 1930s were a bleak time in the United States (US) and around the world. Globally, Europe was beginning to fall into World War II and Japan had invaded China. The US was in the midst of the Great Depression, during which unemployment reached 25 percent and millions lost their homes. During this decade of turmoil, four individual drought events occurred in near-sequential order (1930–31, 1934, 1936, and 1939–40) throughout the Midwest plains states. Sometimes called "the breadbasket of the world," this highly fertile region of the US had been used for agriculture for generations. However, in 1935 alone, nearly 46.6 million acres of crops in this region failed. Because of successive seasons of drought, the land and plants were unable to recover, and soon large tracts of land were barren. These barren lands, coupled with little rain, large, flat open land, and high winds created one of the worst environmental disasters in US history.

The Dust Bowl, as it is known, laid waste to nearly 100 million acres of prime farmland in western Kansas, eastern Colorado, and parts of the Oklahoma and Texas panhandles. This led to one of the largest human migration events in US history. However, the drought was not the only cause of these large dust storms, which could dump inches of dirt, blocking doors and burying farm equipment. It was soon determined that poor land use and improper use of new farming equipment, such as the tractor and plow that destroyed topsoil, made these storms inevitable. During this time, an abundance of agricultural commodities were grown in the Midwest. Over-cultivation along with over-tilling created less fertile and looser soil. Crops failed due to low nutrition because of poor tillage and soil conservation and retention practices, along with drought conditions (severely limited rainfall and irrigation reserves). This barren land became vulnerable to **erosion**. The Dust Bowl led to the development of land use and land management practices, including **terracing** and **contouring**. As a result, government agencies were created to repair farmland and promote anti-erosion practices among farmers, even providing incentives for farmers that used soil conservation methods. Once they were put in place, these practices helped protect the region from a similar fate during droughts in the 1950s, which actually affected a larger area.

EROSION The loss of soil from a location.
TERRACING A style of agriculture that involves creating levels of planting rows on a hill, much like steps. Terracing is a very common practice in mountainous Asian rice farms.
CONTOURING A style of agriculture that involves planting crops with the lay of the land.

China is currently experiencing the loss of productive farmland as a result of poor land management practices, creating another dust bowl scenario in which dust from storms in the desert northwest regularly reduce visibility not only in Beijing but also in other countries, such as Japan, North Korea, and South Korea. The National Oceanic and Atmospheric Administration (NOAA) reported in 2001 that dust from these storms covered areas of the US Southwest as well.

URBAN SPRAWL

Urban sprawl in its most basic form is the growth of a highly developed and populated area outward away from an urban center. In a grander sense, urban sprawl incorporates much more than this outward growth. Urban sprawl also involves the altering of **land use**, increased use of resources, and increased centralized waste. Urban sprawl is not a new phenomenon. Numerous cities throughout history have experienced urban sprawl and dealt with the ensuing challenges. Large cities such as Athens, Tikal, Angkor, Paris, Phoenix, Chicago, and London struggled and still struggle with urban sprawl. All of these cities struggled with growing smartly and supporting a growing population. They all had their own unique challenges, but regardless of geographic area or historical context, all shared similar challenges associated with urban sprawl.

URBAN SPRAWL The increase in area of a population center as it expands beyond its center.
LAND USE The way in which a particular parcel of land is used.

History and Measurement of Urban Sprawl

The ancient city of Tikal, located in what is now Guatemala, reached the height of its success between 600 BCE and 900 CE. Archeological excavations suggest that the city may have been approximately 10 square miles (sq mi) at its peak. It is estimated the population around 830 CE was 120,000—an astonishing number of inhabitants by ancient standards, an even greater feat considering the lack of springs,

1. What were two issues that led to the Dust Bowl?

2. Describe changes that were put in place to prevent a similar future event.

Angkor Wat, Cambodia

rivers, or lakes to support the people and agriculture of this major city. The Tikal people were able to survive for more than 1,000 years primarily by collecting and storing rainwater. A high average rainfall (about 52 inches per year (in/year) in this part of Central America), coupled with high average temperatures and a very intensive style of agriculture, supported the growing population of Tikal. However, scientists theorize that near the time of Tikal's peak, a drought hit the area. This lack of rainfall and possible nutrient loss from erosion severely limited the food production capabilities of the Tikal people. Within the next 70 years, both Tikal and, to a greater extent, the Mayan civilization as a whole began to crumble.

Just as Tikal was beginning to wane, Angkor, an ancient city found in what is now Cambodia, was rising to power. The city reigned as a super city-state from the ninth to the fifteenth century CE. Angkor was the capital city of the Khmer civilization and was home to the largest spiritual temple ever built, Angkor Wat. Angkor Wat and the grounds surrounding the temple covered an area of over 200 acres. The city itself spanned an estimated 1,000 square kilometers (sq km) and was home to nearly 750,000 people at its peak. As Angkor continued to grow, there was an increased need for food and water to sustain the population. This required the clearing of tracts of land for agricultural fields, and the digging of more channels and canals. Recent archeological studies theorized that a combination of canal sedimentation and extreme weather fluctuations from drought to monsoon caused the water supply to collapse. Angkor slowly declined as its people were forced to close down canals and divert water. By the seventeenth century the city was deserted, and it would eventually be overgrown and enveloped by the jungle.

Impacts of the Industrial Revolution and Beyond on Land Use

The issues of urban sprawl and urbanization increased dramatically during the Industrial Revolution, but this period also saw more advances in solving these same problems than at any previous time in history. New technology allowed advancements in water supply and waste removal. Other technological advancements in factory equipment, mechanical agricultural equipment, and tools increased the productivity of every trade. This meant that fewer people were required to work the land, but more people were required to process the commodities grown on the land and produce finished products. These advances drew people to urban areas, where factories and processing plants were located, which increased the burden on the surrounding land.

While developing cities and towns could adjust to this increase in population, long-established cities like Paris and London required major redevelopment to support more people in an already heavily populated area. Paris, situated around the Seine River, was forced to develop a means for waste removal. This led Napoleon III to hire architect Georges Haussmann in 1853 to develop a system of sewers to move the waste to the Seine River. His planning increased the sewer system to approximately 386 miles of sewer by 1870, nearly four times its previous size. The sewer system was also as mechanical as possible, requiring little hands-on work, a drastic change from the original sewer works that were cleaned by hand. Haussmann also divided the city into 20 districts, allowing city leaders to manage the city more like several small towns than one large city.

The redevelopment of Paris came nearly 200 years after the Great London Fire of 1666. Overcrowding, poor building codes, and poor infrastructure resulted in a massive fire that tore through the urban center of London. At the time, most homes were made of wood and pitch, and what started as a fire at a small bakery in the early hours of Sunday, September 2, soon engulfed a large portion of the city. By September 5, an estimated 13,000 homes were burned to the ground, leaving thousands of Londoners homeless. This and a lesser fire in 1676 caused King Charles II to appoint six commissioners to completely redevelop London's center and changed the primary building material from timber to bricks. Similar to London, Chicago faced problems with urbanization in a disastrous fire that started October 8, 1871, and burned for three days, destroying approximately four sq mi and claiming the lives of more than 300 people. Again, tightly packed buildings and poor building materials exacerbated the situation.

Urban sprawl can also create other challenges for cities. Phoenix, currently the sixth largest metropolitan area, by population, in the US, is in the arid Southwest. As the population of Phoenix has increased over the years, so has water demand. Phoenix has an annual average rainfall of only seven inches, and during the summer average temperatures top 100°F. These factors in an area with increasing population have led some planners and environmental scientists to raise concerns about water shortages in the near future. Already, Phoenix imposes regular water restrictions to limit household use during the driest times.

It should be noted that a city's location, culture, and general geography influence the problems it has with urban sprawl. Because of this, defining and measuring urban sprawl can be difficult. For example, a city surrounded by mountains will face different problems and expand differently than a city with the same population sitting on flat or gently rolling land. Oceans, lakes, and rivers also control the expansion of urban areas. However, to better control urban sprawl and to efficiently plan for the development of cities, centralized characteristics have been established to define and measure the effects of sprawl. These characteristics include: street connectivity, centeredness, mixed use, and density.

The commonly measured characteristics of urban sprawl are each comprised of several component factors that influence the degree to which each characteristic influences the quality of life in a city. Street connectivity, for example, is a measurement of how connected the streets and roads are, and is influenced by the size of city blocks. Areas that are sprawled may have longer blocks and, especially in residential areas, have a large number of cul-de-sacs. This type of roadway plan forces traffic into smaller areas because there may only be a few major roads available to reach a community's business, commercial, and industrial districts or dining, entertainment, and retail areas.

Diminished street connectivity also decreases the use of public transit for commuting because of limited access, and the resulting increased vehicular traffic on main thoroughfares makes alternatives to automobile transportation, such as walking or biking, more difficult. Cities like Rochester, NY, and Atlanta, are designed with these larger blocks and dead-end features. However, older metropolitan areas such as New York City and San Francisco have much smaller blocks that interconnect. This interconnection allows travelers using all modes of transportation to navigate more directly to their desired location, with less congestion.

City Centers: Concentrating Activities in Specific Zones

Centeredness refers to a city having a strong downtown or main street area. These are areas that have high concentrations of either employment or population. These urban centers draw commercial activity and provide jobs at a greater rate than cities with amenities spread throughout a metropolitan area. They also foster alternative means of transit and allow people to perform multiple tasks in one location. For the most part, cities with the best centeredness are smaller, less-populated areas such as Honolulu, Columbia, SC, and Springfield, MA. This is because it is easier to have a concentrated city center when there is a smaller population. In fact, among the largest US cities, only New York City and San Francisco rank high on the list of most centered. Their high ranking can be attributed to their multiple city centers. For example, New York is divided into five boroughs, and each of these boroughs has several concentrated districts. Some of the New York City boroughs are physically separated by water. As a result, the city is not a contiguous landmass.

Multiple city centers allow both New York City and San Francisco to operate almost as a conglomeration of several smaller cities, thus directing traffic, people, and capital to various centralized areas. Unlike New York City and San Francisco, most large metropolitan areas in the US are not very centered at all, with commercial districts scattered throughout. Examples of these types of areas include Vallejo, CA, Riverside, CA, and Fort Lauderdale, FL.

Mixed-Use City Layouts

Mixed-use describes an urban area that includes residential, commercial, and industrial buildings dispersed among one another. Similar to the advantages of city centeredness, mixed-use allows citizens to live, work, and play within a smaller section of a larger city, usually close to public transportation. The idea of mixed-use is best exemplified in downtown New York. Large buildings with storefronts on the ground floor also contain offices, apartments, or a mixture of floors above them.

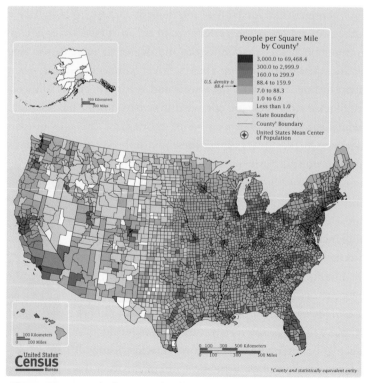

Figure 10.1 Population Density from 2010 US Census Data

This efficient way of arranging urban space is a necessity where real estate is very expensive, but it can be mimicked in smaller metropolitan areas as well. In addition to New York City, other areas that rank high in mixed-use are Jersey City, NJ, Oxnard, CA, and New Haven, CT. These cities provide the best opportunity for residents to conduct their activities within the smallest areas, reducing commute times and using less land for development, thus providing for farmland or natural areas. Cities that sprawl, on the other hand, force people to travel greater distances to live, work, and engage in recreation. The least efficient cities in terms of mixed-use include Raleigh, NC, Riverside, CA, and Greensboro, NC. These cities are designed and zoned to keep their residential, commercial, and industrial buildings highly separated.

Density

Finally, density is another key factor used when calculating urban sprawl. Simply measured as the population in a given area, the measurement of population density can quickly show evidence of urban sprawl. Consider cities with large suburban areas that surround the more central urban areas compared to large metropolitan areas such as New York City and Chicago. Many of the most sprawling areas in regards to density can be found in the Southeast. Cities such as Atlanta, Greensboro, NC, and Knoxville, TN have very low and very sprawling populations situated throughout a large suburban area. These low-density cities often are coupled with low mixed-use areas, such as in Greensboro, NC. These low-density areas often do not have major stores or groceries among the residential areas and require the population to travel greater distances than those living in areas with higher density.

The top five most sprawling cities are: Riverside, CA, Greensboro, NC, Raleigh, NC, Atlanta, GA, and Greenville, SC. It should be noted that for the most part, these cities are in the Southeast, which historically was known for agriculture, not industry. The top five least sprawling cities are New York City, Jersey City, NJ, Providence, RI, San Francisco, and Honolulu. It should also be noted that these cities were historically industrial centers or, in the case of Honolulu's island setting, are geographically restricted.

Impacts of Urban Sprawl

Urban sprawl creates problems for cities that may not be immediately obvious. As in the examples of Tikal and Angkor, food and water supply can become an issue. Other major issues that can be exacerbated by urban sprawl are sanitation, waste management, increased air pollution, strains on utilities and infrastructure, strains on local ecology, and soil degradation and erosion.

The primary problem of urban sprawl is that as a population grows, more food is required to feed increasing number of people. As a city branches out farther from its urban center, more land is needed for development, and farmland is often repurposed for these needs. As the demand for food increases, the land available to produce it decreases. This loss of land has increased over time, as well. While food production capability is at an

Los Angeles

"Major issues that can be exacerbated by urban sprawl are sanitation, waste management, increased air pollution, strains on utilities and infrastructure, strains on local ecology, and soil degradation and erosion."

all-time high, and there is an increase in the globalization of food importation and exportation, uncontrolled and poorly planned urban expansion can lead to serious issues with food production.

The loss of farmland is not the only effect that sprawl has on the environment. The problems that industrial-era Paris dealt with are still issues that modern urban areas must address. As urban areas age and expand, controlling and managing waste becomes problematic. Wastewater treatment plants must be upgraded, substations must be built and added, and sewer piping must be added and tied into existing networks. In some cases, **biosolids** are used to fertilize and amend the soil of rural and agricultural fields. And while biosolids can be a beneficial addition to soils, too much can cause **nitrogen pollution**, which can contaminate the groundwater and surrounding waterways. It is essential to maintain healthy water coming into urban and suburban areas as well as ensure that waste is effectively removed.

Human waste is not the only waste that must be managed as cities expand. Household waste, such as packaging material, food scraps, and plastic, also increases as urban areas expand. Food waste is biodegradable; whereas, most landfill waste does not degrade easily or at all. Excessive food waste also perpetuates the reality that modern "first world" humans are not very ecologically or financially responsible.

Much like the situation with vanishing farmland, as areas expand there is more waste to remove while space for landfills diminishes. In New York City, garbage is collected and then shipped out on barges to landfills outside of the city. As intensive as this waste hauling effort sounds, if New York were as sprawling as Riverside, CA, the same waste would have to be shipped even farther away. Increased waste hauling distances make each additional ton of garbage produced by growing cities that much more expensive to dispose of properly. Longer hauling distances for trash removal translates to increased fuel usage and additional costs for taxpayers (as well as the increased traffic, resulting in a greater carbon footprint).

Air Pollution

Air pollution is another issue connected to sprawl. The farther from the center of an urban area that residential areas are located, the greater the distance workers must travel to and from their jobs. When longer commuting distances are combined with poorly connected roads, low mixed-use areas, and traffic congestion, travel times inevitably increase. More importantly, more miles driven by commuters contribute to the motor vehicle air pollution problems detailed in Chapter 7, including primary pollutants and

BIOSOLIDS The organic accumulation of treated sewage sludge.
NITROGEN POLLUTION (EUTROPHICATION) An overabundance of the nutrient nitrogen, which runs off agricultural land and is harmful to the environment, primarily to aquatic ecosystems.

particulate matter, as well as secondary pollutants like smog and brown clouds. Urban sprawl thus directly contributes to diminished air quality for its residents, not to mention the increased greenhouse gas emissions from vehicles burning more fossil fuels.

Settlement Expansion Requires More Natural Resources

Similar to the problem of dealing with human waste are the issues of the general infrastructure and utilities in a growing city. Roads must be widened, added, or rerouted to handle the higher traffic as more and more people need to get to places of employment and commerce. But roads are not the only part of a city strained by sprawl. Electric, natural gas, water, sewage, and other essential public services and utilities are often strained as well. It is necessary to not only run the required cables or piping to connect new developments into city infrastructure, but also to ensure that there is enough supply and that systems can handle the additional loads. Expansion of urban areas, especially sprawling suburban areas, requires more power, and occasionally additional sources of power are needed to avoid power interruptions. For example, New York City often struggles with supplying enough power during peak times, especially on hot summer days when air conditioner use is highest. New York must occasionally supplement this demand with power imported from neighboring New England and Quebec, Canada.

It is also important to understand that with urban sprawl there is not only a strain on the resources used by the human population but also a high cost to the ecological areas surrounding an urban area. Sprawl can lead to habitat loss through deforestation and wetland loss. Habitat loss in turn puts a strain on animal populations because food and other resources are limited, forcing different species into competition for these dwindling resources. Ecosystems as a whole are strained by absorbing increased pollution and water runoff from previously permeable soil surfaces areas that are now paved.

Wetlands are natural low-lying areas that help with flood control and retain soil nutrients. The root systems of water-tolerant plant species form massive complex and stable underground matrices to help absorb excess water to limit the occurrence of flooding and to reduce or prevent soil erosion. When wetlands are disrupted or destroyed to build a housing development, highway, or other project, extensive engineering measures must be taken to create artificial flood control systems, such as underground sewer lines and drainage culverts.

When terrestrial ecosystems are disrupted, there is often increased degradation of the soil quality and increased erosion. While this is discussed in greater detail later in this chapter, it is important to note that soils can be lost to erosion during construction and degraded because of loss of nutrients, compaction, and topsoil loss. These phenomena can leave the remaining soils unable to produce as much vegetation as they previously supported.

MID-CHAPTER QUESTIONS

1. Briefly describe urban sprawl.

2. What problems are associated with urban sprawl?

3. What are some measures that could have been used to prevent the collapse of the ancient cities of Tikal and Angkor?

Makati City, Manila, Philippines, a megacity and one of the most populated urban areas in the world

URBANIZATION

Urbanization refers to populations moving from rural to urban areas. This is a phenomenon that has been occurring throughout the history of human beings. Most major cities throughout the world began as small settlements located adjacent to a waterway, which provided many uses, including potable water, food (fishing), irrigation (fresh water sources), and transportation and trade routes. The majority of the global population continues to live near coastal zones and waterways. However, the rate of urbanization has grown drastically in the last two centuries. Previously, urbanization was restricted by food production. Because of the limited amount of surplus created by farms in ancient times, only a small fraction of the population was able to live in urban areas and still be supported by the agriculture of the time. Even as late as 1800, only about five percent of the world's population lived in urban areas. However, as the Industrial Revolution began to take hold, the need for people in urban areas, where many of the factories were located, increased. At the same time, the Industrial Revolution brought technological advances to agriculture. This meant that farmers could grow more food and required less labor to do so. This increase in food productivity meant that more people could be sustained from the same amount of farmland, with fewer workers needed. Consequently, more people sought work in non-agricultural fields.

After the Industrial Revolution, urbanization of developed countries grew rapidly. For example, Chicago's population was only 15 residents at its founding in 1820. By 1854, it had increased to approximately 55,000. Near the turn of the century in 1898, the population was nearly 1.7 million people. This rapid growth was commonplace in the US and Europe. The population of people living in urban areas grew to nearly 50 percent by 1920. At present it is estimated that nearly 80 percent of Americans live in cities or suburban areas.

Developing nations have not urbanized as rapidly as developed nations. In 2000, only about 45 percent of the population in developing nations had become urbanized. There are several reasons for this slower movement away from an **agrarian** lifestyle.

There are fewer jobs available in urban areas of developing nations. Furthermore, there are fewer financial resources available to increase food production. This lack of abundant food production means that a large population of people living in an urban setting would not be supported by the agriculture industry. It is estimated that by 2030 approximately 57 percent of people in developing nations will live in urban areas, which does not reflect an estimated increase in industrialization or greater productivity in these economies. This estimate is based on increased overall population and overcrowding in rural areas. For example, a small 10-acre family farm may support both parents and their children. However, as these children reach adulthood and marry, the same farm is not capable of supporting the extended family. This, in turn, forces the children to find their own farm, if possible. In most cases, the members of this younger generation migrate to more urban areas in search of livelihoods. All too often, jobs are difficult to obtain. As a result, these newly urbanized migrants are forced to live in **shantytowns**. Shantytowns are makeshift settlements near urban centers where deeply impoverished people live in houses

URBANIZATION The increase in population density as people move from rural areas to more urban areas.
AGRARIAN A lifestyle centered around agriculture and rural life.
SHANTYTOWN A makeshift settlement built out of rudimentary or improvised building materials, such as corrugated metal sheets and scrap lumber.

"It is estimated that by 2030 approximately 57 percent of people in developing nations will live in urban areas, which does not reflect an estimated increase in industrialization or greater productivity in these economies. This estimate is based on increased overall population and overcrowding in rural areas."

|||||||||||||||||||||||||||||||||||||||||||||||||||||||||||||||||||||||||||||||||||||||||||||||||||||||||||||||||||||||||||||||||||||||||||||||||||||||||||||||

made of rudimentary or improvised building materials. Shantytowns may lack even the most basic necessities, such as clean running water and electricity. Shantytowns were common during the Great Depression in the US as well. These towns were commonly referred to as "Hoovervilles," after President Herbert Hoover, who was in office during the stock market crash of 1929.

In 2007, the world reached a demographic threshold when for the first time more than half the global population resided in urban areas. This increase has resulted in the formation of 26 **megacities**, cities with populations above 10 million people. In fact, the 10 largest cities on the planet have populations over 20 million people.

As of 2011, these cities included, but were not limited to:

- Tokyo, Japan
- Guangzhou, China
- Seoul, South Korea
- Shanghai, China
- New Delhi, India
- Mumbai, India
- Mexico City, Mexico
- Sao Paulo, Brazil
- Manila, Philippines
- New York City, USA

Interestingly, both China and India have three megacities, while the US has only two: New York and Los Angeles.

However, with this rapid urbanization come many concerns. City planners must ensure that the infrastructure can manage such population growth. Housing, utilities, and basic necessities like

MEGACITY A very large urban area with a population above 10 million people.

A shantytown

food, water, and electricity can be difficult to provide for so many people. Typical urban planning concerns are not the only dilemmas faced by most of the world's megacities. Growing poverty and substandard construction increase the possibility of catastrophic loss of life from natural disasters. Urban dwellers, especially those in impoverished areas, are more vulnerable to pandemic disease than those in rural areas of the same size. Finally, there is great concern about the ecological impact of urbanization. Due to the sheer size of these cities, the wastes they produce can be immense. This can be seen in the megacity of Manila, which is home to an enormous trash mountain that also acts as a community for approximately 150,000 people who sift through the estimated 6,700 tons of trash that is added daily for items to sell and salvage.

MID-CHAPTER QUESTIONS

1. **What are the most populated countries in the world? Compare this with the information on megacities.**

2. **Describe why people move to urban areas.**

SMART GROWTH POLICIES

Because of the concerns about urbanization around the globe, scientists and city planners are developing methods to handle growth and expansion as efficiently as possible. This effort has resulted in a variety of approaches known as **smart growth policies**. The purpose of these policies is to help cities adapt to the needs of rising populations without worsening the problems of urban sprawl, while at the same time meeting transportation challenges, managing waste removal, and protecting air quality. Policies can vary from city to city, based on need, geography, culture, and demographics. Smart growth policies emphasize the need to encourage growth with minimal changes in land use.

As described earlier, there are four main characteristics considered when measuring urban sprawl:

- Road connectivity
- Centeredness
- Mixed-use
- Density

Policymakers target these characteristics when addressing smart growth goals, resulting in unique policies adopted by towns and cities to deal with urban sprawl. In general, however, these policies fall under ten separate principles:

- **Mixing Land Use**. The first principle is mixing land use. By building residential, commercial, and office buildings in close proximity to one another, people can, in some cases, work, shop, and live all within walking distance. This minimizes car traffic and air pollution; saves time and money because people can make fewer trips; and can improve health by encouraging people to walk more.

- **Compact Building Design**. Another principle is utilizing compact building design. Maximizing efficiency in both residential and retail space requires the

SMART GROWTH POLICIES Policies enacted by local, regional, and state governments to reduce urban sprawl and maintain controlled and regulated growth.

development of less real estate to support the same task. This can be seen in the recent trend of building "small houses," some of which are as small as 144 square feet (sq ft). This principle comes on the heels of a time when home sizes increased over 200 sq ft. on average between 1993 and 1999, while family size decreased. Retail size has also increased by nearly four times on a per-consumer basis.

- **Variety in Housing Types**. Creating a range of housing types within a community is a smart growth policy that allows residents of different income brackets to live in proximity to one another. It can include both single-family homes and multi-family units, but it ultimately provides for a variety of housing at different price ranges to accommodate a wide subset of the population.

- **Walkable Communities**. Developing walkable communities is another principle of smart growth. The benefits of having a walkable community are similar to that of developing a mixed-use area. In communities that are walkable, people are able to easily reach work and shops by foot, limiting automobile traffic and congestion while promoting health through physical activity. In order to be walkable, communities need streets with public walkways, highly connective streets, and mixed-use areas.

- **A Sense of Community**. Fostering a strong sense of unique community is also an important principle. This plays on residents' desire to take pride and ultimately care of their own neighborhoods. By having communities more interested and involved in their neighborhoods and communities, buildings that may be dilapidated or abandoned are removed or replaced (or renovated such as with brownfields). Developing land in the urban core, rather than building in suburban or rural areas, preserves land outside of urban areas while drawing people toward the city center.

- **Preservation**. Another key for maintaining land-use is preserving natural eco-systems and agricultural areas. Policies aimed at land conservation not only maintain habitat, ensure areas of natural buffering from storms and pollution, and protect the food supply, but they also provide residents with a connection to the natural world close to home. Creating green spaces in cities by adding parks or community gardens increases the quality of life for all residents.

- **Redevelopment.** Another important principle is strengthening and redeveloping existing communities. For decades, when cities needed to grow they tended to expand out. This generally occurs at the cost of neglecting the inner parts of cities. Money is allocated for new projects while older communities are neglected and liable to fall into ruin. Reinvesting in these areas has the potential to create new space for homes and businesses while minimizing sprawl.

Financial assistance from public and private sources can help to alleviate some of the burdens in depressed areas. Infrastructure restoration addresses only part of the problem. The local residents need more job opportunities within the area to gain a sense of self. As they become more involved in the process, local ownership, personal responsibility, and community involvement can help to sustain the process and contribute to continued success and growth.

■ **Transportation.** Providing a variety of transportation options is also important to smart growth. This includes public transit, such as rail, bus, subway, or trolley, as well as facilities that encourage active modes of transportation like biking and walking. The ultimate goal is to ease the burden on roads, minimizing congestion and commuting times.

■ **Affordability.** Making development of these areas affordable and cost effective will drive the reconstruction and revitalization of these areas, minimizing the development of outlying fringe areas in a city. Easing zoning and building restrictions to make redevelopment in the inner core a profitable answer can help draw private investors, bankers, and contractors into redevelopment projects.

■ **Stakeholder Involvement.** By enlisting the input of all **stakeholders** in city planning, municipalities provide their constituents with a sense of civic engagement and involvement in their community. Drawing communities together can also encourage people to shop at local stores, dine at local restaurants, and conduct other business locally, helping to spur economic activity. Stakeholders must consider the negative and positive impacts on the local residents for potential failures and project success. When both public and private groups work together to guide development of cities, not only are all voices heard but sprawl is also controlled.

PRESERVATION: PORTLAND'S SMART GROWTH POLICY

Portland, Oregon, has been experimenting with and tuning its growth policies for more than 35 years. Beginning in 1979, Portland enacted an Urban Growth Boundary (UGB) that created a circle around the center of Portland. This line separated the urban center from farmland and natural areas. Since creating this boundary, the city limits have expanded only slightly, even though Portland's population has grown greatly.

Portland was able to do this through the use of smart growth policies that allowed the city to grow without sprawl. These policies included increasing single-family dwelling density, increasing street connectivity, and enhancing the walkability of the city. Portland actually started increasing the density of single-family homes in the late 1960s. This effort intensified in the 1990s, however, causing a jump from an average density of five homes per acre in 1994 to eight homes per acre in new developments by 1998. This allowed Portland's population to grow while the city remained more or less within its previous borders.

Increasing street connectivity eases vehicular traffic and congestion and has the added benefit of allowing homes to be placed closer together since there are fewer cul-de-sacs. Increasing street connectivity also promotes alternative means of commuting, including mass transit, bicycling, and walking. In fact, according to a 2011 study by Rutgers University and Virginia Tech, Portland has the highest share of bike commuters in the nation.

As mentioned, Portland has also strived to increase the city's walkability. This was done in part by increasing street connectivity, but also by creating mixed-use areas so that multiple types of buildings could be located near one another. The result has been that more places are accessible by more people using more modes of transport.

MID-CHAPTER QUESTIONS

1. Describe two smart growth policies and how they help decrease urban sprawl.

2. Why are smart growth policies beneficial for urban areas?

SOIL DEGRADATION

A key concern as urbanization of areas continues to expand is **soil degradation**. Although soil degradation can include erosion, it is only one facet of soil degradation and reduced soil quality.

Soil quality is not determined by a universal set of measurements. In fact, the use for the soil determines what qualities of the soil need to be monitored. For example, a farmer may be more concerned with soil fertility and the availability of nutrients like nitrogen (N), phosphorus (P), and potassium (K). However, an environmental scientist may be concerned about potential run-off as well as the **leaching** of nutrients and contaminated water into the ground water system. Developers may be concerned more with soil structure and texture and how it will affect buildings and the construction of footers and foundations. Even though these different stakeholders have different interests in the same area, the test parameters are the same.

There are many features of soil that are tested when assessing soil quality, including soil texture, color, and **redox potential**. Such features are generally grouped into three categories: physical, chemical, and biological quality. Each category has a minimum of three to four testable soil quality indicators. Soil scientists use a **minimum data set (MDS)** of parameters revolving around certain soil features. While more parameters can be tested to get more specific results, an MDS is a short list of soil parameters that are able to tell scientists much about the health of a soil sample.

The MDS parameters for testing the physical characteristics of soil are:

- Texture
- Topsoil depth
- Rooting zone depth
- Infiltration (drainage)

Soil texture refers to the ratio of silt, sand, and clay in a soil's makeup. At the most basic level, soil texture is divisible into 12 types of soil, ranging from all sand, all silt, or all clay, to various combinations of these.

Soil types are determined by particle size.

- Clay: < 0.002 mm
- Silt: 0.002 – 0.05 mm
- Sand: 0.05 – 2 mm
- Gravel: 2 – 75 mm

The textural triangle in Figure 10.2 shows these divisions. However, these 12 types only begin to narrow down the variety of soil textures. Depending on the exact percentages and types of sand, silt, and clay, there are countless combinations of soil textures across the world.

SOIL DEGRADATION The decrease of soil quality from alterations in the ecosystem.

LEACHING The action of water and chemicals flowing through the soil into groundwater.

REDOX POTENTIAL The potential of a chemical to add or lose electrons; also known as oxidation-reduction potential.

MINIMUM DATA SET (MDS) The smallest number of parameters that can be tested to create a reasonable assessment of a system.

Soil Textural Triangle

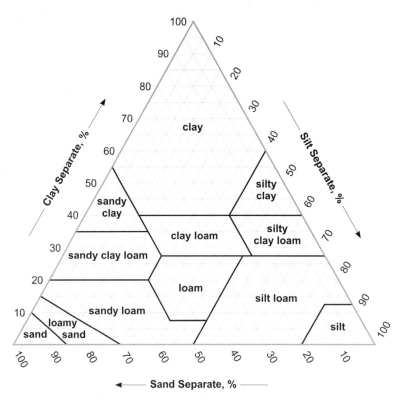

Figure 10.2 USDA Soil Texture Triangle

Topsoil depth measures the surface profile layer thickness. Topsoil contains many nutrients and much of a soil's organic matter, which helps sustain plants. It also generally holds more water and is the layer of soil that erodes if not protected.

Rooting zone depth is a measurement that describes the depth to which roots can grow. This measurement helps scientists determine the location of available nutrients, at what depth water can be often found, and the amount of soil compaction present.

Infiltration (drainage) is a measurement that describes the rate that water can permeate through the soil (generally the topsoil). This measurement allows scientists to determine how much water can flow into a soil over a period time. Infiltration measures the number of inches or millimeters of water that pass through the soil in one hour. These physical measurements help stakeholders establish important soil aspects, including runoff, erosion, water-holding capacity, and possible soil productivity, among other characteristics.

The chemical characteristics of a soil are measures of the **extractable nitrogen (N), phosphorus (P), and potassium (K)**, pH, electrical conductivity, and soil organic matter. Extractable N, P, and K are three of the most important plant nutrients; measuring them helps to indicate soil fertility properties. Soil pH is a measurement of hydrogen (H^+) ion concentration. When H^+ ions are high in concentration, the soil is very acidic. Low concentrations of H^+ ions (or high in OH^-; hydroxide ions) result in the soil being basic. The pH scale ranges from 0 (acidic) to 14 (basic or alkaline); pH 7 is neutral and contains equivalent amounts of hydrogen (H^+) and hydroxide (OH^-) ions.

EXTRACTABLE N, P, AND K The amount of nitrogen, phosphorus, and potassium in a soil that can be used by plants.

Most plants grow well only within a small pH range (generally between 6 and 7 for crops). Some crops can tolerate pH levels outside the "normal" range. Blueberries and cranberries require acidic soil (about <4.5 – 5.5 pH) to grow. Sugar beets and cotton prefer alkaline soils (>7.5 pH).

Electrical conductivity is a method used to measure the salinity of a soil. In general, plants, especially crop plants, cannot tolerate even moderate levels of salt.

Perhaps the most important feature to a soil is its soil organic matter content. Soil organic matter can include plant and animal waste, as well as human biosolids. Organic matter can alter the physical makeup of a soil. For example, organic matter, because of its high surface area, can increase water holding capacity, increase cation exchange capacity (CEC), and decrease runoff. Organic content also adds nutrients like N, P, and K to the soil naturally. It also can provide nutrients beneficial to microorganisms, which aids in plant growth. The chemical characteristics of a soil help stakeholders determine the fertility of the soil and whether or not the soil needs **amendments** added.

The biological characteristic of soil is tested by measuring microbial biomass, **mineralizable N** (nitrogen), and soil respiration. The microbial biomass measure is the amount of microscopic organisms found in the soil; these microbes include beneficial bacteria, fungi, and protozoans that help break down organic matter and release important nutrients into the soil system. For example, *Rhizobium* bacteria break down organic forms of nitrogen and digest them into organic forms such as NH_4^+ and NO_3^-, which plants can use.

Rhizobia are nitrogen-fixing bacteria that convert atmospheric nitrogen to ammonia, which becomes available for plant metabolism. Some of these bacteria form root nodules on plants, especially on legumes; the nodules are where nitrogen-fixing occurs. Farmers use this natural process to their advantage. It is a common practice to alternate soybeans and corn in a field each year. The soybeans provide nitrogen to grow corn the following year. Soy is planted the next growing season to restore soil fertility. The cycle repeats again and again.

Nutrients like nitrogen, whether added to the soil through organic matter or through fertilizers, cannot be used by plants in their unprocessed state. Many of these materials must be processed by bacteria and mineralized before they are used by plants. For this reason, another important measurement is the amount of mineralizable N. This measures the amount of nitrogen available in a soil to be mineralized.

As these microorganisms live and eat, they must be able to breathe, or respire. Soil respiration measures the ability of gases to pass through the soil. It should be understood, though, that this does not mean only oxygen (O_2). Many of the essential bacteria live under **anaerobic** conditions as opposed to **aerobic** conditions. Therefore, soil respiration includes many gases such as O_2, carbon dioxide (CO_2), and even gaseous N_2.

When analyzed, these parameters give soil scientists and other stakeholders insight into the soil quality and health of a soil system. If the soil is monitored over time, it can help land managers and scientists maintain the health of the soil, prevent soil degradation, and create action plans to remediate any soil degradation problems.

Soil degradation can consist of several different factors, including nutrient loss, water compaction, runoff/infiltration problems, pollution, and topsoil loss/erosion. However, because soil systems are so complex, each of these factors affects, and is affected by, every other factor. For example, when there is a loss of nutrients in a soil, plants will not grow, which makes erosion likely, which can reduce topsoil depth.

AMENDMENTS Substances, including fertilizers, $CaCO_3$, and organic matter, added to the soil to improve soil quality. Chelated fertilizers provide plant-usable forms of micronutrient metals, such as iron, copper, zinc, and manganese.

MINERALIZABLE N The amount of available nitrogen that can be converted from organic forms of nitrogen to inorganic forms.

ANAEROBIC Lacking oxygen.

AEROBIC With or having oxygen.

Nutrient losses can occur in a number of different ways. Losses can occur when topsoil erodes away and the key nutrients are lost with the topsoil. Nutrients can also be lost because they are completely used by plants and not replenished. If a farmer continually planted and harvested without fertilizing the field or growing a **cover crop** to replace nutrients in the soil, it would soon lose its fertility and be unable to sustain plant life. When an area is in its natural state, without human activity or intervention, or is managed properly, the soil constantly replenishes its nutrients cyclically, meaning that plants use the nutrients, then die and decay, replenishing the nutrients. In the case of managed soil, these nutrients are added before each planting to foster growth.

Compaction can occur naturally during periods of drought in soils that have a heavy percentage of clay. More often, this happens with soils subjected to lot of traffic. As vehicles, equipment, and livestock continually travel over an area, the soil particles are pushed closer and closer together. If this continues, compaction can stop water from flowing into the soil and can also block plant roots from growing into the soil, regardless of nutrient content. Severe compaction can lead to barren hard soil with limited infiltration, possibly causing increased flooding and runoff.

Runoff and infiltration problems are common in urban areas and can be caused by several factors. It should be noted that while soils can develop runoff and infiltration problems due to compaction, they are not always directly related. Runoff and infiltration problems can occur because of alterations to upland areas and contour changes, construction and pavement, and changes in vegetation. When areas upland have land use alterations, this can affect the rate that water flows through them, which can translate to changes to down-land areas as well.

Consider a soft, sloping hill upland that has soil added to the top of it. The additional soil increases the slope of the hill. As rain hits the top of this steeper hill, its acceleration is increased, similar to a car traveling down a very steep hill compared to a very shallow hill. As this water velocity increases, it picks up more energy and can remove more soil down-land from the hill than before soil was added to the hill. This erosion event can occur when contour changes happen at any given site as well.

COVER CROP A crop, such as winter wheat, used to cover a field during non-growing seasons in order to retain soil and replenish nutrients.

"Pollutants alter the chemical makeup of the soil, including increasing or decreasing the pH, increasing the electric conductivity, or putting toxic chemicals into the soil. All of these effects can kill or inhibit the growth of plants, which can leave the land barren and more susceptible to erosion."

Construction and pavement affect soils the same way. However, instead of picking up more velocity, less water is absorbed into the soil system upland, which results in more water running over a smaller amount of land. Change in vegetation can also affect runoff and infiltration. For example, grasses are generally short plants with broad root patterns that weave into each other, allowing these plants to trap soil and slow the flow of water. Crops like corn, however, are tall plants with root systems that do not branch out as much and remain separate. Thus, corn plants leave soil more susceptible to runoff and can alter the infiltration rate between the plants.

Pollution can come in a variety of forms, including **hydrocarbons**, volatile organic compounds, salts, acids or bases, and even excess nutrients. These pollutants alter the chemical makeup of the soil, including increasing or decreasing the pH, increasing the electric conductivity, or putting toxic chemicals into the soil. All of these effects can kill or inhibit the growth of plants, which can leave the land barren and more susceptible to erosion.

HYDROCARBON A simple compound consisting of only hydrogen and carbon, such as methane or propane.

HYPOXIC A condition in waterways in which the concentration of dissolved oxygen is lower than 5 ppm.

MID-CHAPTER QUESTIONS

1. **What is a minimum data set and why is it important?**

2. **What are some issues that can arise as soil degrades?**

HABITAT LOSS

Another major concern that arises with urbanization is habitat loss. Habitat loss from urbanization can occur both directly and indirectly. Direct losses can occur from events like deforestation, riparian zone losses, and grassland destruction, as well as losses of estuaries. Indirect habitat losses are caused by upland changes that destroy habitats down-grade. For example, indirect losses can be caused by "dead rivers," (rivers that cannot support life or support very little life), **hypoxic** estuaries, and other forms of estuary destruction.

Direct losses of habitat may be the most well-known and best understood effects of an increase in urban development. As more people move into a region, more land is needed to build housing. Often, this land is found in wooded tracts, grasslands, or farmlands. This land must be cleared of plants, trees, and root systems. Infrastructure, such as water mains, sewer mains, and storm water mains, must be laid to handle the supply and discharge of this new construction. These land-use changes can completely alter a landscape.

However, the indirect loss of habitat, while often overlooked, cannot be ignored. Development not only affects the immediate area, but it also can have direct effects on areas down-grade of the site. As was described in Chapter 2, when there are no or little guidelines in effect, areas like the Cuyahoga River and parts of Lake Erie were labeled "dead" because of the poor water quality caused by point source pollution. While this type of pollution is heavily monitored and regulated, non-point source pollution is nearly untraceable. This type of pollution can lead to hypoxic estuaries and general degradation of estuaries, which can result in fish kills and shellfish bed destruction.

Habitat loss, whether from direct or indirect causes, has broad-reaching effects, including increased erosion, loss of natural pollution filtration, and decreased storm surge buffering, not to mention the loss in biodiversity. Erosion, which is discussed in greater detail in the next section, is a great threat. This loss of soil can leave land barren and pollute rivers and other waterways when the eroded soil in the water blocks sunlight or carries pollutants with it.

As habitat is lost, the land's ability to naturally filter pollution is lost as well. Estuaries and forested areas act like the kidneys or the liver in the human body, filtering out pollutants through both microbiological digestion as well as through plant absorption. As these organisms absorb or break down these pollutants—whether heavy metals, chlorinated solvents, or excess nutrients—they purify the water before it reaches rivers or streams. However, when these areas are lost or destroyed, these pollutants are able to run directly into neighboring waterways.

Decreased storm surge buffering is also a very important effect of habitat loss. Estuaries and coastal woodlands act as windbreakers and coastal sponges during major storms. As sea levels rise from storm surges, estuaries are able to absorb the extra water and disperse it over a large area. However, if this area is converted or diminished, there is less area for the water to disperse into. This loss of natural buffers near the coast increases inland flooding and storm surge damage farther away from the coast. Forested areas perform a similar task when high winds are present, as they act as a wind break for large open land. When these areas are destroyed or clear cut, it leaves open space for wind to blow; when houses are built in place of these forested areas, they take the brunt of the wind. However, unlike trees that can dissipate the wind and bend with it, houses are often damaged by wind and create wind tunnels that force the wind between structures.

When habitat is lost there can be a loss of biodiversity. This can be in the form of geographical extinction or in the form of diminished genetic diversity. While biodiversity is discussed in more detail in Chapter 2, it is important to understand how land-use and habitat loss affect it. When habitat is lost it may completely wipe out a species from an area, which can impact the entire food web, or it can put a strain on other species. Those species that have large home ranges are impacted especially hard. For example, a male grizzly bear has a home range that averages between 200 and 500 sq mi. But when areas of their habitat are lost, these bears must compress into a smaller areas. This increases competition for food or forces the bears into contact with urban settings.

MID-CHAPTER QUESTIONS

1. **What is hypoxia and why is it important?**

2. **Describe two effects of habitat loss.**

EROSION

One of the largest concerns with land use from an environmental perspective is erosion. Erosion, as mentioned in the case study at the beginning of this chapter, is the loss of soil (not just dirt) from a region. It is important to understand the difference between soil and dirt. Dirt itself consists of the soil particles sand, silt, and clay. Informally, dirt can also be particles of biological origin, such as sloughed off skin cells and pet dander (large components of household dust). These particles only make up the soil texture and are a small component of the soil structure. Soil, on the other hand, consists of the dirt and additional organic material, nutrients, and beneficial microbiotic organisms. These components determine the quality of the soil and sustain life. As erosion occurs, all of these components are lost, which can ultimately leave the affected region devoid of life.

The rate of erosion can actually be calculated using a complex formula knows as the Revised Universal Soil Loss Equation, or **RUSLE** (pronounced Russell).

It is a function of the factors of:

- Soil Erodibility (or how easily a soil can erode (K))
- Rainfall (R)
- Vegetation (V)
- Length and Slope of Topography (LS)
- Conservation Practices (P)

The RUSLE equation is:

$$SE\ (A) = f\ [K \times R \times V \times LS \times P]$$

Avg Annual Soil Loss (A) = Soil Erodibility × Rainfall × Vegetation × Topography × Conservation Practices

All the factors, except conservation practices (P), can be quantified. The P variable can be subjective and open to interpretation. However, there is a P rating system based on conservation practice activities to help quantify the variable. Some of the variables can change from year to year, such as rainfall and vegetation. As a result, RUSLE is a guideline and tool, rather than an actual complete analysis, when used for soil conservation and land-use management.

Erosion is divided into two different categories: **aeolian** and **alluvial**. Aeolian erosion, also known as wind erosion, occurs when wind moves dry particles away from their original location. The Dust Bowl is a prime example of extreme aeolian erosion, as are sandstorms that occur in the desert regions. These wind storms move massive amounts of soil as they blow through an area. In some cases, wind can restructure the topography of the land.

Aeolian erosion does not only occur during major wind storms. As soil particles dry, they can be susceptible to aeolian erosion. As the particles dry they are not held together through water adhesion, making them easier to move with even low levels of wind. In fact, one common soil order, **mollisol,** is made up of wind-deposited soils. Mollisols are very granular in nature, which is easier for the wind to carry. Found predominately in the Midwest in wide open plains, this soil type is often moved by the wind. Mollisols are naturally fertile and are beneficial to agriculture. However, when the soil is plowed or disturbed, this type of soil can move downwind in high volume.

Alluvial erosion is the result of water. Alluvial erosion occurs when rainwater washes away particles, river water erodes the bank, or a hurricane storm surge erodes beachfront or estuary soils. There are four types of erosion associated with water erosion: raindrop, sheet, rill, and gully.

Raindrop erosion, as the name suggests, occurs when water droplets hit the soil and particles are dislodged from the soil structure and flow with water across the soil. This type of erosion can be noticed if an object is left outside on the ground in the rain. After the rainstorm, the parts of the object in contact with the soil will have a slight layer of dirt particles that have splashed up on it. The eroded dirt observed in such a demonstration may be minute, but precipitation in sufficient quantity can cause substantial raindrop erosion to occur.

Sheet erosion occurs when enough water has been absorbed by the soil that an entire layer of soil moves at once. This type of erosion occurs most frequently in areas where there is a significant grade. An extreme example occurs during very rainy periods in mountainous areas. During these times, mudslides can occasionally occur when the ground becomes so saturated with water that the soil's cohesion forces cannot hold together. Much like an avalanche, the mud slides down the hill. The force of this form of sheet erosion is enough to move a house off its foundation. Sheet erosion is not limited to this extreme, though, and it can also occur on barren hillsides or small inclines on fill dirt at construction sites.

More common than sheet erosion is rill erosion. Rill erosion occurs when rainwater runoff creates small, stream-like channels in the soil. These channels are formed when water moves across the surface of barren soil, cutting a pathway through particles that are looser than others. These pathways continue downhill until they reach a low-lying spot or level ground and are deposited.

If the flow of water is great enough rill erosion may become gully erosion. This type of alluvial erosion occurs when deep channels are formed in the soil. Some gullies can grow big enough to become dangerous to vehicles or equipment.

Soil texture and soil moisture also come into play when dealing with erosion. Different soil particles erode more easily than others. The one caveat to this is soil moisture. As particle size goes, sand is the largest, followed by silt and then clay. Therefore, it could be assumed that clay erodes more easily than silt or sand. However, this assumption is only half correct. Clay does erode faster than either—if the soil is dry. Clay, unlike silt or sand, has a unique structure that when damp, adheres tightly to other clay particles and holds water very well. These particles remain tightly adhered to each other until the soil is very dry. Conversely, silt particles hold less water and sand particles are very porous, holding very little water. Because of this dynamic, sand and silt particles are more affected by alluvial erosion than clay.

As these particles travel downwind or downstream, various particles fall out at different times as the velocity slows. Sand particles (which are the largest of the soil particles) settle out sooner than silt particles. This phenomenon is noticeable at the mouths of large rivers and perhaps no more evident than at the mouth of the Mississippi River. As the Mississippi flows into Gulf of Mexico, a large delta fan forms. This fan is primarily silt, as the sand particles that eroded downriver fall out of solution as the water slows away from the head waters. While delta fans bring benefits such as fertile river beds for fish nurseries and shellfish beds, there are also, as with erosion in general, many problems.

Erosion in the worst case forms like the Dust Bowl, and large sheet erosion can cause health issues and injuries to people. However, erosion has a wide array of ecological issues that may be missed by the lay person. Problems with erosion can involve loss of plant nutrients; loss of topsoil; silting up of streams, rivers, and other waterways; increased **turbidity**; and hypoxic water conditions.

The loss of plant nutrients occurs when organic material and nutrients bound in fertile topsoil erode away with the topsoil. When these nutrients are lost, it can stress

TURBIDITY Cloudiness or haziness of water.

or limit the plants that can grow in that area. This decrease in plant coverage and size only compounds the issue of erosion, since it means a shrinkage of the root system, which holds together the soil and absorbs and slows water as it flows across the soil.

If plant growth is hampered long enough, topsoil loss may follow. Soils are made up of multiple layers, ranging from the uppermost surface layer, which may be an O layer (organic layer made up of leaf litter, compost, or manure) or an A layer (first true soil layer). The topsoil is generally highly fertile and fairly permeable to water. This means that it can grow plants and absorbs water well. When this layer is lost, land can become barren and water runoff increases.

Because erosion is the movement of plant soils from one area to another, it is important to understand that not only is the loss of soil an issue, but also the deposition of soil can be a problem. When aeolian erosion occurs, eroded soil can enter waterways or other land areas. However, alluvial erosion almost always results in the deposition of soil particles in some form of waterway. In some cases, waterways can become so full of sediment that they begin to fill, or silt up. Not only does this change the entire ecosystem, as it may bury plants and push fish and other animals to deeper waters, but it can also affect the way storm water runoff is handled, which may lead to increased flooding.

Even if waterways do not fill with eroded soil, there are still environmental impacts caused by erosion. Increased turbidity, for example, can prevent sunlight from penetrating to the waterway's bottom. Turbidity can be caused by abundance of algae in the waterway or because of sediments that are trapped in suspension. If a waterway is too turbid, plant life is not able to grow on the water's bottom. This lack of plant life causes a twofold problem. First, a lack of abundant plant life can stress fish and other organisms that feed on the plants, which can decrease biodiversity. A lack of plant life can also cause hypoxic conditions in the water, as the plant life is responsible for creating the dissolved oxygen in the water.

Hypoxia is a decreased abundance of dissolved oxygen (DO) in the water. Like animals on land, fish need oxygen to survive. A concentration of DO above 5 parts per million (ppm) is sufficient for most fish. However, in hypoxic waters, DO can drop to near zero ppm, or **anoxic** conditions. Hypoxia can cause fish kills leaving segments of waterways dead. Erosion can actually cause hypoxia in water both directly and indirectly. Erosion increases turbidity, which can kill plant life that generates DO in the water. Erosion can also fill the waterway, making it shallower. Shallow water heats up faster than deeper water and stays warmer longer. High water temperatures cause DO to be released into the atmosphere, thus diminishing the concentration of oxygen in solution. However, erosion can cause hypoxia indirectly as well. Sometimes as soil particles flow into waterways, they carry pollutants. Some pollutants bind readily with the oxygen in water, reducing the DO available to aquatic life.

Because of concern about the harmful effects of erosion, people often go to great lengths to minimize the loss of soil particles. Erosion-abatement practices vary depending on the land use, but all such techniques represent attempts at easing the burden of soil loss caused by human activity.

Erosion from agriculture can be massive, because this soil is tilled and replanted several times each year. As crops are harvested and the soil is tilled,

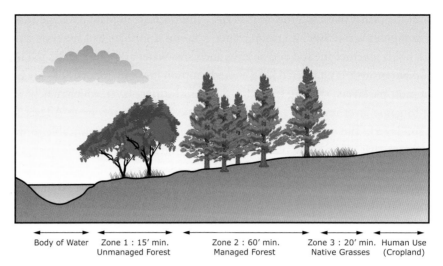

Body of Water | Zone 1 : 15' min.
Unmanaged Forest | Zone 2 : 60' min.
Managed Forest | Zone 3 : 20' min.
Native Grasses | Human Use
(Cropland)

Figure 10.3 Riparian buffer zones

the soil is loosened, and roots and remaining plant materials are worked under the surface of the soil. In order to combat the resulting potential soil loss, some farmers have turned to minimal-till or no-till operations. This style of farming greatly reduces the amount of loose soil and keeps unused parts of plants in place, holding the soil in place. On top of this practice, many farmers also plant a cover crop that helps to anchor the soil while replacing nutrients used in growing the previous cash crop.

Farms found in areas with landscape contours often employ specialized practices to limit erosion. As mentioned in the case study at the beginning of the chapter, planting crops along the contours of the land, rather than in straight lines, slows water as it moves downhill. Terracing involves creating different levels of field up a hillside in step-like fashion. This practice causes water to catch and slow at each step before it moves down the hill. Strip cropping is also an effective method in which farmers may plant a large strip of one crop, such as corn, followed by another strip of a different crop, such as hay. This alternation of crops slows water because the root systems are different and trap water instead of having continuous channels.

Construction sites employ erosion control methods as well. Most notable are sediment fences. These porous fences outline construction sites that have been cleared and are being built upon. These fences are porous enough to allow water to flow through them but hold the sediment back inside the construction zones. Another useful method of limiting erosion is storm drain bags. These bags, set just underneath the grate of storm drains, catch sediment but are porous enough to allow water to pass through them.

Riparian buffer zones are also important tools used in agricultural, construction, and urban settings. These areas are narrow strips of undisturbed forested areas that run parallel to waterways. Much like a cover crop, riparian zones stop sediment and slow water as it passes into the waterway.

RIPARIAN BUFFER ZONES A strip of undisturbed forest land running parallel to the shoreline of a waterway, designed to protect the waterway from the land's use.

MID-CHAPTER QUESTIONS

1. Describe the two types of erosion.

2. What effects can erosion have on waterways?

3. What are some ways that erosion can be prevented?

CONSERVATION

As discussed earlier, urban sprawl ultimately converts one form of land use to another. The conversion of land use can have crippling effects on ecosystems and species, and in some cases involves the loss of food production capabilities for human beings. These effects have led planners and policymakers to create smart growth policies that help curb urban sprawl. While minimizing urban sprawl is an important goal of these strategies, a related goal of smart growth is to protect and conserve land as it is currently used. This conservation initiative serves as a way to prevent land losses and to maintain and protect viable ecosystems

The US Department of Agriculture (USDA) lists nine different types of types of land, three of which (barren land, tundra, and perennial snow) will be omitted here because there is little interaction between these types of land and urban areas.

The other types of land according to the USDA are:

- Urban areas
- Agricultural land/crop land—agricultural land includes all food production land classes; crop land is the next level down and does not include orchards, groves, vineyards, nurseries and horticultural zones
- Rangeland
- Forest land
- Water, which includes oceans, lakes, rivers, streams, and estuaries
- Wetlands, both forested and non-forested

The key to land use conservation is how urban areas interact with these types of land.

There has been much discussion about the loss of farmland, or crop land, due to urban sprawl. According the American Farmland Trust, an acre of farm land is lost every minute. If this loss was to continue at this pace, conventional farming would eventually cease to exist. Besides the fact that farmland consists of large areas of open land that require no clearing to be developed, there is another reason why farmland is an attractive purchase for developers. Row-crop land, such and corn and soybean fields, tends to be flat and well drained, which means that water flows well through it. This is beneficial for developers because it opens many options for infrastructure and home design. Well-drained soils are essential for septic systems, while poorly drained soils must either be tied into a sewer system or have a large above-ground septic mound. Both options are expensive to install, and while tying into the sewer system is more aesthetically pleasing to a homeowner, it comes with a monthly cost. Well-drained soils also are beneficial for the construction of basements because water does not stay in the soil long and therefore will not seep through basement walls. These factors, coupled with the ease of development and often low price makes crop land especially desirable for new construction.

There is a growing push to protect crop lands from development because of the importance of food safety. Groups like the American Farmland Trust work with farmers, consumers, and policymakers, advocating and educating for crop land conservation. Apart from these types of advocacy organizations, both federal and state government agencies work together to preserve farmland. By creating subsidies

and tax advantages for farmers, these agencies help make farming more profitable for the farmer and lessen the financial incentives to sell out to developers. Furthermore, governmental agencies have or are developing **easements** to protect farmlands. These easements act as a financial pledge from the government (in most cases local or county government) to the farmer that the land will remain farmland. The easement acts like municipal wildlife refuge, while still remaining a working private farm. Steps like this work to ensure that cropland is not lost to urban sprawl. Millions of acres of farm cropland have been taken out of production by the federal government, not the result of sprawl. The US federal government has the authority to convert 25 percent of all farmland back to a natural state. The Conservation Reserve Program (CRP) has the authority to convert 32 million acres of farmland and unlimited acreage under the Conservation Reserve Enhancement Program (CREP).

Rangeland is very similar to cropland, with the exception that it does not depend on having a commodity grown and raised. Rangeland consists of large tracts of mostly flat land used to raise a variety of livestock, such as cows and sheep. This land, like cropland, is appealing to developers because of the openness, relatively flat contour, and large expanses that can be purchased (real estate in large parcels is often much cheaper than in small parcels). However, unlike cropland, rangeland soil does not have to be well-drained, as it generally supports only grasses and small herbaceous plants. This feature makes rangeland a less profitable opportunity for development than cropland, but it is still sought after by some developers.

Rangeland conservation is a priority, as it affects food security as well. Many private and public organizations are involved in conserving rangeland. Easements are a tool used to protect rangeland from destructive uses.

Forested areas are another prime land type for developers. Although there is more work involved with clearing the land of trees and removing stumps, the fact is that there are large open tracts of this type of land available. Forested areas are often cheaper than cropland or range land in a similar location because there is no revenue-making ability outside of sale (unless the land is timbered occasionally). However, while there may not be a large monetary value for forested land, it has several important purposes.

Forested areas are prime habitat for an array of animals. Birds, mammals, reptiles, amphibians, and insects all use forested areas for food and shelter. In some cases, the presence of endangered or threatened animals can stop the development of these tracts of lands. For example, the spotted owl has on several occasions stopped even logging of privately owned lands in Washington State. Often, though, this is not the case. As areas are clear-cut the native animals are forced out into neighboring tracts of forest, or into urban areas. This puts stress on the animal populations, as competition increases for food and space.

Forested areas also are responsible for the production of a large amount of O_2 and the sequestering of carbon from the atmosphere. Vegetation, especially trees and small shrubs, requires CO_2 for respiration and energy production. As trees intake CO_2 and sunlight,

they form glucose for themselves and release O_2 back into the atmosphere. Forested areas balance out the respiration of animals as well as the sum of byproducts associated with the burning of fossil fuels.

Well-managed forested areas provide wood for lumber and heating as well as pulp for paper products. As these areas are clear-cut this renewable resource is lost to the area, which can cause wood-based products to become more costly to produce, leading to price increases. Forests are also valued as recreation spots for camping, hunting, and other sporting activities. Forested areas are of keen interest to several groups, both private and public.

Groups like the Arbor Day Foundation increase awareness and educate the public about the importance of forested areas. They also plant and donate trees to be planted all around the country. The Arbor Day Foundation also works with urban areas to plant and create green places in cities, awarding some with the designation of "Tree City." Private citizens also buy land to prevent development and to reforest. Ted Turner, owner of Turner Broadcasting System and Time Warner, owns over two million acres of land. While most of this land is used as open ranchland and is home to over 50,000 head of bison, some of the land is replanted and reforested to replenish lost habitats. Government agencies both local and federal also purchase and protect forested areas. In some cases, these agencies purchase land for use as parks, managed forestry areas, and wildlife refuges to protect these lands from development. And agencies like the forestry service and the EPA monitor and sometimes block development of privately owned land when engendered or threatened species are found.

Water-use areas are generally not developed for housing. However, there are examples of water-use areas being utilized. In San Leandro, CA, salt marshes were filled in to create building sites. The shores of waterways are much sought after because of the waterfront amenities, which makes these areas very popular and more valuable to developers than agricultural/crop land or rangeland. While the water may not be lost to development, the water ecosystem can be disturbed or greatly affected. Consider the effects that urban areas had on the Cuyahoga River outlined in the case study at the beginning of Chapter 2. Pre-existing urban centers and newly developed waterfront properties can pollute and stress the animals of water ecosystems. There may be increased fishing in areas that have been developed, increased waterway traffic in the form of boating and jet skiing, runoff pollutants from residential and industrial sites, as well as sediment runoff due to erosion.

Because of the importance of water-use areas as nurseries for fish and animals, food supplies, human enjoyment, and natural filtration and buffering capacities that water-use areas have, many groups—both private and public—work together to protect and restore these habitat areas. Groups like Ducks Unlimited, Great Lakes Protection Fund, and American Rivers work to protect these areas through advocacy as well as by purchasing land and restoring habitats and native species. Government agencies like the EPA and state natural resources agencies also work to protect waterway habitats.

Wetland use areas, as classified by the USDA, include forested and non-forested areas. These areas, which are primarily swamp and bog lands, are not developed for the most part because of the highly saturated soils and non-stable topography. However, they can be affected by urban sprawl and are often overlooked during planning. These areas, which generally have little monetary or aesthetic value, serve a vital ecological role. Wetlands act as filters for the surrounding urban and agricultural land; because of their saturated condition and high populations of decomposers they are able to absorb and break down much of the runoff from these areas. However, as more land is paved and formerly forested land is developed, runoff and pollution increase, which can overburden the natural decomposition of these wetlands. For conservation purposes, wetlands are often associated with water use areas, though, and many of the same organizations and agencies that protect water use areas also work to protect wetlands.

MID-CHAPTER QUESTIONS

1. How does the USDA classify types of land by the way it is used?

2. What are two reasons that croplands are so valued for development?

DISPOSAL OF HAZARDOUS WASTE AND SOLID WASTE

Another problem associated with large urban areas is the volume of waste generated by large population centers. This waste includes everyday garbage; human solid waste; and hazardous materials, which may include household hazardous materials, such as paints, cleaners, and solvents, or industrial hazardous wastes that may include powerful acidic and basic chemicals, industrial cleaners, and other chemicals. Industrial hazardous waste also includes nuclear waste. As discussed earlier, the amount of wastes that are generated by urban areas can be astounding. The megacity Manila generates nearly 6,700 tons of trash a day. The issue that planners and citizens alike have to deal with is what to do with the waste.

Waste management methods employed by major cities include intensive recycling for household wastes and hazardous wastes, municipal composting and mulching programs, transportation of wastes to landfills away from the urban center, and in the case of human solid waste field application, as amendments to the soil.

Household recycling programs have now been adopted by many municipalities across the US. But nowhere are they more important than large urban areas that generate tons of garbage daily. The use of these recycling programs not only reduces the volume of trash and solid wastes that are thrown away, but also can save cities

millions of dollars in exportation fees. For example, New York City only recycled an estimated 7 percent to 14 percent of its waste prior to 2001. Exportation fees for removal of the waste headed for landfills are estimated to reach $1 billion annually. Meanwhile, waste prevention programs could save an estimated $100 million dollars annually. Major cities such as Los Angeles have seen the possibilities of saving money through recycling. Compared to New York's meager recycling rate, Los Angeles recycles an estimated 46 percent of waste and city managers hope to increase this to 70 percent.

Hazardous waste can also be recycled. Materials such as heavy metals and solvents are often recycled through licensed hazardous waste recycling centers,

"Waste management methods employed by major cities include intensive recycling for household wastes and hazardous wastes, municipal composting and mulching programs, transportation of wastes to landfills away from the urban center, and in the case of human solid waste field application, as amendments to the soil."

such as CycleSolv, LLC, a company based in Wilmington, DE. The drive to recycle hazardous wastes, as opposed to more traditional methods of incineration or burying, stems from the Resource Conservation and Recovery Act (RCRA) passed by Congress in 1976 and revised in 1986. RCRA's main objective is "to promote the protection of health and the environment and to conserve valuable material and energy resources." Through this law, nearly two million tons of hazardous materials are recycled annually.

Municipal composting and mulching programs also help reduce the amount of waste that enters landfills. In fact, an estimated 25 percent of landfill waste is lawn and kitchen waste, which includes leaves, grass clippings, and vegetable peelings. These wastes, when properly composted, can be turned into beneficial soil amendments in just a few months. However, when placed in landfills, the decomposition rates are much slower. The same materials may take years to break down. San Francisco has implemented both recycling and composting programs. As of 2002, San Francisco recycled or composted 63 percent of all city wastes.

Many urban areas do not have landfills inside their urban setting. If the facilities are available, they are usually not large enough to support the volume of waste that is generated daily. Consequently, many urban areas send their waste to landfills outside the area. As discussed above, this process can be quite expensive.

The great volume of human waste is also a problem in urban areas. Because of its composition, it must be handled carefully to avoid the spread of disease. But it can also be a highly nutrient-rich soil amendment that is often applied to fields for agricultural or restoration uses. This waste may be sprayed on, tilled in, or trenched into the soil to provide beneficial nutrients like nitrogen.

The overlaying problem is that while these policies are necessary to remove the waste from these urban areas safely and efficiently, people do not want recycling centers or landfills near their residences. This is often called the "not in my backyard" syndrome, or NIMBY. While this is an understandable position to have, the problem remains. All too often, the problem is passed along until it reaches an area where people are impoverished or otherwise have no political influence. This has led the EPA, along with state agencies, to work together to provide education for groups affected by dump waste sites. This includes education and hearings to give all stakeholders a voice in these matters. In some cases they step in to protect people under the National Environmental Policy Act or under the Civil Rights Act.

An innovative practice in solid waste disposal is converting landfills into other land uses after they have been closed. One example of this is Fresh Kill Park in Staten Island, New York. The Fresh Kill landfill was the largest landfill in the world, at over 2,200 acres; it handled a majority of the daily household waste from New York City. After receiving more than 28,000 tons of waste daily for over 50 years, the landfill was closed. However, city planners did not simply decommission the site. They capped and repurposed the landfill as a park that includes wetlands, creeks, and many other amenities.

MID-CHAPTER QUESTIONS

1. Describe the benefit that a recycling program can have in an urban area.

2. What is NIMBY and how can this affect waste disposal?

INDUSTRIAL PROCESSES

As urban areas increase in size and population, industrial and agricultural trades are forced to keep pace. These groups have needed to streamline production, while increasing production and decreasing energy and pollution output. This is not always an easy task considering that, especially in the case of agriculture, available land decreases as urban areas increase. Historically these industries were able to adapt to provide the necessary goods, including increasing the use of fertilizers and pesticides, clear-cutting land, and dumping excess waste. However, in today's world of environmental awareness and green sustainable living, people may not approve of these practices, and in some cases, are illegal. This mindset has led many industry and agricultural leaders to employ sustainable and more responsible business practices to meet the changing world.

There is a growing trend in crop farming and ranching to become more sustainable. As mentioned earlier, farmers have adopted several practices to limit soil erosion, including no-till farming, contour farming, and planting cover crops. However, responsible farming does not stop at erosion control. There are many methods that farmers employ to become more sustainable, including several different **best management practices** (BMPs).

Responsible Ranching and Farming

There are two main types of BMPs farmers generally employ: those that manage water quality and those that manage nutrients; in some cases the two types overlap. Water quality BMPs are practices that help keep water clean and pollution-free. These practices can include the erosion control techniques described earlier, and also pest management, crop rotation, and nutrient management.

Pests, a category that includes insects, parasites, and fungi, are often controlled with the use of chemical sprays and pesticides. However, **integrated pest management** (IPM) has begun to take a foothold in the agricultural industries. Integrated pest management is a method of managing pests while reducing total volume of pesticides used. This is done using a multilateral process.

Action thresholds must be set prior to responding to a threat. Economic pest population threshold levels are set to determine when the pest threat can cause financial losses; the threshold must be met before a control method is enacted. The presence of one or two pest organisms found in an acre of crop may not warrant an application of pesticide. However, the presence of 100 pest organisms in an acre of crop may warrant action. Economic threshold levels may be an average of few insects per leaf or less. Economic threshold levels are specific to pest species and crops.

Pests must be properly identified and monitored. In some cases, pests and weeds may exist naturally with certain crops and do little to no harm to crop production. In some cases, one organism that is not a pest may look similar to a real threat. Proper identification ensures that pesticides are not being used on organisms that are not harming a crop. Pest prevention methods including crop rotation, planting pest-resistant varieties of crops, and planting pest-free root stocks can prevent or minimize the infestation of pest organisms. Control methods should only be considered after these steps are taken. Control should begin with the most harmless and pest-specific control methods available. This may include pheromone management to disrupt mating, trapping, or mechanical control including weeding, and spraying. Only as a last resort should producers use the broadcast spraying of a non-specific, broad-spectrum pesticide.

IPM has been found to be very effective as well as cost-efficient. For example, New Hampshire apple growers saved $450,000 in 1999 on spraying application

INTEGRATED PEST MANAGEMENT (IMP) An agricultural method aimed at reducing the total volume of pesticides that are sprayed.

ACTION THRESHOLD A level of pest population that must be present before a control method is enacted.

As end users move away from the **IPM** foundation, they will experience...

Pesticides

Increasing...
• **Costs**
• **Environmental impacts**

Other Tools
Cultural controls (grazing, crop rotations, tillage, cultivation, reseeding, etc.); mechanical controls (prescribed fire, mowing/clipping. etc.); genetics and host plant resistance; pheromones; sterile-male techniques.

Decreasing...
• **Sustainability**
• **Species diversity**

Biological Control
The use of natural enemies, such as parasites, predators and naturally occuring pathogens, to reduce the competitive advantage of exotic invasive weed and insect pests, nematodes and plant pathogens.

Figure 10.4 Integrated pest management

using IPM. Furthermore, Missouri greenhouse tomato growers noted a 30 percent increase in production using IPM. It is estimated that the introduction of IPM across the country has prevented over two million pounds of excess pesticide use in the US.

Crop rotation is another important method to improve soil quality. Crop rotation involves planting different crops on the same fields and alternating each year. This practice usually involves the rotation of two to three crops. For example, one year a crop of corn may be planted, the following year it may be soybeans, and in the third year the crop is oats. This order repeats over and over again. Each plant uses and produces different nutrients while it grows. As crops are rotated, the nutrients that the previous plant produced and stored in the soil are used by the next plant, which in turn produces or stores different nutrients in the soil used by the third crop. This cycling of nutrients requires less field application of nutrients, reducing the potential for runoff reaching nearby waterways and saving money in the process.

Nutrient BMPs are distinct from water BMPs, even though they can greatly affect water quality. As with IPM, there are several steps to ensure that the right amount of nutrients is applied to the soil. The first and perhaps most important step is soil testing. Testing provides famers and managers a starting point to assess their direction for nutrient management. Following the recommendations of the test can help determine what type of nutrient is needed, as well which specific fertilizer to use. For example, ammonium NH_4^+ and nitrate NO_3^- based fertilizers both provide nitrogen to the soil, but they react differently in the soil and have different runoff properties. Proper application methods ensure that as much of the nutrients are bound in the soil as possible. This can come in the form of tilling, disking, or in the case of anhydrous ammonium (a gas form of fertilizer), injecting it below the surface of the soil. The use of animal manure is also suggested because, when applied properly, it does not runoff as easily as some of the other forms of nutrients. Finally, controlling erosion and water usage also help keep nutrients in the soil.

Responsible farming practices are interconnected. Proper nutrient management prevents nutrients from flowing into water sources. Plant coverage decreases erosion, keeping nutrients in the soil. This means that fewer nutrients are needed to fertilize crops and there is less runoff, preventing pollution. Meanwhile, stronger, healthier plants need less pesticide control, which also helps keep excess pesticides out of the water.

Livestock ranchers can also employ BMPs to reduce their impact on the environment. For example, installing stock fences near water boundaries can keep livestock out of waterways. This prevents bank erosion and keeps animal wastes out of the water supply. Ranchers also collect and compost animal waste for crop fertilization, reducing the need for chemical-based fertilizers. Livestock farmers can also use methane digesters to break down excess wastes. These prevent methane from escaping into the atmosphere while also producing heat and electricity. These practices, while only a few examples, help keep excess nutrients and gases from polluting water and air while also improving ranch land health.

Industrial Example: Brazil and Beef

While these BMPs are used often in developed countries, developing countries and countries with less stringent environmental laws are less likely to employ these methods. An example of irresponsible agricultural land management can be seen in the Brazilian beef industry. Brazil is the second largest beef producer in the world, with nearly 8.6 million tons of beef raised in 2006 alone; nearly one-quarter of this beef was exported. In the past decade, demand for Brazilian beef has grown seven-fold. As this demand has grown so has the need for pasture land. However, large portions of Brazil are covered by the Amazon Rainforest. In order to fill the demand, large tracts of land have been cleared. By some estimates, 1.9 million hectares of rainforest were lost annually from 1986 to 2005, an estimated 60 percent to 75 percent of which has been used for pastureland. The loss of this forested land has far-reaching repercussions. Not only is there a loss of habitat and possible biodiversity at the local level, but also a loss of oxygen creation and carbon storage. By some estimates, the Amazon Rainforest is responsible for nearly 20 percent of the world's oxygen and is able to absorb up to six tons of carbon per hectare each year. This rapid deforestation and its ensuing effects cause many international environmental groups such as Greenpeace and the Rainforest Action Network to express concern. In response, the Brazilian government continues to shut down illegal ranch operators while also putting pressure on purchasers of beef that comes from protected areas.

Global rainforest losses are also caused by agricultural and timber harvesting activities. Some of these activities are illegal or do not comply with local, national, or international regulations. Illegal harvesting of exotic woods in the rainforests is rampant. Limited financial and enforcement resources in the rainforest nations cannot keep pace with the illegal activities.

BUSINESSES GOING GREEN: BRAZIL AND ITS BEEF

Brazil's growing beef industry has recently come under fire because of the deforestation of the Amazon. In 2009 Greenpeace released a report titled "Slaughtering the Amazon," naming several major cattle farming companies and their role in the illegal destruction of the rain forest. Since then, four of the biggest cattle producers in Brazil signed contracts agreeing to protect the Amazon and the rainforest. Among these was JBS-Friboi, the world's largest producer of beef. JBS-Friboi has plants in Brazil, Argentina, the United States, and Australia.

JBS-Friboi has implemented several important environmental policies to increase its sustainability and to protect the rainforest. Among its sustainable policies, the company has implemented modern effluent treatment systems to control waste and manure runoff. It also works to increase recycling and the use of energy-efficient equipment to minimize greenhouse gas emissions.

Perhaps more important are the company's steps to decrease its impact on the rainforest. One policy includes several reforestation projects involving new tree plantings. This initiative is coupled with the recognition and protection of areas deemed Areas of Permanent Preservation, or APPs. These APPs are habitats protected from deforestation, much like wildlife refuges or protected forested areas in the United States. Another practice that JBS-Friboi employs to protect the rainforest is geo-referencing and satellite monitoring of its cattle ranches. This monitoring ensures that no ranchland encroaches on the rainforest.

Efforts like these have not only protected the natural resources surrounding JBS-Friboi's ranches, but have also led to cost reductions, translating into improved financial results for the company.

Industrial Example: Soybean Importation into China

As food demands grow, there is an increased need for nutrients and supplies. In some cases, the demand outweighs the ability of a country to produce enough food and products must be imported. Such is the case with China. For centuries China was the leading producer of soybeans. The plant itself was and still is revered for its ability to fix nitrogen to the soil, thus improving its fertility. However, soybeans are used for both human consumption and animal feed, and are an important ingredient in a number of industrial products, including paint, fabrics, and plastics. Over the last two decades, population growth in China has outpaced its ability to produce enough soybeans. This is primarily due to an expanded demand for meat (especially pork, which comprises nearly 75 percent of China's overall meat production), a limited water supply, and the fact that an important staple of pig feed is the soybean. Soybeans, high in protein, are essential to building muscle tissue on livestock. Because of an increased demand for pork both domestically and abroad (China produces about half of the world's pork), China has become the world's largest importer of soybeans, at nearly 60 percent of the global demand, or 57 million metric tons. This demand is not expected to decrease anytime soon. By 2014, China is expected to increase their importation to nearly 67 million metric tons. Previously, the US was the largest exporter of soybeans, but the continent of South America eclipsed the US in 2003. This shift happened for two reasons. First, the US began growing more corn as the ethanol industry grew while soybean production decreased. Second, China began looking for emerging markets that had large areas of land that could be cultivated. Brazil was an especially viable option for this growth.

Between the years of 1996 and 2002, Brazil's production of soybeans increased nearly three-fold, while at the same time US production decreased. In fact, Brazil is second only to the US in soybean production, followed closely by fellow South American nation Argentina. Brazil is looking to expand its soybean production to meet China's growing need. In April 2011, China agreed to invest $7 billion in Brazil to increase soybean production. However, with this increased production comes the need for more agricultural land that may ultimately come from the Amazon Rainforest.

MID-CHAPTER QUESTIONS

1. Describe three best practices for the management of croplands or ranchlands.

2. How has the Brazilian beef industry affected rainforests in that country?

3. Describe the effects of increased demand for Chinese-raised pork.

ENVIRONMENTAL MISCONCEPTIONS: THE FAMILY FARM

By and large, the family farm as conceived in the popular imagination is disappearing. Only 30 percent of the 2.1 million farms in the US will pass on to the next generation, and of these farms less than 10 percent will pass to the generation after that. While one reason for this decline in family farms is the lack of desire on the part of children to follow in their parents' footsteps, another major reason is expense. As technology continues to develop, many small family farms are unable to afford new advances. Meanwhile, large corporate farms with financial backing stay current with technological advances.

This investment, while expensive in the beginning, often results in increased yields and/ or increased bottom lines. This in turn creates larger profits for larger farms. Meanwhile, smaller family farms, which may lack the capital to purchase new technology, are forced to compete with these corporate farms that can produce more products at cheaper prices.

Many family farmers are forced to subsidize farming with other work, close the farm, or sell to these larger corporate farms. As these changes occur, farmland and the surrounding rural areas can be impacted both financially and aesthetically. A family farm that produces food and distributes its food to the surrounding area puts money in the local economy several ways, including the profits from the farmers and profits from the stores selling the produce. However, when corporate farms take control of these farms, produce may be sent out of the area and all revenue is returned to the corporation, which may be in another state. Aesthetically speaking, corporate farms operate differently than rural family farms. Increased use of manure pools for fertilizers are common, as is larger, more industrialized equipment, which detracts from rural settings.

CHAPTER SUMMARY

The way land is used and how well it is managed is of paramount importance. When managed poorly, soil quality degrades. As this happens, nutrients are lost, erosion occurs, and water quality is diminished. The Dust Bowl of the 1930s is a prime example of how poor land management practices can have catastrophic effects.

As the global population increases, the world becomes more and more urbanized. People tend to flock to urban areas in search of work. The rate of urbanization has increased rapidly since the Industrial Revolution, leading to the development of megacities with populations of over 10 million people.

As urban areas grow, the phenomenon of urban sprawl can take a toll on the quality of life. As this sprawl increases, surrounding land, especially farmland, is converted to make way for more housing, often in the form of suburban residential developments. City planners have begun to institute smart growth policies aimed at preventing urban sprawl by increasing population density and increasing street connectivity, among other techniques.

Urban sprawl is not the only issue facing large urban areas. Management of human waste, household garbage, and industrial wastes become more difficult as cities grow. A number of waste management practices can ease this burden, including increased numbers of landfills, recycling, and municipal composting programs. However, residents often do not want these centers near their homes, an occurrence known as the NIMBY syndrome.

Decreasing urban sprawl through slower development is not the only form of protection that non-urban land needs. Managers of agricultural land, including crop land and rangeland, also need to use conservation techniques, including best management practices and integrated pest management techniques, to minimize their effects on neighboring environments, including forested areas and wetlands.

REFERENCES

American Farmland Trust. (2011). Sustainable agriculture. Retrieved from http://www.farmland.org/programs/environment/solutions/farming-practices.asp

Anderson, J. R., Harty, E. E., Roach, J. T., & Witmer, R. E. (1976). *A land use and land cover classification system for use with remote sensor data* (Geological Survey Professional Paper No. 964). Retrieved from http://landcover.usgs.gov/pdf/anderson.pdf

Barrionuevo, A. (2011, May 26). China's interest in farmland makes Brazil uneasy. *The New York Times.* Retrieved from http://www.nytimes.com/2011/05/27/world/americas/27brazil.html?pagewanted=all

Cederberg, C., Persson, U. M., Neovius, K., Molander, S., & Clift, R. (2011). Including carbon emissions from deforestation in the carbon footprint of Brazilian beef. *Environmental Science & Technology, 45*(5), 1773–1779. Retrieved from http://www.ibcperu.org/doc/isis/13743.pdf

City Population. (2011). Megacities. Retrieved from http://www.citypopulation.de/world/Agglomerations.html

Clean Water Action Council. (2009). Land use and urban sprawl. Retrieved from http://www.cwac.net/landuse/index.html

Cook, B., Miller, R., & Seager, R. (2011). *Did dust storms make the Dust Bowl drought worse?* Lamont-Doherty Earth Observatory. Retrieved from http://www.ldeo.columbia.edu/res/div/ocp/drought/dust_storms.shtml

Flaskerud, G. (2003, July). *Brazil's soybean production and impact.* Fargo, ND: North Dakota State University Extension Service. Retrieved from http://www.ag.ndsu.edu/pubs/agecon/market/eb79.pdf

Ikerd, J. (2002, November 27). Farm economy state of the union address: The logical consequences of industrial agriculture. Retrieved from http://newfarm.rodaleinstitute.org/features/1102/ikerd_address/index.shtml

Institute for Local Self-Reliance. (2001). The paradigm shift in NYC's solid waste management. Retrieved from http://www.ilsr.org/recycling/NYC/NYCmain.html

JBS-Friboi. (2011). JBS-Friboi sustainability practices. Retrieved from http://www.jbs.com.br/ir/

Kirkman, E. (2007). Architecture in the era of Napoleon III. Retrieved from http://www.arthistoryarchive.com/arthistory/architecture/Haussmanns-Architectural-Paris.html

Lilly, J. P. (1997). *Best management practices for agricultural nutrients.* North Carolina Cooperative Extension Service. Retrieved from http://www.soil.ncsu.edu/publications/Soilfacts/AG-439-20/

Lindsey, R. (2003, April 23). Escape from the Amazon. NASA Earth Observatory. Retrieved from http://earthobservatory.nasa.gov/Features/LBA_Escape/

Luninarium Encyclopedia Project. (2010). Great London Fire 1666. Retrieved from http://www.luminarium.org/encyclopedia/greatfire.htm

Mydans, S. (2006, May 21). Manila: Sifting for a living on trash mountain. *The New York Times.* Retrieved from http://www.nytimes.com/2006/05/21/world/asia/21iht-city7.1790859.html?pagewanted=all

New York City, Parks & Recreation. (n.d.). Freshkills Park. Retrieved from http://www.nycgovparks.org/park-features/freshkills-park

Pierzynski, G. M., Sims, J. T., & Vance, G. F. (2005). *Soils and environmental quality* (3rd ed.). Boca Raton, FL: Taylor & Francis Group.

Polopolus, L. C. (n.d.). Athens, Greece: A city-state that grew from optimaility in the golden era to excessive urbanization by the 21st century [Lecture transcript]. Retrieved from http://www.clas.ufl.edu/users/kapparis/AOC/ATHENS.htm

Smart Growth Network. (2010). Getting to smart growth: 100 policies for implementation. Retrieved from http://www.smartgrowth.org/pdf/gettosg.pdf

Smart Growth America. (2010). Measuring urban sprawl. Retrieved from http://www.smartgrowthamerica.org/sprawlindex/MeasuringSprawl.PDF

Tuan, F. C., Fang, C., & Cao, Z. (2004, October). *China's soybean imports expected to grow despite short-term disruptions* (USDA Report No. OCS-04J-01). Retrieved from http://www.ers.usda.gov/publications/OCS/Oct04/OCS04J01/ocs04j01.pdf

"Urban sprawl" responsible for collapse of ancient Cambodian city of Angkor. (2009, June 24). *Thaindian News.* Retrieved from http://www.thaindian.com/newsportal/health/urban-sprawl-responsible-for-collapse-of-ancient-cambodian-city-of-angkor_100208779.html

The urbanization of the world. (n.d.). Retrieved from http://www.faculty.fairfield.edu/faculty/hodgson/Courses/so11/population/urbanization.htm

U.S. Department of Agriculture, Economic Research Service. (2012, October 10). Soybeans and oil crops: Trade. Retrieved from http://www.ers.usda.gov/Briefing/Soybeansoilcrops/trade.htm

WATT Publishing. (2011, April 21). China increasing soybean imports due to record pig numbers. Retrieved from http://www.wattagnet.com/China_increasing_soybean_imports_due_to_record_pig_numbers.html

APPENDIX 1

MAIN US GOVERNMENT AGENCIES

United States Environmental Protection Agency (EPA)

The EPA handles a range of more than 100 environmental laws and issues and oversees environmental policies for the nation. It sets up and enforces specific rules about clean air and water, waste cleanup, recycling, pesticides and other chemicals, and limiting pollution. It oversees everything from certifying which appliances use energy efficiently to making sure polluters clean up waste sites to determining which animals are considered endangered species and therefore must be protected.

United States Department of Agriculture (USDA)

The USDA is a cabinet-level department that sets farm policies for the country. The department also regulates and inspects meat, poultry, aquaculture, and dairy.

United States Forest Service (USFS)

The USFS protects more than 150 designated national forests, including fighting forest fires. Forest fire fighting activity accounts for more than 40 percent of the department's budget.

Natural Resource Conservation Service (NRCS)

The NRCS regulates conservation of grazing land, the Great Lakes and many river basins, wildlife habitats, and wetlands. The NRCS also works to limit soil erosion and other damage caused by natural disasters such as floods and hurricanes.

Department of Health and Human Services (HHS)

The HHS studies environmental problems that affect public health. The Agency for Toxic Substances and Disease Registry tracks dangerous pollutants, such as asbestos, lead, and formaldehyde. The Centers for Disease Control (CDC), based in Atlanta, provides information to the public about air pollution, climate change, and other environmental problems that can affect people's health. The HHS oversees the Food and Drug Administration.

Food and Drug Administration (FDA)

The FDA, part of the Department of Health and Human Services, is concerned with protecting the public from diseases, including testing food and medicine for safety and inspecting factories. The FDA sets regulations for seafood, grains, and fruits and vegetables, inspects food imported from other countries, and manages recalls when there are food-related disease outbreaks.

National Parks Service (NPS)

The NPS operates and preserves about 400 properties around the country, including national parks, forests, monuments, and historic sites.

Office of Energy Efficiency and Renewable Energy (EERE)

The EERE funds projects to develop cleaner, naturally replenished sources of energy, such as solar and wind power, which can reduce the need for high-polluting fossil fuels like oil and coal.

Office of Environmental Management (EM)

The Office of Environmental Management oversees the cleanup of waste created by the development of nuclear weapons and nuclear energy.

National Oceanographic and Atmospheric Administration (NOAA)

Under the Department of Commerce, the NOAA operates the National Ocean Service (NOS), which sets aside marine sanctuary environments and coral reefs for protection. The NOS tracks risks to the ocean from rising sea levels and other natural disasters. It also operates the National Marine Fisheries Service (NMFS), which enforces rules about fishing, keeps track of fish populations, and works to protect endangered marine species from overfishing.

APPENDIX 2

APA STYLE

APA style is a set of rules and guidelines for manuscript preparation based on the psychology literature that was developed by the American Psychological Association (APA). APA style is a standard format for academic research writing and is used extensively in the social sciences. The *Publication Manual of the American Psychological Association* (2010) is the style's official guide. The information in this chapter comes from the sixth edition of the *Publication Manual* and its affiliated website.

The *Publication Manual* provides guidelines for formatting a research paper and referencing sources. It provides specific information about organizing the content of the research paper; using effective writing style and avoiding bias in language; employing Standard English grammar and punctuation; and using tables, figures, and graphs to illustrate a research paper. The *Publication Manual* also guides authors through the process of submitting papers for publication. The purpose of this chapter is to focus on the guidelines the *Publication Manual* sets forth for most undergraduate papers.

The *Publication Manual* also includes detailed information about documenting sources,—giving credit to the sources that were used to prepare a manuscript. Following these guidelines can help a writer avoid plagiarism. Every type of source used in a research paper must be cited—from journals and books to music and videos. The APA's website (http://apastyle.org) and its accompanying blog (http://blog.apastyle.org) are among the best resources for the most up-to-date information on citing electronic sources.

FORMATTING A PAPER

Each research paper should have four core components:
- Title page
  - Includes the title of the work, running head, and byline
  - May also include school and instructor information
- Abstract
  - Provides a short summary of research and findings
- Body text
  - Includes an introduction with a background of literature consulted, method of research, results, and a discussion of the results
- References
  - Includes all sources referenced in the paper

The following basic guidelines should be used when formatting a paper:
- Use 8½ × 11 in. (22 × 28 cm) paper (standard)
- Use double spacing between lines
- Use a 12-point serif font, such as Times New Roman
- Number each page on the right-hand side at the top of the page
- Use 1-in. margins on each side
- Indent the first line of each paragraph to ½ in. (1.3 cm)
- Align the text to the left, leaving the right margin ragged and unjustified

■ Present a title page, abstract, body text, and references, in that order

Some papers may feature other collateral items, such as appendices, author notes, footnotes, tables, figure captions, and figures. They should be placed in this sequence after the references.

Organization is important to help the reader follow the flow of ideas from existing research to original findings. The APA has established common formatting styles to create uniformity in published material that is recognizable to a broad readership. Perhaps most important is that writers remember to not worry about perfectly formatting the paper in APA style until the revision stage. Becoming preoccupied with formatting early on will slow writing progress.

Title Page

The title page includes the title of the paper centered in the upper third of the page. This is followed by a byline, which includes the author's name. In the upper-left corner of the title page, the running head (see the next section for more information) should be identified. Also include a page header that includes the running head to the left and the page number in the upper-right corner.

Running Head

The research paper's title page should include a page header—called a running head—that will appear on each page of the document. Usually a shortened version of the paper's title (two to three words, no more than 50 characters) is used as the running head. For example, if the title of the document is "Everything You Need to Know about APA Citations," an appropriate running header might be "APA CITATIONS." The running head should be flush left in all caps. In the top-left corner of the title page, type "APA CITATIONS" flush left and the page number flush right.

Abstract

An abstract is a summary of the research paper and its findings. It is an extremely important paragraph that allows readers to immediately determine if they are interested in reading the paper. This section begins on page 2 with the header "Abstract" centered on the page with an initial capital A followed by lowercase letters. Abstracts should be brief and usually range between 150 and 250 words. The text should be flush left (without an indention) beneath the title and Arabic numerals should be used for any numbers.

Headings

Using levels of headings provides a hierarchy for the sections in a paper; in effect, they provide the reader with an outline of the paper. Avoid use of only one subsection heading or one subsection within a section. The same level of heading should be given to all topics of equal importance (e.g., Method, Results). At least two subsection headings should be used within a section; otherwise, none should be used. A heading structure for all sections should use the same top-to-bottom progression, regardless of the number of levels of subheading. APA style uses five possible levels of headings, which follow each other sequentially. Thus, if only one level is used, use Level 1; if two are used, use Levels 1 and 2 (the most common combination in most research papers), in that order; if three are used, use Levels 1,

2, and 3, in that order, and so on.

Level 1: Centered, boldface, initial capital letters on important words; on the line above the paragraph

Example:

BASIC FINDINGS

Level 2: Flush left, boldface, initial capital letters on important words; on the line above the paragraph

Example:

Demographic Analysis

Level 3: Indented, boldface, sentence-case heading followed by a period, on the same line of copy as the beginning of the paragraph that follows.

Demographic analysis. The demographic analysis shows that among participating physicians…

Level 4: Indented, boldface, italicized, sentence-case heading followed by a period, on the same line of copy as the beginning of the paragraph that follows.

Demographic analysis. The demographic analysis shows that among participating physicians…

Level 5: Indented, italicized, sentence-case heading followed by a period, on the same line of copy as the beginning of the paragraph that follows.

Demographic analysis. The demographic analysis shows that among participating physicians…

Punctuation and Spacing

Punctuation provides the pace for a sentence and tells the reader where to pause (commas, colons, or semicolons); stop (periods, question marks, or exclamation points); or deviate (parentheses, dashes, or brackets). The different kinds of punctuation in a sentence usually designate different kinds and lengths of pauses. Modern word-processing programs provide the appropriate space for each character, so hit the spacebar only once after commas, colons, and semicolons. Do not add extra spaces around dashes, parentheses, or brackets.

APA style suggests—but does not require—two spaces after punctuation marks at the end of a sentence in draft manuscripts. Because requirements vary across publications, when submitting a manuscript for publication, consult the publication's style guidelines regarding spacing after end punctuation.

Following is a quick guide to some punctuation rules required in APA style.

Period

Periods are used in reference lists after the author's name, the year, the title of a book or article, and the close of the reference; an exception to this close-reference rule is references that end in a website address (electronic references), which do not end with a period.

When in-text citations are used at the end of a sentence, the period should follow the citation. When in-text citations appear at the end of a long, indented quote, periods should not follow the in-text citations. In that case, the period appears at the end of the quote but before the in-text citation. See "Quotations of 40 Words or More," which appears later in this section, for an example.

Colon

Colons appear between the publication location and the publisher listed in individual references. In text, a colon should not be used after an introductory clause that is not a complete sentence. If two independent clauses are separated by a colon, capitalize the word that begins the second clause.

Semicolon

Although semicolons are usually used to separate two independent clauses (complete sentences), a semicolon should also be used to set off items in a series when one or more of these items already includes commas, regardless of whether the items are complete sentences—for example, "The sisters were challenged to ride a bike for two hours; juggle a ball, a book, and a toy car for 10 minutes; and walk on a treadmill for 30 minutes."

Comma

In in-text citations, a comma should be used to set off the year of publication within parentheses. In text, use a comma between all elements in a series of three or more items, including before *and* and *or*.

Quotation Marks

Double quotation marks should be used in the following situations:

- To introduce a word or phrase that is used as slang, a coined expression, or an example of irony
- To identify an article or chapter title in a periodical or book when the title is mentioned in text
- To reproduce or cite material from a published source (only up to 40 words)

Double quotation marks should not enclose quotations of 40 words or more.

Quotations of 40 Words or More

Quotations of 40 words or more should be in a paragraph by themselves, should be indented five spaces without the customary first-line indent, and should not include quotation marks. These block quotations should also be followed by a citation that includes a page number. The citation is presented after the closing punctuation of the block quotation. If the quoted text contains quotation marks, double quotation marks should be used. Note the following example:

> Candy manufactured at the offshore facility was tainted, but testing of product made domestically revealed that it was safe. Representatives

from the manufacturer claimed that the company was unaware of any problems with ingredients or machinery at the offshore plant prior to the discovery of the poisoned product. (Bradenforth, 2007, p. 238)

Italics

Use italics for introduction of a new, technical, or key term (but only on first use of the word; do not italicize the word again if it is used in subsequent sentences). Also use italics in the following instances:

- Letters used as statistical symbols
- Periodical volume numbers in the reference list
- Anchors on a scale (e.g., a survey asks respondents to rate customer service on a scale of *1* to *5*).

Parentheses

Parentheses are used in the following circumstance:

- To set off reference citations in text
- To separate letters that identify terms in a series within a sentence or paragraph
- To enclose the citation or page number of a direct quote
- To introduce an abbreviation
- To enclose numbers that represent formulas, equations, statistical values, or degrees of freedom

Avoid use of back-to-back parenthetical text.

Hyphens

A hyphen should not be used on common fractions used as nouns (e.g., Two thirds of the students missed class); however, a hyphen should be used when the fraction is used as a descriptor (e.g., The student council requires a two-thirds majority to pass a new rule). Hyphens should also be avoided in compounds in which the first word is an adverb (e.g., The nearly vetoed legislation has finally passed) and in situations where there is no possible way a compound term could be misread without it (e.g., The health care industry lobbied Congress for this law). Do not use a space before or after a hyphen.

Dashes

APA distinguishes em dashes (two hyphens placed side by side with no space in between: —) from en dashes (which are slightly longer than a hyphen: –). Note that some word-processing programs include em dash and en dash symbols, often a combination of keystrokes or accessible from the symbols menu. As shown in the examples in the paragraphs that follow, do not add spaces before or after em dashes and en dashes.

An em dash should be used to either highlight a clause or to indicate a diversion from the sentence's primary clause (e.g., The test subjects—who were unaware of the change—disliked the nature of the treatment).

An en dash is used between words of equal weight in a compound adjective (e.g., "medication–nutrient interaction") and between page ranges (e.g., 112–114).

Using Numbers in a Document

Generally, APA style uses numerals to express numbers 10 and larger and words for numbers one through nine. One primary exception to this rule is when a number greater than 10 begins a sentence. In this case, the word should be spelled out (e.g., Forty-eight men were surveyed).

There are several exceptions in which numbers less than 10 are listed in numeric form, generally related to presenting a specific quantity measurement, such as in the following instances:

- When the numbers precede a unit of measurement or a percentage symbol
- When the numbers are used for a mathematical or statistical function
- When used to represent time, dates, ages, scores, or points on a scale
- When placed in a numbered series, parts of book chapters or tables, or in a numbered list of four or more
- When included in a research paper's abstract

If the number of days, months, or years are an approximation, write out the numbers (e.g., The ships takes approximately eight days to reach Portugal). A zero should be written before decimals and numbers that are less than one, except in decimal fractions where the number cannot be greater than one. Plurals of numbers should be written by adding -s or -es, without an apostrophe.

Abbreviations

APA style recommends minimal use of abbreviations, as they can often cause more confusion than clarification and can hinder reader comprehension. Generally, an abbreviation should be used only if (a) it is well known and a reader would be familiar with it, or (b) it saves considerable space and prevents repetition.

A writer must decide whether to spell out an expression or group name every time or spell it out initially and abbreviate it thereafter. If abbreviating, the term must be written out completely the first time, followed by its abbreviation in parentheses. Afterward, the abbreviation can be used without any further explanation.

Do not write out standard abbreviations for units of measurement on first use, but do not use the abbreviation if a specific measurement is not given (e.g., It was 3 cm in length; It was measured in centimeters).

A sentence can begin with an abbreviation or acronym that appears in all capital letters but not if it is all lowercase letters. Some abbreviations are accepted as words in APA style and do not require explanation, including the following well-known terms: IQ, REM, ESP, AIDS, and HIV.

Periods are used with abbreviations for initials of names (e.g., William S. Sanderson), to abbreviate the United States when used as an adjective (e.g., U.S. Navy), in identity-concealing labels for study participants (e.g., participants S. P. and J. M.), and with Latin and reference abbreviations (e.g., i.e., etc.).

Periods should not be used with abbreviations of state names, capital letter acronyms, or metric and nonmetric measurements; one exception is the abbreviation for inch (in.), which includes a period because of the likelihood of its confusion with the word "in."

In general, use Latin abbreviations only in parenthetical material and use the English translations of Latin abbreviations in running text (e.g., use "e.g." in parentheses and use "for example" in text). However, "et al." (and others) and "v." (for versus) should be used for citations, both parenthetical and in text (APA, 2010, pp. 106–111).

Percent and Percentages

The symbol for percent (%) should be used only when it is preceded by a numeral (e.g., 5%). The word "percent" should not be spelled out after a numeral. When a number is not given, the word "percentage" should be used (e.g., a significant percentage of women in the group preferred the reformulated product). In table headings or legends, use a percent symbol in lieu of the word "percentage" to conserve space.

Lists

Elements or ideas in a series can be enumerated to clarify their relationship. This is particularly important when a sequence is lengthy or difficult to understand. Three different forms are possible: a within-sentence list, a numbered list, or a bulleted list.

Example of a within-sentence list:
The student's three choices were (a) living in the dorm with a roommate, (b) living alone in the dorm, or (c) living at home.

Listing within a Sentence with Internal Commas

When listing items within a paragraph or sentence with items that include commas, use lowercase letters in parentheses and semicolons, as shown in the following example:
- The respondents were broken into three groups: (a) high communication apprehension, scoring more than 35; (b) moderate communication apprehension, scoring between 18 and 35; and (c) low communication apprehension, scoring below 18.

Numbered Lists

To list paragraphs in a numbered sequence, such as itemized conclusions or successive steps in a procedure, number each paragraph or sentence with an Arabic numeral followed by a period, as shown in the following example:

1. We divided the study sample into three groups based on income.
2. We further subdivided these three groups into subgroups based on race/ethnicity.
3. We calculated the average monthly income for each of these subgroups.

Bulleted Lists

Numbered lists may imply an unintended and unwanted hierarchy such as chronology or importance. In such cases, a bulleted list, as shown in the following example, is an option:
The physicians were asked questions about the following factors:
- How long they have been in practice
- How many patients they see per week on average
- How many of those patients have private insurance

Each item in the bulleted list should be indented. Items in a bulleted list may be complete sentences or parts of a longer sentence introduced with a colon, but all items in the list should be parallel (e.g., they should all start with the same part of speech or same conjugation, form, or tense of a verb).

REFERENCES AND INTERNAL CITATION STYLE

Proper documentation of sources includes two important steps: creating a reference list and using internal citations. APA guidelines require a structured reference list and parenthetical in-text citations of each source listed in the references. It is critical to carefully follow APA guidelines for placement and style of citations and references. Footnotes and endnotes are occasionally used, but they are secondary to parenthetical citations. Content footnotes are used to clarify or expand on information in the text, and copyright permission footnotes are used to identify the source of quotations. Neither type should be used in place of parenthetical citations in an APA-style research paper.

Citation Style

For parenthetical citations, include author name(s) and year of the publication. If using a direct quotation or paraphrasing a particular passage, the page number must also be included. APA style offers a variety of acceptable citation formats. Example 1 illustrates an effective way to mention the authors in the text of the sentence; it is particularly useful if the writer wishes to describe the cited author in some way. The style of Example 2 results in a complete statement without using the cited author's name in the sentence. Example 3 shows a direct quote from the reference material coupled with mention of the author's name in the sentence. Example 4 combines a direct quote and a complete statement that does not mention the author's name in the sentence.

Example 1:
According to Booth, Colomb, and Williams (2003), you should avoid plagiarism.

Example 2:
You should avoid plagiarism (Booth, Colomb, & Williams, 2003).

Example 3:
According to Booth, Colomb, and Williams (2003), "In all fields, you plagiarize when you use a source's words or ideas without citing that source" (p. 202).

Example 4:
Many authorities have commented on the topic, but this is one of the most effective descriptions: "In all fields, you plagiarize when you use a source's words or ideas without citing that source" (Booth, Colomb, & Williams, 2003, p. 202).

If a source has two to five authors, use all the names of the authors in the first citation, but in later citations, refer to secondary authors with the abbreviation "et al." If a source has six or more authors, in all citations—including the first—list only the first author followed by "et al." and the date (e.g., Smith et al., 2007). Note that if citing the same source more than once in the same paragraph, it is not necessary to include the year in the succeeding citations. See Example 5 for an illustration.

Example 5:

Plagiarism can harm your career (Booth et al., 2003). Several prominent historians have lost credibility because they had plagiarized from the works of others (Weaver et al., 2009). It is best to create your own original content and exercise caution when quoting and summarizing the content of others (Booth et al.).

Some citation styles do not meet the criteria listed previously, including the following:

- Personal communications
- Anonymous works
- Works without publication dates
- Classical works

See Figure APA.1 for examples of these unusual styles.

REFERENCE TYPE	IN-TEXT CITATION STYLE	REFERENCE STYLE	EXPLANATION
Personal communications that include letters, memos, e-mail, nonarchived discussion groups, personal interviews, and telephone conversations	S. H. Hanson (personal communication, January 1, 2007), or (S. H. Hanson, personal communication, January 1, 2007)	Not included in reference list	Cite personal communication in-text only
No publication date given	(Hamilton, n.d.)	Hamilton, G. (n.d.). *Hope is the verb*. Boston, MA: Cambridge Press.	When no date is given, write n.d. in parentheses for in-text and reference list mentions
A work with no identified author, not designated as anonymous	("College Bound," 2007)	College bound. (2007). *Journal of Teacher Education, 45*(3) 26–31.	In the reference list, alphabetize by title
Works with group authors	(American Psychological Association, 1994)	American Psychological Association. (1994). *The APA manual of style*. Washington, DC: Author.	Alphabetize group authors, such as associations and universities, by the first significant word of the name
A work's author is designated "anonymous"	(Anonymous, 2007)	Anonymous. (2007). *Let's build bridges*. New York, NY: Prentice Hall.	In the reference list, only a work that is explicitly identified as written by "Anonymous" includes the word, which is alphabetized as such.
Classical works	(Plato, trans. 1938), or (Freud, 1931/1997)	Not required	Reference entries are not required for major classical works. That includes ancient Greek and Roman works and the Bible. In cases of the Bible, identify which version was used in the first in-text citation—for example, "(1 Cor. 13:1) [King James Version]."

FIGURE APA.1 APA citation style for unusual references

Reference Style

The APA reference style is preferred for many reasons, but primary among them is that APA style is perhaps the most common form of organizing, citing, structuring, and verifying information in universities today. APA reference style provides all the basic building blocks that make it easier to learn other styles, such as MLA, Turabian, and Chicago style, and underscores the importance of professionalism and rigor in writing. All references should be listed in alphabetical order by the first authors' last name or, if no author is listed, by the title of the source.

Assembling a Reference List

An APA reference list is more than just a simple listing of works cited. Each type of reference—a journal article, a book, a website, or a newspaper article, for example—has its own unique style. The idea behind the reference list is to give readers as much information as possible to seek out the references and gain a deeper understanding of the logic expressed in the paper by reading them. The following are general guidelines for an APA reference list:

- Sources should be arranged alphabetically by the author's last name. If there is no identified author, alphabetize the reference listing by the first main word of the title, excluding "A," "An," or "The."
- Double space or leave one blank line between each line of type in a reference list.
- The first line of a reference is set flush left, but any subsequent lines in the same reference are indented one-half inch (known as the hanging indent).
- Periods separate most parts of a reference, including (a) after the author name(s), (b) after the date, (c) after the closing parenthesis for the date of publication, and (d) at the end of the reference (except for an electronic reference, which requires no period). Periods should also be used after the first and middle initials of each author.
- Commas are used between the author's last name(s) and initials; to separate authors; between the book or periodical title and the volume number; after an issue number and before a page number; and between a volume number and page number. A colon is used to separate the city of publication and the publisher's name.
- The author's names in a reference should be listed as last name first, followed by a comma, and then the first and middle initials, and finished with a period. When there are eight or more authors, list only the first six and abbreviate the remaining authors using ellipsis points ("..."), followed by the final author. If a group or entity is the author, spell out its full name as the author. If a second author of a book or magazine is listed with the word "with," he or she should be listed in the reference in parentheses—for example, "Porter, J. (with Rutter, K. L.)." To reference an edited book, list the editor's name in the author position and follow it with the abbreviation "Ed." or "Eds." in parentheses. If there is no author, the title of the work should be moved to the beginning of the reference.
- The year the work of a reference was copyrighted should follow the authors' names (or title, if there are no authors), appear in parentheses, and have a period at the end outside of the parentheses. For magazines, newspapers, or newsletters, the year, followed by the exact date (month and date) of the publication should be listed in parentheses. If no date is available, "n.d." should be written in parentheses and should be followed by a period.

■ The title of an article or chapter comes after the date, followed by the title of the work, periodical, or book. Only the first word of the title and subtitle (if there is one) should be capitalized. The title should not be italicized or have quotation marks around it. All nonweb references should end with a period. Web-based references should include as much of the previously listed information as possible and the digital object identifier (DOI) if available or the web address of the source. If the last item in the reference is a DOI or a website address, it should not end with a period.

■ The city of publication follows the title of any book or brochure. Regardless of how well-known a city is, write a comma and the appropriate two-letter abbreviation for the state or territory that is used by the U.S. Postal Service. Spell out country names. A colon should follow the city, state, or country of publication. If the publisher is a university that has the same name as the state or province (e.g., Ohio State), do not repeat the state or province in the publisher location.

■ The publisher's name follows the city of publication. The name of the publisher should be as brief as possible, eliminating terms such as "Inc.," or "Co.," but the words "Books" and "Press" should be kept in the reference. If two or more publisher locations are given, give the first listed or the publisher's corporate office, if specified. A period should follow all listings.

■ "Page" and "pages" should be cited as "p." and "pp." in instances where book chapters are listed. Periodical page numbers go at the end of the reference, following the title of the journal, and "p." or "pp." is not used. Book page numbers go between the title and the city of publication. All page numbers should include the entire article or chapter, and the beginning and end numbers should be separated by an en dash. Page numbers for entire books are not listed.

■ Appropriate abbreviations for use in reference section and in-text citations include the following:

- chap. = chapter
- ed. = edition
- Rev. ed. = revised edition
- 2nd ed. = second edition
- Ed. (Eds.) = editor (editors)
- Trans. = translator(s)
- n.d. = no date
- p. (pp.) = page (pages)
- Vol. = volume (as in Vol. 4)
- Vols. = volumes (as in four volumes)
- No. = number
- Pt. = part
- Suppl. = supplement
- Tech. Rep. = technical report

■ U.S. states and territories should be indicated with the appropriate two-letter abbreviation used by the U.S. Postal Service. City names and country names should not be abbreviated (APA, 2010, p. 187).

Examples of References

Refer to the *Publication Manual* or its companion website (http://apastyle.org) if citing a resource that is not included among the examples that follow. Different sources have different requirements and rules. Books, journal articles, magazine articles, websites, and other sources each have particular requirements that give proper credit and help readers locate the reference material. If any part of the reference is not included, this amounts to failure to properly credit a source. The following 11 examples illustrate some of the more common reference styles.

Example 1: A book with a single author.

Klein, N. (2000). *No logo*. New York, NY: Picador.

Book author: The author's last name is listed first, followed by the author's first and middle initials (if applicable). The period that follows the initial is also the period that follows the first element (author's name) of the References citation.

Date of publication: The year the book was published is included in parentheses, followed by a period.

Book title: The title is italicized with all words except the first in lowercase. If there is a colon in the title, the first word following the colon is also capitalized. If the book has several editions, the edition of the text goes in parentheses following the title. This element is followed by a period.

Publication information: For all cities, include the state (e.g., Newbury Park, CA), even if the city is well known. A colon is placed after the state and followed by the name of the publisher. Omit superfluous terms such as "Publishers," "Co.," or "Inc.," but keep the words "Books" or "Press."

Example 2: A book with two to seven authors.

Rubin, R. B., Rubin, A. M., & Piele, L. J. (2000). *Communication research: Strategies and sources* (5th ed.). Belmont, CA: Wadsworth.

Book author: The author's last name is listed first, followed by the author's first and middle initials (if applicable). A comma follows the name of the first author, even when there are only two authors to list. Type "&" before the last author is listed. Authors are listed in the order they are listed on the book cover.

Date of publication, book title, and publication information: Follow the format applied in Example 1.

Example 3: A book with eight or more authors.

Brown, L. V., Ecks, T. Z., Walters, F. A., Zim, A., Ricks, J., Bynum, C. T., ... Olsen, L. (2007). *Research methods for undergraduate students*. New York, NY: Text Press.

Book author: The author's last name is listed first, followed by the author's first and middle initials (if applicable). With more than seven authors, list only the first six authors and abbreviate the remaining authors using ellipsis points ("…"), followed by the final author. Do not type "&" before the final author.

Date of publication, book title, and publication information: Follow the format applied in Example 1.

Example 4: An article with only one author in a scholarly journal.

Kramer, M. W. (2005). Communication in community theatre groups. *Journal of Applied Communication Research, 33,* 159–182.

Article author: The author's last name is listed first, followed by the author's first and middle initials (if applicable).

Date of publication: The year the article was written is included in parentheses, followed by a period.

Article title: The article title is not italicized nor enclosed in quotation marks, and only the first word of the title and the subtitle should be capitalized. The title is followed by a period.

Journal title: The journal title is italicized and all words in the title are capitalized except articles and prepositions ("a," "the," "and," "an," "of").

Publication information: Provide the volume number (in italics) and the page numbers (not italicized) of the article. If the periodical uses successive pagination in its volumes, it is not necessary to include the issue number. If the pagination is not successive, the issue number should be included in parentheses and not italicized—for example, *Consulting Psychology Journal: Practice and Research, 45*(2), 10–36.

Example 5: An article with multiple authors in a scholarly journal.

Rosenfeld, L. B., Richman, J. M., Bowen, G. L., & Wynns, S. L. (2006). In the face of a dangerous community: The effects of social support and neighborhood danger on high school students' school outcomes. *Southern Communication Journal, 71,* 273–289.

Article author: The author's last name is listed first, followed by the author's first and middle initials (if applicable). Type "&" before the last author is listed. Authors are listed in the order they appear on the article. With more than seven authors, list only the first six authors and abbreviate the remaining authors using ellipsis points ("…"), followed by the final author. Do not type "&" before the final author.

Date of publication, article title, journal title, and publication information: Follow the format applied in Example 4.

Example 6: A magazine article.

Marano, H. E. (2004, August). Rock around the doc. *Psychology Today, 9,* 47–52.

Article author: The author's last name is listed first, followed by the author's first and middle initials (if applicable).

Date of publication: The year and month the article was written is included in parentheses as "(year, month)."

Article title: The article title is not italicized, and only the first word of the title and subtitle should be capitalized.

Periodical title: The periodical title is italicized, and all words in the title are capitalized except articles and prepositions ("a," "the," "and," "an," "of").

Publication information: Provide the volume number (italics) and the page numbers of the article (not italicized). If the periodical uses successive pagination in its volumes, do not add the issue number. If the pagination is not successive, the issue number should be included in parentheses and not italicized—for example, *Communication Connection, 2*(2), 3–7.

Example 7: An online magazine or news article.

Marano, H. E., & Schwartz, B. G. (2004, August). Rock around the doc. *Psychology Today, 9,* 47–52. Retrieved from http://www.psychologytoday.com

Article author, date of publication, article title, periodical title, and publication information: Follow the format applied in Example 6.

Retrieval information: The rule for electronic resources is to list the information that will help readers find the resource. Do not include the date the document was retrieved unless there is an expectation that the material cited will change over time. Some documents include a digital object identifier (DOI), which is a number that provides a consistent means to find an online document. If the cited publication has a DOI, it is usually prominently displayed at the top of the online document. If the research document includes a DOI, include it at the end of the reference, after the page numbers. For example, Marano, H. E., & Schwartz, B. G. (2004, August). Rock around the doc. *Psychology Today, 9,* 47–50. doi:10.1187/0142-9052.78.1.298. If no DOI is available, give the home web page for the periodical, not the specific link to the article. Web pages often disappear or change, and this avoids citing expired web addresses.

Example 8: An article from a newspaper database.

Russell, P. R. (2007, May 11). Saving energy is a hot topic: Energy to develop ways to conserve. *New Orleans Times-Picayune,* p. Money 1. Retrieved from www.timespicayune.com

Article author: Follow the format applied in Example 7.

Date of publication: The year, month, and day the article was written are included in parentheses (year, month, day).

Article title, periodical title: Follow the format applied in Example 6.

Publication information: Follow the format applied in Example 7.

Retrieval information: The rule for electronic resources is to list the information that will help the reader find the resource. Do not include the name of the database where the article was found; instead list the newspaper's home web page address. Do not close the web page address with a period.

Example 9: An article from a newspaper with one author and nonconsecutive page numbers.

> McBride, J. (2007, May 30). Pantex crew returns today: Guards union ratifies 5-year pact. *Amarillo Globe-News,* pp. A1, A6.

Article author: Follow the format applied in Example 7.

Date of publication: Follow the format applied in Example 8.

Article title, periodical title: Follow the format applied in Example 6.

Publication information: For newspapers, include the section and page number. Unlike journal citations, newspaper references do require a "p." or "pp." before the section and page number(s). If the pages are not continuous, list the page on which the article begins, insert a comma and a space, and then list the page where the article continues (e.g., pp. A1, A6).

Example 10: An article with no author, from a newspaper.

> Asarco gets approval to auction land in Salt Lake City. (2007, May 30). *Amarillo Globe-News,* p. D6.

Article author: If an article has no author, do not write "Anonymous." The article title is placed first. It is not italicized, and only the first word of the title and subtitle should be capitalized.

Date of publication: Follow the format applied in Example 8.

Article title, periodical title: Follow the format applied in Example 6.

Publication information: Follow the format applied in Example 7.

Example 11: An Internet source.

> How to publish with APA. (n.d.). Retrieved from American Psychological Association website: http://www.apastyle.org

Heading title: Websites and web pages often do not have identified author(s). In such a case, the website section heading is used at the beginning of the reference. It is not italicized, and only the first word of the title and subtitle should be capitalized.

Date of publication: A date is also not often available, so it is acceptable to reference that there is no date identified by typing (n.d.) after the heading title.

Internet site title: Identify the publisher of the resource as part of the retrieval information.

Retrieval information: The rule for electronic resources is to list the information that will help readers find the resource. Only include the complete web page address if the home page of the organization housing the document does not have a search function or if the website is large and hard to navigate, making it unlikely that the reader will be able to find the document from the home address. Do not close the web page address with a period.

Example 12: A picture from a website.

> Pollock, J. (1953). *Greyed rainbow* [Painting]. Retrieved from
>   http://www.artic.edu/aic/collections/artwork/83642?search_id=1

Artist or photographer: Follow the format applied to authors in Example 6.

Title: The title of the picture is italicized and only the first word of the title should be capitalized. The title is followed by the medium (e.g., painting, photograph, etc.) in brackets.

Retrieval information: Follow the format applied in Example 8.

Example 13: A picture from a book.

> Pollock, J. (1953). *Greyed rainbow* [Painting]. In E. G. Landau, *Jackson Pollock*
>   (p. 230). New York, NY: Abradale Press.

Artist or photographer: Follow the format applied to authors in Example 6.

Title: Follow the format applied in Example 12.

Book author and title: The word "In" is followed by the author's name. First and middle initials (if applicable) precede the author's last name, which is followed by a comma. The title of the book is italicized and only the first word and any proper nouns are capitalized. The page number(s) or plate number for the artwork is set in parentheses and is not italicized.

Publication information: Follow the format applied in Example 1.

GLOSSARY

A

abiotic Related to events, reactions, or interactions that occur in the absence of living organisms (including with natural and man-made objects such as rocks, dams, or oxygen).

action threshold A level of pest population that must be present before a control method is enacted.

acute Impacts over the short term.

add-on controls Equipment added to existing pollution control strategies to destroy or capture pollutants.

adsorption The adhesion of molecules to a surface.

aeolian Pertaining to the wind and its effects on topography.

aerobic With or having oxygen.

agrarian A lifestyle centered around agriculture and rural life.

agronomy The science of agriculture and its economic values.

air pollutants Substances that—when present in high concentrations in the air—constitute a threat to human or environmental health.

air pollution control The various policies and processes that have been employed to reduce or eliminate the release of pollutants into the air.

air quality index A scale that provides daily data regarding air quality.

alluvial Pertaining to water and its effects on topography.

ambient air Air accessible to all humans and animals.

amendments Substances, including fertilizers, $CaCO_3$, and organic matter, added to the soil to improve soil quality. Chelated fertilizers provide plant-usable forms of micronutrient metals, such as iron, copper, zinc, and manganese.

anaerobic Lacking oxygen.

analog forest A designed sustainable forest that mimics native forests and is used as an economic resource.

anoxic Having very little or no dissolved oxygen.

anthropogenic pollution Air pollution caused by human activity.

apex predator Predator at the top of a food web that does not have a predator of its own.

apical bud The end or terminal bud of a branch or stem.

aquaponic system An agricultural production technique in which plants and aquatic animals are raised in a symbiotic manner. Animal waste is used to fertilize the plants, and the plants then serve as a filter to produce clean water that is returned to the animal tank.

area sources Facilities with individual sources of emissions that are not point sources but that, when taken together, represent a significant amount of pollution.

arid Dry, lacking water or moisture.

atmosphere The gaseous medium surrounding the Earth.

autotroph An organism capable of synthesizing its own food from inorganic substances, using light or chemical energy.

B

best management practices (BMPs) A set of land management guidelines used to reduce or prevent environmental disruptions in farming operations.

bias Prejudice for or against a particular view.

biodiversity The variety of living organisms inhabiting a particular area.

biofuels A source of energy produced from renewable biomass, such as wood, crops, and waste.

biogenic pollution Air pollution from natural sources.

biome Large geographic area with a particular climate.

biosolids The organic accumulation of treated sewage sludge.

biosphere The Earth's spheres, including surface, water, and atmosphere, which support all living organisms.

biotic Related to events, reactions, or interaction involving living organisms.

body mass index (BMI) A simple guide using weight versus height, combined with gender, to determine an ideal weight range.

brackish Containing a mixture of both freshwater and saltwater.

brine Salt water.

bycatch Any water dwelling species that is unintentionally extracted and discarded during the effort to capture a specific type of fish.

C

CAFE standards The average fuel economy (mpg) that a vehicle manufacturer's fleet must meet each year.

carbon cycle A natural process in which carbon is released and absorbed to sustain life.

carbon offset An action undertaken to reduce the emissions of greenhouse gases in response to an action that created emissions.

carnivore An organism that feeds only on other animals.

carrying capacity The maximum number of individuals of a species that can survive over long periods of time.

catalytic converter Device attached to exhaust system on an automobile to covert toxic air pollutants into nontoxic emissions.

cation-exchange capacity The quantity of positively charged ions that a soil can hold.

chronic Impacts over the long term.

Clean Water Act (CWA) Establishes regulations for the discharge of pollutants into water systems in the US and sets regulations for quality standards for surface water.

Climate change A change in the world's overall climate, sustained for a significant amount of time (usually over decades) due to natural factors and processes or from human activity.

cohort-component method Demographic method that uses the components that cause population change, such as migration, fertility, and mortality, in combination with the cohorts, or people born in a given year, factored together with international migration rates to determine projected numbers of people in future years.

colony collapse disorder A term first used in 2006 to describe the significant loss of bee colonies in North America. There are many proposed reasons for such disappearances, such as biotic pathogens or Varroa mites, or environmental stresses such as malnutrition and pesticides.

commodity An item that has a marketable value.

community water systems Direct, in-home, year-round water service; the principle source of drinking water for most US residents.

companion planting A method of agriculture in which plants that grow well and benefit from one another are planted in close proximity.

complete combustion Combustion that results when incineration of waste, air, and heat produces only CO_2 and water vapor.

composting The practice of layering "brown" organic material with "green" organic material and allowing it to decay in a ventilated outdoor area, creating an inexpensive and rich fertilizer while reducing waste.

contouring A style of agriculture that involves planting crops with the lay of the land.

control technology The equipment and processes that reduce stationary air pollution.

conventional pollutants Pollutants that can be treated through the use of conventional water treatment systems.

cover crop A crop, such as winter wheat, used to cover a field during non-growing seasons in order to retain soil and replenish nutrients.

criteria air pollutants (CAPs) Substances that can potentially cause adverse health and environment effects such as respiratory damage and acid rain.

cross-pollination The placement of pollen from one plant into the flower of another plant; used to create specific traits in the offspring.

D

deforestation The removal of trees from large areas of land.

demographics Data that describe the statistical characteristics of a specific population, including age, gender, race, education, and income.

desalination The process of removing minerals and bacteria from saltwater to make it suitable for human consumption.

desert Biome defined by high temperatures, little moisture, and little biodiversity.

desertification The removal of topsoil, generally from extended drought, overgrazing, or overfarming.

detritivore An organism that feeds mainly on dead and decaying material.

developed nations Nations with advanced industrial and technological capabilities as well as sustainable economic productivity.

developing nations Nations with per capita incomes below $12,275 per year. Income does not necessarily reflect development status.

development taxonomy A ranking system of countries' development that takes into consideration multiple of factors, such as personal income, life expectancy, and literacy; replaced the older classification systems of First, Second, Third, and Fourth World and developed or developing economy.

development threshold The minimum level of a criterion used in development taxonomy.

dominant Refers to a gene that is expressed when at least one dominant allele is present.

dry acid deposition Occurs when acid particles suspended in the atmosphere drop to the Earth's surface in gas or particulate form.

easement The right of a person or group to use another's land.

E

ecological niche A specialized role or placement for an organism within an ecosystem.

ecology The study of ecosystems and habitats.

ecosystem The interaction between living organisms and non-living components such as air, soil, and water, within the different environmental parts of an area.

ecosystem diversity The variety of ecosystems in a region.

ecosystem overfishing The destruction of an entire ecosystem as the result of removing too many of one species from an environment.

ectotherm Organisms that regulate body temperature with external stimuli; also known as cold-blooded organisms.

electromagnetic energy Energy reflected or emitted in the form of electrical and magnetic waves with the ability to travel through space.

emission points The areas or pieces of equipment that emit an air pollutant.

endemic Restricted to a single locality or region.

endotherm Organisms that regulate own body temperature using internal bodily functions; also known as warm-blooded organisms.

environmental movement A grassroots social movement to increase awareness about issues impacting the natural environment.

erosion The loss of soil from a location.

eutrophication The abnormal growth of toxic algae.

extractable N, P, and K The amount of nitrogen, phosphorus, and potassium in a soil that can be used by plants.

F

factory farming A farming technique that allows for the mass production of food through the confinement of animals.

famine Widespread lack of food caused by climatic and/or political policies.

feral Domesticated animals that have been released and turned wild.

fertility rate The ratio of live births in an area to the population of that area.

fill material Earthen matter used to create mounds or fill holes in developments or industry. This material comes from many sources and can be contaminated by industrial, mining, or other waste.

fission A nuclear reaction in which a massive nucleus splits into smaller nuclei with the simultaneous release of energy.

food web A complex grouping of interrelated food chains in an ecological community.

fusion A nuclear reaction in which two nuclei combine to form a nucleus with the release of energy.

G

gangue The material from an ore deposit as a result of mining. It has no commercial value and is removed during processing as waste.

gaseous emissions Pollutants such as carbon monoxide, sulfur dioxide, VOCs, and nitrogen oxides released during industrial processes.

genetic diversity The range of genetic variations within a species or population.

genetically modified organism An organism that has had genes added or deleted for specific results.

geo-specific Specific to a certain area or geographical location.

geographical extinction The loss of a species from a specific area.

geosphere The area of the earth that includes the topography and geographical outcroppings and shapes.

grassland Biome defined by moderate temperatures, open fields, and grasses.

green completion A process used to eliminate or collect the VOC emissions produced from natural gas wells with a completion combustion device or a collection procedure that allows for the resource to be used for energy production.

Gross National Product (GNP) The total value of the goods and services produced by a country, measured annually.

groundwater Water located beneath the Earth's surface, typically collected in aquifers or wells.

growth overfishing The situation in which too many young fish are extracted before they mature.

H

hazardous air pollutants (HAPs) Significant toxins that can cause severe health problems such as cancer and birth defects.

herbivore An organism that feeds only on plants.

heterotroph An organism that cannot synthesize its own food and is dependent on complex organic substances for nutrition.

high-risk groups Groups of individuals who are more likely to be susceptible to injury or harm.

hominid Human-like organisms.

hunger Lack of food for a region or group of people.

hydraulic fracturing ("fracking") A process in which pressurized liquid is used to break through rock to release fossil fuel deposits.

hydrocarbon A simple compound consisting of only hydrogen and carbon, such as methane or propane.

hydrologic cycle The continuous movement of water above, below, and on the surface of the Earth, in gaseous, liquid, and solid form.

hydrosphere The water on, underneath, and above the surface of the Earth, including atmospheric water.

hypothesis An educated guess proposing an explanation for the occurrence of a phenomenon.

hypoxic A condition in waterways in which the concentration of dissolved oxygen is lower than 5 ppm.

I

incomplete combustion Combustion that results when products other than CO_2 and water vapor are produced by incineration.

inductive reasoning A pattern of thinking in which observations are used as a means for creating general rules.

integrated pest management (IMP) An agricultural method aimed at reducing the total volume of pesticides that are sprayed.

intergenus Involving members of different species but of the same genus.

interspecies Involving members of the same species.

interspecies competition The interactions between two different species.

intraspecies competition The interactions between two members of the same species.

invasive species A non-native species introduced into an ecosystem that can disturb the balance when in competition with native species.

K

K-type reproduction Style of reproduction characterized by low births, high energy in, and high survivability.

kwashiorkor A type of protein-energy malnourishment that is characterized by muscle atrophy and organ failure.

L

land use The way in which a particular parcel of land is used.

leaching The action of water and chemicals flowing through the soil into groundwater.

limiting factor Something that restricts the growth of a desired entity.

lithosphere The outermost layer of the Earth and the upper section of the mantle. The crust is only a small portion of the lithosphere.

M

malnourishment Lack of food and proper nutrition and its effect on people.

marasmus A type of malnutrition often associated with protein-energy malnourishment that is characterized by edema and sagging skin.

marine dumping The discarding of trash into the ocean.

maximum contaminant level goals Values that provide a threshold for measuring the level of contaminant in drinking water; these numbers represent levels at which the contaminant poses no known health risk to humans.

maximum contaminant level The highest amount of a contaminant that can be present in drinking water used for human consumption.

megacity A very large urban area with a population above 10 million people.

megafauna Large animals generally found on Earth up to the Ice Age.

microclimate A small area that has a different climate than neighboring areas; may be as small as a few square yards.

mineralizable N The amount of available nitrogen that can be converted from organic forms of nitrogen to inorganic forms.

mineralization The transformation (by specialized bacteria) of organic forms of nitrogen, phosphorus, and potassium into inorganic forms that can be absorbed by plants.

minimum data set (MDS) The smallest number of parameters that can be tested to create a reasonable assessment of a system.

mobile sources Sources such as highway vehicles and off road equipment that emit compounds known or suspected to cause cancer or other serious health and environmental effects.

modernization An evolutionary process in which society changes to support the needs of its inhabitants.

mollisol A soil order characterized by fertile, wind-deposited soils.

mountaintop removal mining The practice of using heavy equipment and explosives to remove the top layer of material of a mountain in order to more easily reach the minerals or fuel.

N

nationalization To change from private ownership to government or public control.

nitrogen fixation Biological process in which bacteria living in soil (and symbiotically with plants) transform and store nitrogen compounds that can be readily used by plants.

nitrogen pollution (eutrophication) An overabundance of the nutrient nitrogen, which runs off agricultural land and is harmful to the environment, primarily to aquatic ecosystems.

non-conventional pollutants Pollutants not classified as priority or conventional pollutants.

non-point source Water pollution that cannot be traced back to a single point of origin.

non-renewable energy resources Energy sources that exist in limited supply and cannot be regenerated once consumed.

nuclear fission The process that occurs when one atom splits into two, releasing energy.

O

off-road mobile sources of air pollution Vehicles and engines used in construction, agriculture, and recreation.

omnivore An organism whose normal diet includes both plants and animals.

on-road mobile sources of air pollution Sources of air pollution such as vehicles, trucks, and motorcycles.

opportunity costs The loss of potential gain from other alternatives when one alternative is chosen.

organic material Carbon-based material generally from a plant or animal.

organic material Decomposed plant and other carbon-based material.

overexploitation Stressing of a species due to overhunting, overfishing, or overcollection.

overfishing A situation in which excessive amounts of fish are captured, reducing the fish population to unsustainable levels.

ozone A reactive gas that consists of molecules with three oxygen atoms (O_3).

ozone-depleting substances Manmade chemicals that destroy the ozone layer.

P

pandemic Widespread or global epidemic, often referring to a disease.

parasitism Form of interaction where one organism survives by feeding on another organism without initially killing it.

particulate control methods Methods to separate particulate matter from the gases in which these materials are contained.

particulates Tiny pieces of matter released into the air through combustion or industrial activities or from sources such as fires or volcanic activity.

permafrost A layer of topsoil that is frozen year-round, found primarily in tundra regions.

permeable The quality of a medium that refers to the ability of liquids or gases to pass through it.

photosynthesis The process by which plants convert light energy into chemical energy.

phytoremediation The use of plants or algae to absorb and clean pollutants in the environment.

piscicide A substance used to kill fish.

plant incorporated protectants Genetically inserted proteins that aid a plant in resistance to a pest.

point source Pollution released in quantities above a particular threshold or standard and that can be traced back to a point of origin.

point sources Large sources of pollutants that come from specific locations and are emitted in quantities above a particular threshold or standard.

population momentum When the population continues to grow larger, (beyond the need to replace population from mortality or emigration) even though average people are having fewer children. This may occur when children are born during an economic transition. Eventually, the number of childbearing adults decreases, resulting in a lower birth rate.

primary pollutants Pollutants that are directly released into the atmosphere, remaining in their original form.

priority pollutants Pollutants that pose a substantial risk to human and environmental health.

privatization To change from government or public control to private ownership.

process vents Openings where gases are vented into the atmosphere.

protein-energy malnourishment The most dangerous form of malnourishment, caused by a lack of sufficient protein.

public lands Land held by the federal government or state governments.

public water systems Water systems that provide water service to at least 25 individuals or have 15 service connections and operate at least 60 days a year.

R

r-type reproduction Style of reproduction characterized by high births, low energy in, and low survivability.

raptor A bird of prey.

recessive Refers to a gene that is expressed when there are two alleles present.

recruitment overfishing The situation in which too many mature adults from a species are extracted, reducing reproduction of the species.

redox potential The potential of a chemical to add or lose electrons; also known as oxidation-reduction potential.

regulation A rule issued by a government agency that has the force of law.

relay planting A method of agriculture where the same plant variety is planted over a staggered time period to ensure crop yield throughout the growing season.

remedial action plan A plan devised to restore a habitat or clean up a contaminant.

renewable energy resources Energy resources that are not depleted through use.

replacement rate The number of people that are needed in order to maintain a population; these can come from either births or migration.

riparian area A vegetative transitional area between a developed or cleared area and a waterway.

riparian buffer zones A strip of undisturbed forest land running parallel to the shoreline of a waterway, designed to protect the waterway from the land's use.

rootstock The portion of a plant used in splicing that includes the roots and a portion of trunk.

RUSLE Acronym for Revised Universal Soil Loss Equation, used to calculate estimated soil loss in tons per acre per year.

S

Safe Drinking Water Act (SDWA) Federal legislation that sets national standards for drinking water quality.

salinity Concentration of salt found in a solution, generally measured in parts per thousand (ppt).

saltwater intrusion A process by which sea water infiltrates freshwater aquifers.

scientific method A multi-step process used in a logical and systematic manner to acquire new information, observe phenomena, and/or disprove or modify existing knowledge.

scion A portion of a branch with growing buds that is attached to the rootstock during splicing.

secondary pollutants Pollutants that are formed when primary pollutants react with substances in the atmosphere.

sewage A subset of wastewater that contains the human wastes urine and feces.

shantytown A makeshift settlement built out of rudimentary or improvised building materials, such as corrugated metal sheets and scrap lumber.

smart growth policies Policies enacted by local, regional, and state governments to reduce urban sprawl and maintain controlled and regulated growth.

Smog Pollutant released when nitrous oxide compounds become trapped in fog and are exposed to sunlight.

soil degradation The decrease of soil quality from alterations in the ecosystem.

sound science Research conducted by qualified persons that leads to verifiable results.

species diversity The variety of species in an ecosystem.

spin The portrayal of information in a way that conveys specific aspects of research and/or data to convey a particular opinion, attitude, or belief.

splicing Method of artificially creating desired plant effects by joining a scion from one plant to the rootstock of another.

stakeholders Any group of people that have a vested interest in an area, event, or outcome.

stationary sources of air pollution Non-moving, fixed sources of air pollution, such as power plants, cement plans, and industrial facilities.

storm water Water produced during precipitation (e.g., rain or snow) as well as water that originates from melting snow and ice.

stratosphere Upper level of the atmosphere located between 10 and 50 km (6 and 30 miles) above the Earth's surface.

strip mining The removal of topsoil and other material to obtain natural resources.

successive planting A method of agriculture in which different varieties of plants are rotated in and out of the same location.

succulents Group of plants often found in dry or arid climates, characterized by fleshy leaves and trunks specially adapted to store water.

surface runoff Excess water that cannot be absorbed into the soil and remains on the Earth's surface.

sustainable development The process of utilizing current resources to meet human and environmental needs without compromising the needs of future generations.

sustainable forest A managed forest environment in which mature trees that are cut are replaced with seedlings.

sustainable seafood Seafood products that are obtained from fishing or aquaculture organizations that do not jeopardize the environment.

symbiotic A relationship between organisms that benefits both parties.

systems perspective Used in sustainable agriculture to make operating decisions based on the local ecosystem, the needs of the surrounding community, and governing bodies overseeing a farm.

T

taiga Biome defined by low temperatures, harsh winter, primarily evergreen trees, and low biodiversity.

temperate deciduous forest Biome defined by moderate temperatures and weather and deciduous trees.

terracing A style of agriculture that involves creating levels of planting rows on a hill, much like steps. Terracing is a very common practice in mountainous Asian rice farms.

theory A hypothesis that has been repeatedly supported through ongoing experimentation and review.

topography The elevation and geographic layout ofan area.

topography The surface features of land including mountains, plains, and plateaus.

total extinction The complete loss of a species from Earth.

trophic cascade The effect of an addition or deletion to an ecosystem that transfers up or down the food web.

tropical rainforest Biome defined by high temperatures, high humidity, and heavy rainfall year around.

tundra Biome defined by very low temperature and very low biodiversity.

turbidity Cloudiness or haziness of water.

turbulence The horizontal and vertical motion of air in the atmosphere.

U

uranium A heavy silvery-white metallic element, radioactive and toxic, easily oxidized, and having 14 known isotopes, of which U238 is the most abundant in nature.

urban sprawl The increase in area of a population center as it expands beyond its center.

urbanization The increase in population density as people move from rural areas to more urban areas.

V

virtual water The total amount of water used to produce a product.

volatility The ease with which a liquid evaporates.

W

wastewater Any water after human use found to contain materials or substances that are harmful to human or environmental health.

wastewater treatment The removal of contaminants from wastewater such that the effluent can be discharged safely back into the environment.

water holding capacity The ability for a soil to retain water from rain or irrigation events.

water pollution Foreign materials added to water.

welfare effects The changes to land, soil, water, climate, and visibility that result from air pollution.

wet acid deposition Occurs when acids suspended in the atmosphere fall to the Earth's surface via rain, snow, or fog.

PHOTO CREDITS

Chapter 1: Opener, p. 2: © arsdigital (Fotolia); p. 5, top: © Georgios Kollidas (Fotolia); p. 5, bottom: © jojje11; p. 6: © Luftbildfotograf (Fotolia); p. 8: © Dudarev Mikhail (Fotolia); p. 9: © adimas (Fotolia); p. 11: © anweber (Fotolia); p. 12: © martin33 (Fotolia); p. 13: © iofoto (Fotolia); p. 14: © herreneck (Fotolia); p. 15: © Boca (Fotolia); p. 16: © Anchels (Fotolia); p. 17: © Andrea Danti (Fotolia); p. 18: © Anioł (Fotolia); p. 19: © T.Tulic (Fotolia); p. 20: © Galina Barskaya (Fotolia); p. 22: © Anobis (Fotolia).

Chapter 2: Opener, p. 26: © Kenneth Sponsler (Fotolia); p. 29: © Les Cunliffe (Fotolia); p. 30: © Aleksander Bolbot (Fotolia); p. 31: © Frederic Bos (Fotolia); p. 33: 2006 by The National Arbor Day Foundation; p. 36: © Richard Carey (Fotolia); p. 37: © Blinztree (Fotolia); p. 38: © Bastos (Fotolia); p. 41: © Alta Oosthuizen (Fotolia); p. 42: © glen gaffney (Fotolia); p. 43: © Les Cunliffe (Fotolia); p. 44: © cubephoto (Fotolia); p. 46: © ETIEN (Fotolia); p. 48: © DLeonis (Fotolia); p. 51: © Tim Markley (Fotolia); p. 52: © Vitos (Fotolia).

Chapter 3: Opener, p. 56: © Krzysztof Czuba (Fotolia); p. 58: © John Casey (Fotolia); p. 61: © bacalao (Fotolia); p. 62: © Vladimir Wrangel (Fotolia); p. 64: © Oleg Kozlov (Fotolia); p. 66: © Adrian Hillman (Fotolia); p. 68: © Distinctive Images (Fotolia); p. 72: © TheFinalMiracle (Fotolia).

Chapter 4: Opener, p. 78: © Dansar@live.it; p. 80, top: © Feng Yu (Fotolia); p. 80, bottom-left: © africa (Fotolia); p. 80, bottom-right: © shirophoto (Fotolia); p. 82: © Scott Latham (Fotolia); p. 83: © Henrik Larsson (Fotolia); p. 84: © Gewoldi (Fotolia); p. 86: © jo (Fotolia); p. 88: © Cifotart (Fotolia); p. 91: © Smithore (Fotolia).

Chapter 5: Opener, p. 94: © alisonhancock (Fotolia); p. 96: © DeshaCAM (Fotolia); p. 97: © Richard Griffin (Fotolia); p. 98: © ASP (Fotolia); p. 101: © Elenathewise (Fotolia); p. 103: © Denis Pepin (Fotolia); p. 106: © Phillip Minnis (Fotolia); p. 107: © Klaus Eppele (Fotolia); p. 109: © abet (Fotolia); p. 110: © alisonhancock (Fotolia); p. 113: © africa (Fotolia); p. 115: © KaYann (Fotolia); p. 118: © ggw (Fotolia); p. 120: © DLeonis (Fotolia).

Chapter 6: Opener, p. 124: © novaga (Fotolia); p. 126, top: © Tommy (Fotolia); p. 126, bottom: © antiksu (Fotolia); p. 127: © bizoo_n (Fotolia); p. 129: © Andrea Danti (Fotolia); p. 130: © federicofoto (Fotolia); p. 131: © africa (Fotolia); p. 133: © Elenathewise (Fotolia); p. 135: © antiksu (Fotolia); p. 140: © Dima_Rogozhin (Fotolia); p. 141: © Papo (Fotolia); p. 142: © Moreno Novello (Fotolia); p. 144: © wildcoastphoto (Fotolia); p. 145: © Brenda Carson (Fotolia); p. 148: © haveseen (Fotolia).

Chapter 7: Opener, p. 152: © multilisks (Fotolia); p. 154: © Stefan Redel (Fotolia); p. 155: © Algost (Fotolia); p. 157: © Juburg (Fotolia); p. 162: © Eric Isselée (Fotolia); p. 164: © photka (Fotolia); p. 166: © Tomasz Bidermann (Fotolia); p. 167: © trekandshoot (Fotolia); p. 171: http://c3headlines.typepad.com; p. 173: © tezzstock (Fotolia); p. 178: © Sergey Tokarev (Fotolia); p. 180: © iQoncept (Fotolia).

Chapter 8: Opener, p. 184: © Danicek (Fotolia); p. 186: © Ritu Jethani (Fotolia); p. 188: © Igor Kovalenko (Fotolia); p. 190: © endostock (Fotolia); p. 192: © cec72 (Fotolia); p. 194: © Kwadri (Fotolia); p. 196, top: © Gunter_Nezhoda (Fotolia); p. 196, bottom: © Y. L. Photographies (Fotolia); p. 197: © Andrzej Tokarski (Fotolia); p. 198: © ermess (Fotolia); p. 200: © Andrea Izzotti (Fotolia); p. 204: © Gary Blakeley (Fotolia); p. 206: © lorcel (Fotolia); p. 207: © Bryan Busovicki (Fotolia).

Chapter 9: Opener, p. 214: © Maria.P (Fotolia); p. 216: © tomas (Fotolia); p. 218: © IRC (Fotolia); p. 244: © Pavle (Fotolia); p. 226: © Jim Barber (Fotolia); p. 229: © andreiorlov (Fotolia); p. 232: © Darren Baker (Fotolia); p. 234: © O.M. (Fotolia); p. 235: © wajan (Fotolia); p. 238: © Laurence Gough (Fotolia); p. 239: © JackF (Fotolia).

Chapter 10: Opener, p. 244: © Željko Radojko (Fotolia); p. 246: © MasterLu (Fotolia); p. 247: © iofoto (Fotolia); p. 249: © PixelThat (Fotolia); p. 252: © simon gurney (Fotolia); p. 253: © Eli Coory; p. 255 (Fotolia): © Radu Razvan (Fotolia); p. 257: © Mykola Mazuryk (Fotolia); p. 258: Natural Resources Conservation Service of the United States Department of Agriculture (USDA-NRCS); p. 260: © AZP Worldwide; (Fotolia) p. 261: © indykb (Fotolia); p. 263: © Yuri Kravchenko (Fotolia); p. 265: © Jun Dangoy (Fotolia); p. 267: © Alexander Kataytsev (Fotolia); p. 268: © Helder Almeida (Fotolia); p. 270: © picsfive (Fotolia); p. 272: © ChristopheB; (Fotolia) p. 276: © Nabok Volodymyr (Fotolia); p. 277: © Alexey Stiop (Fotolia)

REFERENCES

Chapter 1

Canning, K. (2009). The art of transformation. *Private Label Buyer*, 23(8), 20–26.

Climate tension. (2005, July 5). *PBS News*. Retrieved from http://www.pbs.org/newshour/bb/environment/july-dec05/climate_7-5.html

Dykstra, P. (2008, December 15). History of environmental movement full of twists, turns. *CNN*. Retrieved from http://articles.cnn.com/2008-12-10/tech/history.environmental.movement_1_fierce-green-fire-american-environmental-movement-philip-shabecoff/2?_s=PM:TECHEuropean Commission. (2010).

Energy 2020. Luxembourg: Publications Office of the European Union. Retrieved from http://ec.europa.eu/energy/publications/doc/2011_energy2020_en.pdf

European Environment Agency. (n.d.). About climate change. Retrieved from http://www.eea.europa.eu/themes/climate/about-climate-change

European Environment Agency. (n.d.). Biodiversity. Retrieved from http://www.eea.europa.eu/themes/biodiversity

European Environment Agency. (2012, March 26). Climate change policies. Retrieved from http://www.eea.europa.eu/themes/climate/policy-context

Environmental Protection Agency. (2010). Air pollution. Retrieved from http://epa.gov/airtrends/2010/report/airpollution.pdf

Fischetti, M. (2011, December 1). Fukushima earthquake moved seafloor half a football field. *Scientific American*. Retrieved from http://www.scientificamerican.com/article.cfm?id=japan-earthquake-moves-seafloor

Ghadar, F. (2005). Population: Shifting demographics. *Industrial Management*, 47(5), 8–13.

Law. (1979). In *Oxford English Dictionary*. Oxford University Press.

National Aeronautics and Space Administration. (2012). Global climate change: Key indicators. Retrieved from http://climate.nasa.gov/keyIndicators/

National Institute for Environmental Studies. (n.d.). Environmental issues in developing countries. Retrieved from http://www.nies.go.jp/gaiyo/panf2002/developing/developing-e.html

National Snow and Ice Data Center. (2012). Arctic sea ice news and analysis. Retrieved from http://nsidc.org/arcticseaicenews/

National Wildlife Federation. (n.d.). Global warming and polar bears. Retrieved from http://www.nwf.org/Global-Warming/Effects-on-Wildlife-and-Habitat/Polar-Bears.aspx

Pool, R. (2011). Fukushima: The facts. *Engineering & Technology*, 6(4), 32–36.

Schleibe, S. (n.d.). What has been happening to polar bears in recent decades? National Oceanic and Atmospheric Administration. Retrieved from http://www.arctic.noaa.gov/essay_schliebe.html

Scientific method. (2013). In *Merriam-Webster Online Dictionary*. Retrieved from http://www.merriam-webster.com/dictionary/scientific%20method

U.S. Census Bureau. (n.d.). International data base: World population summary. Retrieved from http://www.census.gov/population/international/data/idb/worldpopinfo.php

U.S. Department of Energy. (2012). Fuel economy guide: Model year 2012 (Report No. DOE/EE-0603). Retrieved from http://www.fueleconomy.gov/feg/pdfs/guides/FEG2012.pdf

U.S. Energy Information Administration. (2009). *Annual energy review*. Retrieved from http://www.eia.gov/totalenergy/data/annual/pdf/aer.pdf

U.S. Environmental Protection Agency. (2009, June 2). Smog/regional transport of ozone. Retrieved from http://www.epa.gov/airmarkt/envissues/smog.html

Vidal, J., & Adam, D. (2007, June 19). China overtakes US as world's biggest CO2 emitter. *The Guardian*. Retrieved from: http://www.guardian.co.uk/environment/2007/jun/19/china.usnews

The World Bank. (2013). World Bank atlas method. Retrieved from http://data.worldbank.org/about/country-classifications/world-bank-atlas-method

World Health Organization. (n.d.). Health statistics: Mortality. Retrieved from http://www.who.int/healthinfo/statistics/indunder5mortality/en/

Chapter 2

American Recreation Coalition. (n.d.). Camping and hiking: Growth in recent years. Retrieved from http://www.funoutdoors.com/research

Arizona-Sonora Desert Museum. (n.d.). Genus yucca. Retrieved from http://www.desertmuseum.org/books/nhsd_yucca.php

Aronova-Tiuntseva, Y., & Herreid, C. F. (2003). Hemophilia: "The royal disease." Retrieved from http://sciencecases.lib.buffalo.edu/cs/files/hemo.pdf

Australian Department of Sustainability, Environment, Water, Populations and Communities. (2002). Rabbits are weeds too! [Invasive species fact sheet]. Retrieved from http://www.environment.gov.au/biodiversity/invasive/publications/too.html

Beck, E. (1979). The Love Canal tragedy. Retrieved from http://www.epa.gov/aboutepa/history/topics/lovecanal/01.html

Berens, D., Boudewyns, C., Chmielewski, S., Flehmer, K., Solin, S., Weber, K., & Wichlacz, A. (n.d.). Extinction, the death of everything: Causes of extinction. Retrieved from http://www.uwec.edu/jolhm/EH4/Extinction/CausesLink.html

Biome. (2013). In *Encyclopædia Britannica Online*. Retrieved from http://www.britannica.com/EBchecked/topic/66133/biome

Bird Houses 101. (n.d.). Bird watching interesting facts and statistics. Retrieved from http://www.birdhouses101.com/Bird-Watching-Interesting-Facts-Statistics.asp

Blue Planet Biomes. (n.d.). World biomes: Biome regions. Retrieved from http://www.blueplanetbiomes.org/world_biomes.htm

Broughton, E. (2004) The Bhopal disaster and its aftermath: A review. Retrieved from http://www.ncbi.nlm.nih.gov/pmc/articles/PMC1142333/

Chesapeake Bay Foundation. (n.d.). Our mission. Retrieved from http://www.cbf.org/page.aspx?pid=515

Cuyahoga River Community Planning Organization. (n.d.). Cuyahoga River Remedial Action Plan. Retrieved from http://www.cuyahogariverrap.org/

Day, K. (1996, December). Agriculture's links to biodiversity. *Agricultural Outlook, AO-236*, 32–37.

Ducks Unlimited. (n.d.). Leader in wetlands conservation. Retrieved from http://www.ducksunlimited.org/conservation

Ecological Society of America. (2007). Biodiversity. Retrieved from http://www.esa.org/education_diversity/pdfDocs/biodiversity.pdf

Earth Institute, Columbia University. (2010, January 22). *2000–2009: The Warmest Decade: Long Term Rise in Global Temperature Unabated*. Retrieved from http://www.earth.columbia.edu/articles/view/2620

Ecosystem. (2013). In *Merriam-Webster Online Dictionary*. Retrieved from http://www.merriam-webster.com/dictionary/ecosystem

Falls Brook Centre International Work: Cuba. (n.d.). Retrieved from http://www.fallsbrookcentre.ca/fbc/wp-content/uploads/2010/09/Cuba-Biodiversity-Restoration.pdf

Ford Motor Company. (2011). Sustainability report 2010/2011. Retrieved from http://corporate.ford.com/microsites/sustainability-report-2010-11/environment-operations-buildings

Greenberg, N. (2011, October 1). Deep ethology. Retrieved from https://notes.utk.edu/bio/greenberg.nsf/0/14f2db31736becfa852571fe004f3765?OpenDocument

Koel, T., Irons, K., & Ratcliff, E. (2000, November). *Asian carp invasion of the upper Mississippi River system* (U.S. Geological Survey Report No. PSR 2000-05). Retrieved from http://www.umesc.usgs.gov/reports_publications/psrs/psr_2000_05.html

Lateral Line, Inc. (2008). All about striped bass. Retrieved from http://www.laterallineco.com/fishing_journal/striped_bass/striped_bass_history_st ripedbass_migration_pattern.html

L.L. Bean. (n.d.). L.L. Bean and the environment. Retrieved from http://www.llbean.com/customerService/aboutLLBean/environment.html

National Oceanic and Atmospheric Administration, National Climatic Data Center. (2010, December). *State of the climate 2010*. National Oceanic and Atmospheric Administration. Retrieved from http://www.ncdc.noaa.gov/sotc/2010/13

National Oceanic and Atmospheric Administration. (n.d.). What is ocean acidification? Retrieved from http://www.pmel.noaa.gov/co2/story/What+is+Ocean+Acidification%3F

National Park Service. (n.d.) Welcome to Bridger-Teton National Park. Retrieved from http://www.fs.usda.gov/main/btnf/home

Parks Canada. (2013, February 22). Mountain pine beetle. Retrieved from http://www.pc.gc.ca/pn-np/ab/banff/natcul/natcul22.aspx

The Outdoor Industry Foundation. (2006, fall). *The active outdoor recreation economy*. Retrieved from http://www.outdoorindustry.org/images/researchfiles/RecEconomypublic.pdf?26

Pierzynski, Gary M., Sims, J. T., & Vance, G. F. (2005). *Soils and environmental quality* (3rd ed., pp. 73–83). Boca Raton, FL: Taylor & Francis.

Scott, M. (2009, June 22). Cuyahoga River fire 40 years ago ignited an ongoing cleanup campaign. *The Plain Dealer*. Retrieved from http://www.cleveland.com/science/index.ssf/2009/06/cuyahoga_river_fire_40_years_a.html

Scott, M. (2010, January 4). After the flames: The story behind the 1969 Cuyahoga River fire and its recovery. *The Plain Dealer*. Retrieved from http://blog.cleveland.com/metro/2009/01/after_the_flames_the_story_beh.html

Smith, D. W., & Bangs, E. E. (2009). Reintroduction of wolves to Yellowstone National Park: History, values and ecosystem restoration. In M. W. Hayward & M. J. Somers (Eds.), *Reintroduction of top-order predators* (pp. 92–125). Oxford, UK: Wiley-Blackwell. doi: 10.1002/9781444312034.ch5

Starbucks. (n.d.). Environmental stewardship. Retrieved from http://www.starbucks.com/responsibility/environment

United Nations Educational, Scientific, and Cultural Organization. (n.d.) World Heritage list. Retrieved from http://whc.unesco.org/en/list

United Nations Environmental Programme. (n.d.). Nagoya 2010: Hardwiring biodiversity and ecosystem services into finance. Retrieved from http://new.unep.org/ Documents.Multilingual/Default.asp?DocumentID=649&ArticleID=6801&l=en&t=long

United Nations Framework Convention on Climate Change. (n.d.). Panama Climate Change Conference—October 2011. Retrieved from http://unfccc.int/meetings/panama_oct_2011/meeting/6247.php

United Nations Habitat. (2008, November 13). Winners of Dubai Award named. Retrieved from http://www.unhabitat.org/content.asp?cid=4143&catid=5&typeid=6&subMenuId=0

USAID. (2011, May 3). Introduction to the Enterprise for the Americas Initiative (EAI) funds. Retrieved from http://transition.usaid.gov/our_work/environment/forestry/intro_eai.html

USAID. (2011, May 2). Introduction to the Tropical Forest Conservation Act (TFCA). Retrieved from http://transition.usaid.gov/our_work/environment/forestry/intro_tfca.html

U.S. Department of Agriculture. (2013, April 30). National Invasive Species Information Center (NISIC): Gateway to invasive species information; covering federal, state, local, and international sources. Retrieved from http://www.invasivespeciesinfo.gov/

U.S. Environmental Protection Agency. (n.d.). History of the Clean Water Act. Retrieved from http://www.epa.gov/lawsregs/laws/cwahistory.html

U.S. Environmental Protection Agency. (2011, August 9). Superfund's 30th anniversary: 30 years of protecting communities and the environment. Retrieved from http://www.epa.gov/superfund/30years/

U.S. Environmental Protection Agency. (2012, May 9). DDT: A brief history and status [Fact sheet]. Retrieved from http://www.epa.gov/opp00001/factsheets/chemicals/ddt-brief-history-status.htm

Waldman, A. (2002). Bhopal seethes, pained and poor 18 years later. Retrieved from http://www.nytimes.com/2002/09/21/world/bhopal-seethes-pained-and-poor-18-years-later.html

Chapter 3

The American Institute of Architects. (n.d.). Why are architects and green buildings so important? Retrieved from http://info.aia.org/toolkit2030/advocacy/architects-green-building.html

The Appalachian Regional Commission. (n.d.). The Appalachian region. Retrieved from http://www.arc.gov/appalachian_region/TheAppalachianRegion.asp

Bryner, J. (2009, September 16). Teen birth rates higher in highly religious states. *Live Science*. Retrieved from http://www.livescience.com/5728-teen-birth-rates-higher-highly-religious-states.html

Cadman, M. (2007, March). *Consuming wild life: the illegal exploitation of wild animals in South Africa, Zimbabwe and Zambia: A preliminary report*. Animal Rights Africa and Xwe African Wild Life.

Centers for Disease Control and Prevention. (2012, August 13). Adult obesity facts [Fact sheet]. Retrieved from http://www.cdc.gov/obesity/data/trends.html

Central Intelligence Agency. (n.d.). The world factbook. Retrieved from https://www.cia.gov/library/publications/the-world-factbook/geos/ke.html

Cohen, J. E. (1995). *How many people can the earth support* (pp. 11–12). New York, NY: Norton Books. Retrieved from http://books.wwnorton.com/books/detail-inside.aspx?ID=13204&CTYPE=G

Dart and Beaumont, 1971, p. 10; Bednarik, 1992, p. 15; Dart and Beaumont, 1967; Vermeersch and Paulissen, 1989, p. 36.

Economy Watch. (2013, May 6). European Union GDP per capita (PPP), US dollars statistics. Retrieved from http://www.economywatch.com/economic-statistics/European-Union/GDP_Per_Capita_PPP_US_Dollars/

Economy Watch. (n.d.). Korea (South Korea) GDP per capita (PPP), US dollars statistics. Retrieved from http://www.economywatch.com/economic-statistics/Korea/GDP_Per_Capita_PPP_US_Dollars/U.S. Food and Drug Administration. (2013, April 24).

How to dispose of unused drugs. Retrieved from http://www.fda.gov/ForConsumers/ConsumerUpdates/ucm101653.htm?utm_campaign=Google2&utm_source=fdaSearch&utm_medium=website&utm_term=pharmaceutical%20waste%20disposal&utm_content=7

Fengler, W. (2010, April 15). Can rapid population growth be good for economic development? [Web log post]. Retrieved from http://blogs.worldbank.org/africacan/can-rapid-population-growth-be-good-for-economic-development

Food and Agriculture Organization of the United Nations. (2002, January). The developing world's new burden: Obesity. Retrieved from http://www.fao.org/FOCUS/E/obesity/obes1.htm

Global Health Council. (2011). Causes of child death. Retrieved from http://www.globalhealth.org/child_health/child_mortality/causes_death/

Green Building Certification Institute. (n.d.). Credential maintenance program. Retrieved from http://www.gbci.org/main-nav/cmp/credential-maintenance-program.aspx

Greenpeace International. (2009, February 24). Where does e-waste end up? Retrieved from http://www.greenpeace.org/international/en/campaigns/toxics/electronics/the-e-waste-problem/where-does-e-waste-end-up/

Guest, R. (2005, July 6). Why has South Korea overtaken Kenya? Because its rulers can limit their greed. *The Telegraph*. Retrieved from http://www.telegraph.co.uk/news/uknews/1493489/Why-has-South-Korea-overtaken-Kenya-Because-its-rulers-can-limit-their-greed.html

Hansen, Z. (Ed.). (n.d.). Population control, India. Retrieved from http://www.colby.edu/personal/t/thtieten/Famplan.htm

International Institute for Applied Systems Analysis. (1996). IIASA population projection results. Retrieved from http://www.iiasa.ac.at/Research/POP/docs/Population_Projections_Results.html

International Monetary Fund. (2013). About the IMF. Retrieved from http://www.imf.org/external/about.htm

Jones, A. (2010, February 14). Case study: Genocide in Rwanda, 1994. *Gendercide Watch*. Retrieved from http://www.gendercide.org/case_rwanda.html

Kane, P., & Choi, C. Y. (1999). China's One Child Family Policy. *British Medical Journal, 319*(7215), 992–994. Retrieved from http://www.ncbi.nlm.nih.gov/pmc/articles/PMC1116810/

Kurtz, S. (2005). Demographics and the culture war. *Policy Review, 129*. Retrieved from http://www.hoover.org/publications/policy-review/article/7123

Labs, E. J. (1997, September). *The role of foreign aid in development: South Korea and the Philippines* (Congressional Budget Office Memorandum). Retrieved from http://www.cbo.gov/doc.cfm?index=4306&type=0

Montgomery, K. (n.d.). The demographic transition. Retrieved from http://www.marathon.uwc.edu/geography/demotrans/demtran.htm

Nash, J. (2010, December 7). Full ranking: America's healthiest and unhealthiest states. *Forbes.com*. Retrieved from http://www.forbes.com/2010/12/06/healthiest-unhealthiest-states-lifestyle-health-uhc-table.html

National Heart Lung and Blood Institute. (2012, July 13). What are overweight and obesity? Retrieved from http://www.nhlbi.nih.gov/health/health-topics/topics/obe/

Passel, J., Cohn, D, & Lopez, M. H. (2011, March 24). *Hispanics account for more than half of the nation's growth in past decade.* Pew Hispanic Center, Pew Research Center. Retrieved from http://www.pewhispanic.org/2011/03/24/hispanics-account-for-more-than-half-of-nations-growth-in-past-decade/

Ploiomyelitis. (n.d.). Retrieved from http://www.princeton.edu/~achaney/tmve/wiki100k/docs/Poliomyelitis.html

Schorr, A. (1965). Income maintenance and the birth rate. *Social Security Bulletin, 28*, 22–30. Retrieved from www.ssa.gov/policy/docs/ssb/v28n12/v28n12p22.pdf

U.S. Census Bureau. (n.d.). U.S. population projections. Retrieved from http://www.census.gov/population/www/projections/2009projections.html

U.S. Environmental Protection Agency. (2011). 2011 U.S. greenhouse gas inventory. Retrieved from http://www.epa.gov/climatechange/emissions/usinventoryreport.html

U.S. Environmental Protection Agency. (2012, November 14). Wastes—Resource conservation—Common wastes and materials: eCycling. Retrieved from http://www.epa.gov/osw/conserve/materials/ecycling/faq.htm#howmuch

U.S. Environmental Protection Agency. (2013, May 2). Mid-Atlantic mountaintop mining. Retrieved from http://www.epa.gov/region3/mtntop/

United Nations Economic and Social Council. (2011, April 14). Speakers link higher education among girls to declining fertility rates as Commission on Population and Development continues session [Press release]. Retrieved from http://www.un.org/News/Press/docs/2011/pop994.doc.htm

United Nations Population Fund. (2007). Peering into the dawn of an urban millennium. Introduction to *UNFPA state of the world population 2007*. Retrieved from http://www.unfpa.org/swp/2007/english/print/introduction.html

Vincent, G. K., & Velkoff, V. A. (2010, May). *The next four decades: The older population in the United States: 2010 to 2050: population estimates and projections* (Current Population Report No. 25-1138). Retrieved from http://www.census.gov/prod/2010pubs/p25-1138.pdf

The World Bank. (2011). Mortality rate, infant (per 1,000 live births). Retrieved from http://data.worldbank.org/indicator/SP.DYN.IMRT.IN

World Health Organization. (2011, June). Electronic fields and public health: Mobile phones [Fact sheet]. Retrieved from http://www.who.int/mediacentre/factsheets/fs193/en/

World Health Organization. (2013). Health and environment linkages initiative. Retrieved from http://www.who.int/heli/en/

World Health Organization. (2013, March). Obesity and overweight [Fact sheet]. Retrieved from http://www.who.int/mediacentre/factsheets/fs311/en/

World Health Organization. (2013). Pneumonia is the leading cause of death in children. Retrieved from http://www.who.int/maternal_child_adolescent/news_events/news/2011/pneumonia/en/

World Health Organization. (2013). Vector-borne disease. Retrieved from http://www.who.int/heli/risks/vectors/vector/en/index.html

Yellowstone National Park. (n.d.). Wildlife—wolves. Retrieved from http://www.yellowstonenationalpark.com/wolves.htm

Zuehlke, E. (2009, April). *Changes in fertility among Muslims in India, Pakistan and Bangladesh.* Population reference Bureau. Retrieved from http://www.prb.org/Articles/2009/karimpolicyseminar.aspx

Chapter 4

Anbumozhi, V., & Bauer, A. (2012). *Impact of global recession on sustainable development and poverty linkages.* Tokyo, Japan: Asian Development Bank Institute. Retrieved from http://www.adbi.org/working-paper/2010/07/08/3933.impact.global.recession.dev.poverty.linkages/

Asante-Darko, K. (2009, September 4). *Africa, the global recession and climate change.* EastWest Institute. Retrieved from http://blog.nielsen.com/nielsenwire/consumer/the-state-of-the-global-consumer-spending-trends/

Birn, A-E., Pillay, Y., & Holtz, T. H. (2009*). Textbook of international health: Global health in a dynamic world* (3rd ed., pp. 150–153). New York, NY: Oxford University Press

Brown, L. R. (2001, May 29). China's dust bowl is growing at an alarming rate. *Grist*. Retrieved from http://grist.org/article/grossman-bites/

California Department of Food and Agriculture. (2012). California agricultural production statistics. Retrieved from http://www.cdfa.ca.gov/statistics/

The Carter Center. (n.d.). River Blindness Program. Retrieved from http://www.cartercenter.org/health/river_blindness/index.html

Central Intelligence Agency. (2012). *The world fact book, 2012–2013*. Retrieved from https://www.cia.gov/library/publications/the-world-factbook/appendix/appendix-b.html#D

Colorado River Management, Arizona Department of Water Resources. (2012). Lower Colorado River Multi-Species Conservation Program. Retrieved from http://www.azwater.gov/azdwr/statewideplanning/crm/environmentalprograms.htm

Greenpeace International. (2009, February 24). Where does e-waste end up? Retrieved from http://www.greenpeace.org/international/en/campaigns/toxics/electronics/the-e-waste-problem/where-does-e-waste-end-up/

Kamakura, W. A., & Du, R. Y. (2011). How economic contractions and expansions affect expenditure patterns. *Journal of Consumer Research, 39*. Retrieved from http://www.bauer.uh.edu/rexdu/how%20economic%20contractions%20and%20expansions%20affect%20expenditure%20patterns.pdf

Erasmus, M. (2011, July 18). Feeding China: Africa's other natural resource. *Consultancy Africa Intelligence.* Retrieved from http://www.consultancyafrica.com/index.php?option=com_content&view=article&id=796:feeding-china-africas-other-natural-resource&catid=58:asia-dimension-discussion-papers&Itemid=264

Feenstra, G., Ingels, C., & Campbell, D. (n.d.). What is sustainable agriculture? UC Sustainable Agriculture Research and Education Program. Retrieved from http://www.sarep.ucdavis.edu/concept.htm

George C. Marshall Foundation. (2009). The Marshall Plan. Retrieved from http://www.marshallfoundation.org/TheMarshallPlan.htm

Gordon and Betty Moore Foundation. (2009). Environmental conservation, program grants: Reducing emission from deforestation and forest degradation (REDD). Retrieved from http://www.moore.org/project.aspx?proj=2964&id=2964

Heakal, R. (2011, July 31). What is the World Bank? *Investopedia.* Retrieved from http://www.investopedia.com/articles/03/042303.asp#axzz1lRen1REM

Hedge funds buying massive tracts of African farmland. (2011, August 10). *Here and Now, Public Radio International.* Retrieved from http://www.pri.org/stories/world/africa/hedge-funds-buy-massive-tracts-of-farm-land-5343.html

The History Place. (1996).The rise of Adolf Hitler: Hitler named chancellor. Retrieved from http://www.historyplace.com/worldwar2/riseofhitler/named.htm

International Monetary Fund. (2011, August 31). The IMF and the World Bank. Retrieved from http://www.imf.org/external/np/exr/facts/imfwb.htm

Nielsen. (2010, September 10). The state of the global consumer: Spending trends [Web log post]. Retrieved from http://blog.nielsen.com/nielsenwire/consumer/the-state-of-the-global-consumer-spending-trends/

Nielsen, L. (2011, February). *Classifications of countries based on their level of development: How it is done and how it could be done* (IMF Working Paper No. WP/11/31). International Monetary Fund.

OECD iLibrary. (2011). Society at a glance 2011: OECD social indicators. http://www.oecd-ilibrary.org/sites/soc_glance-2011-en/04/01/g4_ge1-01.html?contentType=&itemId=/content/chapter/soc_glance-2011-6-en&containerItemId=/content/serial/19991290&accessItemIds=/content/book/soc_glance-2011-en&mimeType=text/html

Pan, X-R., Yang, W-Y., Li, G-W., Liu, J., & National Diabetes Prevention and Control Cooperative Group. (1997). Prevalence of diabetes and its risk factors in China, 1994. *Diabetes Care, 20*, 1664–1669. Retrieved from http://care.diabetesjournals.org/content/20/11/1664.short

Patton, D. (2008, April 7). Africa at large: China eyes idle farmland. *Afrika.no: The Norwegian Council for Africa.* Retrieved from http://www.afrika.no/Detailed/16472.html

Plumrose. (n.d.). Sustainability. Retrieved from http://www.plumroseusa.com/sustainability.php

Plumrose USA breaks ground on $70 million facility. (2012, 1st quarter). *View Point: Council Bluffs, Iowa Chamber of Commerce Newsletter.*

The Rain Forest Foundation. (n.d.). Gabon [Fact sheet]. Retrieved from http://www.rainforestfoundationuk.org/Gabon

Recycle Works. (n.d.). Old computers are not deleted: The electronics recycling process. Retrieved from http://www.recycleworks.org/ewaste/ewaste_process.html

Schwartzman, S. (2000). Brazil: The social agenda. *Daedalus, 129*(2), 29–56. Retrieved from http://www.schwartzman.org.br/simon/daedalus.htm

Urban Habitat Chicago. (n.d.). True nature foods rooftop garden. Retrieved from http://www.urbanhabitatchicago.org/projects/true-nature-foods/

Welby, C. W., & Gowan, M. E. (Eds.). (1998). *A paradox of power: Voices of warning and reason in the geosciences.* Boulder, CO: The Geological Society of America.

World Health Organization. (n.d.). Water sanitation and health: Water related diseases. Retrieved from http://www.who.int/water_sanitation_health/diseases/oncho/en/

The World Bank. (2012, February). Brazil country brief. Retrieved from http://web.worldbank.org/WBSITE/EXTERNAL/COUNTRIES/LACEXT/BRAZILEXTN/0,,menuPK:322351~pagePK:141132~piPK:141107~theSitePK:322341,00.html

The World Bank. (2012, February). Data: Brazil. Retrieved from http://data.worldbank.org/country/brazil

The World Bank. (2011, May 17). *Emerging market growth poles are redefining global economic structure.* Retrieved from http://web.worldbank.org/WBSITE/EXTERNAL/COUNTRIES/LACEXT/BRAZILEXTN/0,,contentMDK:22916098~menuPK:322347~pagePK:1497618~piPK:217854~theSitePK:322341,00.html

Chapter 5

The adoption of genetically modified crops: Growth areas [Web log post]. (2011, February 23). *The Economist online.* Retrieved from http://www.economist.com/blogs/dailychart/2011/02/adoption_genetically_modified_crops

Agropolis Museum. (2011). History of food and agriculture. Retrieved from http://museum.agropolis.fr/english/pages/expos/fresque/la_fresque.htm

Bloy, M. (2002, October 11). Irish potato famine. *The Victorian Web.* Retrieved fromhttp://www.victorianweb.org/history/famine.html

Centers for Disease Control and Prevention. (2011). Food borne pathogens. Retrieved from http://www.cdc.gov/foodborneburden/index.html

Cendrowicz, L. (2010, March 9). Is Europe finally ready for genetically modified foods? *Time Business.* Retrieved from http://www.time.com/time/business/article/0,8599,1970471,00.html

Coleman-Jensen, A., Nord, M., Andrews, M., & Carlson, S. (2011, September). *Household food security in the United States in 2010* (USDA Economic Research Report No. ERR-125). Retrieved from http://www.ers.usda.gov/publications/err-economic-research-report/err125.aspx

Dervaes Institute. (2011). Food production. Retrieved from http://urbanhomestead.org/urban-homestead

Environmental Protection Agency. (2013, January). Plant incorporated protectants. Retrieved from http://www.epa.gov/oppbppd1/biopesticides/pips/

European Commission. (n.d.). Health and consumers: Food: Genetically modified food and feed—What are GMOs? Retrieved from http://ec.europa.eu/food/food/biotechnology/gmo_en.htm

Food and Agriculture Organization of the United Nations. (1999). Agricultural trade fact sheet: Agricultural trade and food security. Retrieved from http://www.fao.org/docrep/003/X6730E/X6730E03.HTM

Food and Agriculture Organization of the United Nations. (2005). Food Commodities by Country. Retrieved from http://www.fao.org/es/ess/top/country.html;jsessionid=D4F0856C80F7F6076552D1CA714FF9F8

Food and Agriculture Organization of the United Nations. (2011). Somalia famine. Retrieved from http://www.fao.org/news/story/en/item/89101/icode/

Genetically engineered tomato plant grows in salty water. (2001, July 25). *UC Davis News and Information.* Retrieved from http://www.news.ucdavis.edu/search/news_detail.lasso?id=5840

Growing Power. (2011). Milwaukee farm. Retrieved from http://growingpower.org/headquarters.htm

Highfield, R. (2007, November 26). GM plant grows with 1/3 of usual water. *The Telegraph.* Retrieved from http://www.telegraph.co.uk/science/science-news/3316059/GM-plant-grows-with-13-of-usual-water.html

Irrigation Museum. (2013). History of irrigation. Retrieved from http://www.irrigationmuseum.org/exhibit2.aspx

Kaufman. L. (2011, June 2). Chemicals in farm run off rattle states on the Mississippi. *New York Times.* Retrieved from http://www.nytimes.com/2011/06/03/science/earth/03runoff.html?pagewanted=all

Meng, X., Qian, N., & Yared, P. (2011, November 22). *Institutional causes of China's great famine, 1959–1961.* Retrieved from http://federation.ens.fr/ydepot/semin/texte1213/NAN2012INS.pdf

Mudge, K., Janick, J., Scofield, S., & Goldschmidt, E. E. (2009). *A history of grafting.* Retrieved from http://www.hort.purdue.edu/newcrop/janick-papers/c09.pdf

Pesticide Management Education Program, Cornell University. (1993, September). Extension toxicology network: Rotenone. Retrieved from http://pmep.cce.cornell.edu/profiles/extoxnet/pyrethrins-ziram/rotenone-ext.html

Shuping, N. (2011, March 7). China GMO corn hits policy deadlock. *Reuters.* Retrieved from http://af.reuters.com/article/cameroonNews/idAFTOE72604L20110307?pageNumber=2&virtualBrandChannel=0

Union of Concerned Scientists. (2009, April 14). Genetic engineering has failed to significantly boost U.S. crop yields despite biotech industry claims. Retrieved from http://ucsusa.org/news/press_release/ge-fails-to-increase-yields-0219.html

United Human Rights Council. (n.d.). Ukrainian famine. Retrieved from http://www.unitedhumanrights.org/genocide/ukraine_famine.htm

United Nations. (2009). *Report to the General Assembly on food procurement in developing countries.* Retrieved from http://www.amun.org/uploads/09_Final_Report/WFP-I-Report.pdf

Unsworth, J. (2010, May 10). History of pesticide use. Retrieved from http://agrochemicals.iupac.org/index.php?option=com_sobi2&sobi2Task=sobi2Details&catid=3&sobi2Id=31

U.S. Department of Agriculture. (n.d.). Biotechnology. Retrieved from http://www.usda.gov/wps/portal/usda/usdahome?contentid=BiotechnologyFAQs.xml&navid=AGRICULTURE

U.S. Department of Agriculture. (2012). Key statistics and graphics. Retrieved from http://www.ers.usda.gov/topics/food-nutrition - assistance/food-security-in-the-us/key-statistics-graphics.aspx#insecure

U.S. Food Aid and Security. (2010). Food aid programs. Retrieved from http://foodaid.org/food-aid-programs/food-aid-facts/

World Health Organization. (2011). Food security. Retrieved from http://www.who.int/trade/glossary/story028/en/

World Hunger. (2010). World hunger statistics. Retrieved from http://www.worldhunger.org/articles/Learn/world%20hunger%20facts%202002.htm

Zexima, K. (2009, May 28). Organic dairies watch the good times turn bad. *New York Times.* Retrieved from http://www.nytimes.com/2009/05/29/us/29dairy.html

Chapter 6

The adoption of genetically modified crops: Growth areas [Web log post]. (2011, February 23). *The Economist online.* Retrieved from http://www.economist.com/blogs/dailychart/2011/02/adoption_genetically_modified_crops

Agropolis Museum. (2011). History of food and agriculture. Retrieved from http://museum.agropolis.fr/english/pages/expos/fresque/la_fresque.htm

Bloy, M. (2002, October 11). Irish potato famine. *The Victorian Web.* Retrieved from http://www.victorianweb.org/history/famine.html

Centers for Disease Control and Prevention. (2011). Food borne pathogens. Retrieved from http://www.cdc.gov/foodborneburden/index.html

Cendrowicz, L. (2010, March 9). Is Europe finally ready for genetically modified foods? *Time Business.* Retrieved from http://www.time.com/time/business/article/0,8599,1970471,00.html

Coleman-Jensen, A., Nord, M., Andrews, M., & Carlson, S. (2011, September). *Household food security in the United States in 2010* (USDA Economic Research Report No. ERR-125). Retrieved from http://www.ers.usda.gov/publications/err-economic-research-report/err125.aspx

Dervaes Institute. (2011). Food production. Retrieved from http://urbanhomestead.org/urban-homestead

Environmental Protection Agency. (2013, January). Plant incorporated protectants. Retrieved from http://www.epa.gov/oppbppd1/biopesticides/pips/

European Commission. (n.d.). Health and consumers: Food: Genetically modified food and feed—What are GMOs? Retrieved from http://ec.europa.eu/food/food/biotechnology/gmo_en.htm

Food and Agriculture Organization of the United Nations. (1999). Agricultural trade fact sheet: Agricultural trade and food security. Retrieved from http://www.fao.org/docrep/003/X6730E/X6730E03.HTM

Food and Agriculture Organization of the United Nations. (2005). Food Commodities by Country. Retrieved from http://www.fao.org/es/ess/top/country.html;jsessionid=D4F0856C80F7F6076552D1CA714FF9F8

Food and Agriculture Organization of the United Nations. (2011). Somalia famine. Retrieved from http://www.fao.org/news/story/en/item/89101/icode/

Genetically engineered tomato plant grows in salty water. (2001, July 25). *UC Davis News and Information.* Retrieved from http://www.news.ucdavis.edu/search/news_detail.lasso?id=5840

Growing Power. (2011). Milwaukee farm. Retrieved from http://growingpower.org/headquarters.htm

Highfield, R. (2007, November 26). GM plant grows with 1/3 of usual water. *The Telegraph.* Retrieved from http://www.telegraph.co.uk/science/science-news/3316059/GM-plant-grows-with-13-of-usual-water.html

Irrigation Museum. (2013). History of irrigation. Retrieved from http://www.irrigationmuseum.org/exhibit2.aspx

Kaufman. L. (2011, June 2). Chemicals in farm run off rattle states on the Mississippi. *New York Times.* Retrieved from http://www.nytimes.com/2011/06/03/science/earth/03runoff.html?pagewanted=all

Meng, X., Qian, N., & Yared, P. (2011, November 22). *Institutional causes of China's great famine, 1959–1961.* Retrieved from http://federation.ens.fr/ydepot/semin/texte1213/NAN2012INS.pdf

Mudge, K., Janick, J., Scofield, S., & Goldschmidt, E. E. (2009). *A history of grafting.* Retrieved from http://www.hort.purdue.edu/newcrop/janick-papers/c09.pdf

Pesticide Management Education Program, Cornell University. (1993, September). Extension toxicology network: Rotenone. Retrieved from http://pmep.cce.cornell.edu/profiles/extoxnet/pyrethrins-ziram/rotenone-ext.html

Shuping, N. (2011, March 7). China GMO corn hits policy deadlock. *Reuters.* Retrieved from http://af.reuters.com/article/cameroonNews/idAFTOE72604L20110307?pageNumber=2&virtualBrandChannel=0

Union of Concerned Scientists. (2009, April 14). Genetic engineering has failed to significantly boost U.S. crop yields despite biotech industry claims. Retrieved from http://ucsusa.org/news/press_release/ge-fails-to-increase-yields-0219.html

United Human Rights Council. (n.d.). Ukrainian famine. Retrieved from http://www.unitedhumanrights.org/genocide/ukraine_famine.htm

United Nations. (2009). *Report to the General Assembly on food procurement in developing countries.* Retrieved from http://www.amun.org/uploads/09_Final_Report/WFP-I-Report.pdf

Unsworth, J. (2010, May 10). History of pesticide use. Retrieved from http://agrochemicals.iupac.org/index.php?option=com_sobi2&sobi2Task=sobi2Details&catid=3&sobi2Id=31

U.S. Department of Agriculture. (n.d.). Biotechnology. Retrieved from http://www.usda.gov/wps/portal/usda/usdahome?contentid=BiotechnologyFAQs.xml&navid=AGRICULTURE

U.S. Department of Agriculture. (2012). Key statistics and graphics. Retrieved from http://www.ers.usda.gov/topics/food-nutrition-assistance/food-security-in-the-us/key-statistics-graphics.aspx#insecure

U.S. Food Aid and Security. (2010). Food aid programs. Retrieved from http://foodaid.org/food-aid-programs/food-aid-facts/

World Health Organization. (2011). Food security. Retrieved from http://www.who.int/trade/glossary/story028/en/

World Hunger. (2010). World hunger statistics. Retrieved from http://www.worldhunger.org/articles/Learn/world%20hunger%20facts%202002.htm

Zexima, K. (2009, May 28). Organic dairies watch the good times turn bad. *New York Times.* Retrieved from http://www.nytimes.com/2009/05/29/us/29dairy.html

Chapter 7

Air and Waste Management Association. (2007, April). Air pollution emission control devices [Fact sheet]. Retrieved from http://events.awma.org/files_original/ControlDevicesFactSheet07.pdf

Air Now. (2010). Air quality index. Retrieved from http://airnow.gov/index.cfm?action=aqibasics.aqi

Bast, J. (2010). *The seven theories of climate change.* Chicago, IL: The Heartland Institute.

Berwyn, B. (2011, December 4). NASA satellite confirms air quality improvements. *Summit County Citizens Voice.* Retrieved from http://summitcountyvoice.com/2011/12/04/nasa-satellite-confirms-air-quality-improvements/

Goodstein, E. (2009, October). The trade-off myth. Center for Progressive Reform. Retrieved from http://www.progressivereform.org/perspenviro_regs_jobs.cfm

Lefsrud, L. M., & Meyer, R. E. (2013). Science or science fiction? Professionals' discursive construction of climate change. *Organization Studies, 33,* 1477–1506.

National Oceanic and Atmospheric Administration, Paleoclimatology Program. (2008, August 20). A paleo perspective on abrupt climate change. Retrieved from http://www.ncdc.noaa.gov/paleo/abrupt/

Piers, F., Andrews, T., Good, P., Gregory, J., Jackson, L., & Zelinka, M. (2013). Evaluating adjusted forcing and model spread for historical and future scenarios in the CMIP5 generation of climate models. *Journal of Geophysical Research: Atmospheres, 118*(3), 1139–1150.

Scafetta, N. (2012). Testing an astronomically based decadal-scale empirical harmonic climate model versus the IPCC (2007) general circulation climate models. *Journal of Atmospheric and Solar-Terrestrial Physics, 80,* 124–137.

Thorning, M. (2011, February 9). The impact of EPA regulation of GHGs under the Clean Air Act on U.S. investment and job growth. American Council for Capital Formation. Retrieved from http://accf.org/news/publication/the-impact-of-epa-regulation-of-ghgs-under-the-clean-air-act-on-u-s-investment-and-job-growth

U.S. Environmental Protection Agency. (2010). Control emissions technologies. Retrieved from http://www.epa.gov/apti/course422/ce1.html

U.S. Environmental Protection Agency. (2011). Cross State Air Pollution Rule (CSAPR).http://www.epa.gov/airtransport/

U.S. Environmental Protection Agency. (2007). Montreal Protocol, backgrounder. Retrieved from http://www.epa.gov/ozone/downloads/MP20_Backgrounder.pdf

U.S. Environmental Protection Agency. (n.d.). Montreal Protocol [Fact sheet]. Retrieved from http://www.epa.gov/ozone/downloads/MP20_FactSheet.pdf

U.S. Environmental Protection Agency. (2003, June). *Ozone: Good up high, bad nearby.* Retrieved from http://www.epa.gov/oar/oaqps/gooduphigh/ozone.pdf

U.S. Environmental Protection Agency. (2010). Pollutants in the ambient air. Retrieved from http://www.epa.gov/oar/oaqps/eog/course422/ap2.html

U.S. Environmental Protection Agency. (2011). Second prospective study. Retrieved from http://www.epa.gov/air/sect812/prospective2.html

U.S. Environmental Protection Agency. (2010). Smog. Retrieved from http://www.epa.gov/oar/oaqps/eog/course422/ap7b4.html

U.S. Environmental Protection Agency. (2010). Source control technology. Retrieved from http://www.epa.gov/apti/course422/ce6.html

U.S. Environmental Protection Agency. (2012, March 6). Understanding the Clean Air Act. (2011). Retrieved from http://www.epa.gov/air/caa/peg/understand.html

U.S. Environmental Protection Agency. (2010). Welfare effects—acid rain. Retrieved from http://www.epa.gov/oar/oaqps/eog/course422/ap7b1.html

Vision Los Angeles. (2011). *Clearer roads, clearer skies.* Retrieved from http://www.visionlosangeles.org/pdf/VisionLA_Report.pdf

Wong, E. (2011, December 6). Outrage grows over air pollution and China's response. *New York Times Online.* Retrieved from http://www.nytimes.com/2011/12/07/world/asia/beijing-journal-anger-grows-over-air-pollution-in-china.html?_r=1&scp=1&sq=Outrage%20Grows%20Over%20Air%20Pollution%20and%20Chinas%20Response&st=cse

Yardley, J. (2008, July 7). Cities near Beijing close factories to improve air for Olympics. *New York Times Online.* Retrieved from http://www.nytimes.com/2008/07/07/sports/olympics/07china.html

Zississ, C., & Bajoria, J. (2008, August 4). *China's environmental crisis.* Council on Foreign Relations. Retrieved from http://www.cfr.org/china/chinas-environmental-crisis/p12608

Chapter 8

Associated Press. (2004, March 16). *Study: ANWR oil would have little impact.* Retrieved from http://www.msnbc.msn.com/id/4542853/ns/us_news-environment/t/study-anwr-oil-would-have-little-impact/#.TweN6WCatCp

Broder, J. (2007, May 23).. California wants strict auto emission rules. *The New York Times.* Retrieved from http://www.nytimes.com/2007/05/23/us/23climate.html

California Environmental Protection Agency. (2009, November 24). *California Ambient Air Quality Standards.* Retrieved from http://www.arb.ca.gov/research/aaqs/caaqs/caaqs.htm

Centers for Disease Control and Prevention. (n.d.). *About CDC.* Retrieved from http://www.cdc.gov/

Centers for Disease Control and Prevention. (2013, May 7). *Agency for Toxic Substances and Disease Registry.* Retrieved from http://www.atsdr.cdc.gov/

Clifford, C. (2011, August 23). BP oil spill fund: $5 billion in claims paid out. *CNN Money.* Retrieved from http://money.cnn.com/2011/08/23/smallbusiness/BP_oil_spill_claims/index.htm

Cufone, M. (2008, November 21). Ocean fish farms and public-resource privatization. *The American Prospect.* Retrieved from http://prospect.org/article/ocean-fish-farms-and-public-resource-privatization

Dallas City Hall. (n.d.). *Jack Evans Police Headquarters: Green building design.* Retrieved from http://www.dallascityhall.com/pdf/ehs/JackEvansPoliceBldg.pdf

Dallas Police Department. (n.d.). *Jack Evans Police Headquarters.* Retrieved from http://dallaspolice.net/index.cfm?page_ID=4658&subnav=51&openid=1

Dalton, T. (2010, November 18). Dominion to close Salem plant. *The Salem News.* Retrieved from http://www.salemnews.com/local/x852123427/Dominion-to-close-Salem-plant

Dowie, M. (2005, July/August). In law we trust. *Orion Magazine.* Retrieved from http://www .orionmagazine.org/index.php/articles/article/122/

Energy Star. (n.d.). Federal Tax Credits for Consumer Energy Efficiency. Retrieved from http://www .energystar.gov/index.cfm?c=tax_credits.tx_index

Goldstein, A. (2006, June 18). Privatization backlash in Indiana. *The Washington Post.* Retrieved from http://www.post-gazette.com/pg/06169/698927-84.stm

Hardin, G. (1968). The tragedy of the commons. *Science, 162*(2859), 1242–1248. Retrieved from http://www.garretthardinsociety.org/articles/art_tragedy_of_the_commons.html

Howe, P. (2011, May 12). Salem, Mass. power plant to close. *New England Cable News.* Retrieved from http://www.necn.com/05/12/11/Salem-Mass-power-plant-to-close/landing_business.html?blockID=521746&feedID=4209

Ifill, G. (2003, May 21). Being green? *The NewsHour with Jim Lehrer.* Retrieved from http://www .pbs.org/newshour/bb/environment/jan-june03/bush_5-21.html

Janssen, W. (1981, June). The story of the laws behind the labels. Retrieved from http://www.fda .gov/AboutFDA/WhatWeDo/History/Overviews/ucm056044.htm

Krupp, F. (2009, March 24). Carbon caps are the best policy. *The Wall Street Journal.* Retrieved from http://online.wsj.com/article/SB123785178691219381.html

Kusnetz, N. (2011, October 21). EPA plans to issue rules for hydraulic fracturing wastewater. *Scientific American.* Retrieved from http://www.scientificamerican.com/article.cfm?id=epa-plans-issue-rules-hydraulic fracturing—wastewater

Library of Congress. (n.d.). *America's story: The first Earth Day.* Retrieved from http://www.americaslibrary.gov/jb/modern/jb_modern_earthday_1.html

McLaughlin, D. (1995). *Silent Spring* revisited. *PBS: Frontline.* Retrieved from http://www.pbs.org/wgbh/pages/frontline/shows/nature/disrupt/sspring.html

Mihelich, P. (2007, June 28). Bald eagle soars off endangered species list. *CNN.* Retrieved from http://articles.cnn.com/2007-06-28/tech/bald.eagle.delisting_1_bald-eagle-golden-eagle-protection-act-eagle-habitat?_s=PM:TECH

More, T. A. (2006). The privatization of public lands. *Proceedings of the 2006 Northeastern Recreation Research Symposium* (GTR-NRS-P-14, pp. 135–141). Retrieved from http://nrs.fs.fed.us/pubs/gtr/gtr_nrs-p-14/18-more-p-14.pdf

National Atlas. (2013, January 14). The Public Land Survey System. Retrieved from http://nationalatlas.gov/articles/boundaries/a_plss.html

National Oceanic and Atmospheric Administration. (n.d.). About NOAA. Retrieved from http://www.noaa.gov/about-noaa.html

National Oceanic and Atmospheric Administration. (n.d.). Fisheries service. Retrieved from http://www.nmfs.noaa.gov/

National Oceanic and Atmospheric Administration. (n.d.). National ocean service. Retrieved from http://oceanservice.noaa.gov/

National Parks Conservation Service. (n.d.). *About us.* Retrieved from: http://www.npca.org/about-us/

Ngowi, R. (2011, December 19). Federal pollution regs threaten Salem power plant. *The Boston Globe.* Retrieved from http://www.boston.com/news/local/massachusetts/articles/2011/12/19/ap_survey_epa_rules_threatens_salem_power_plant/

Schoen, J. (2004, October 25). How long will the world's oil last? *MSNBC.* Retrieved from http://www.msnbc.msn.com/id/5945678/ns/business-oil_and_energy/t/how-long-will-worlds-oil-last/#.TweSh2CatCp

Sinclair, U. (1906). *The Jungle.* Retrieved from http://www .online-literature.com/upton_sinclair/jungle/

Smithsonian National Zoological Park. (n.d.). *Bald eagle* [Fact sheet]. Retrieved from http://nationalzoo.si.edu/animals/birds/facts/factsheets/fact-baldeagle.cfm

Solomon, D. (2011, July 29). EPA unveils air-quality rules for natural-gas hydraulic fracturing *The Wall Street Journal.* Retrieved from http://online.wsj.com/article/SB10001424053111904800304576474462644360884.html

U.S. Department of Agriculture. (n.d.). Animal and Plant Health Inspection Service. Retrieved from http://www.aphis.usda.gov/

U.S. Department of Agriculture. (n.d.). Food Safety and Inspection Service. Retrieved from http://www.fsis.usda.gov/

U.S. Department of Agriculture. (n.d.). Natural Resources Conservation Service. Retrieved from http://www.nrcs.usda.gov/wps/portal/nrcs/main/national/home

U.S. Department of Energy. (2011, November 29). Crude oil and total petroleum imports top 15 countries. Retrieved from http://ftp.eia.doe.gov/pub/oil_gas/petroleum/data_publications/company_level_imports/current/import.html

U.S. Department of Energy. (n.d.). DOE environmental management. Retrieved from http://www .em.doe.gov/Pages/EMHome.aspx

U.S. Department of Energy. (n.d.). Energy efficiency and renewable energy. Retrieved from http://www.eere.energy.gov/

U.S. Department of Energy. (n.d.). The National Environmental Policy Act of 1969. Retrieved from http://ceq.hss.doe.gov/nepa/regs/nepa/nepaeqia.htm

U.S. Department of Labor, Bureau of Labor Statistics. (2013, May 13). Table 2: Reason for layoff.; Extended mass layoff events, separations, and initial claimants for unemployment insurance, private nonfarm sector, selected quarters, 2012 and 2013. [Press release: Economic News Release]. Retrieved from http://www.bls.gov/news.release/mslo.t02.htm

U.S. Department of the Interior. (n.d.). Bureau of Land Management. Retrieved from http://www .blm.gov/wo/st/en.html

U.S. Energy Information Administration. (n.d.). EIA: Frequently asked questions. Retrieved from http://205.254.135.24/tools/faqs/

U.S. Environmental Protection Agency. (2002, December). *Brownfields redevelopment efforts are big in the heart of Dallas* (EPA Report No. 500-F-02-155). Retrieved from http://nepis.epa.gov

U.S. Environmental Protection Agency. (2011, December 12). CERCLA overview. Retrieved from http://www.epa.gov/superfund/policy/cercla.htm

U.S. Environmental Protection Agency. (2012, February 17). Clean Air Act. Retrieved from http://www.epa.gov/air/caa/

U.S. Environmental Protection Agency. (2013, April 25). Cleaning up the nation's hazardous waste sites. Retrieved from http://www.epa.gov/superfund

U.S. Environmental Protection Agency. (2013, March 28). Exxon Valdez. Retrieved from http://www.epa.gov/osweroe1/content/learning/exxon.htm

U.S. Environmental Protection Agency. (2012, June 25). National Environmental Policy Act. Retrieved from http://www.epa.gov/compliance/basics/nepa.html

U.S. Environmental Protection Agency. (2011, January 28). Oil Pollution Act overview. Retrieved from http://www.epa.gov/osweroe1/content/lawsregs/opaover.htm

U.S. Environmental Protection Agency. (2011, January 27). Oil Spill Liability Trust Fund. Retrieved from http://www.epa.gov/osweroe1/content/learning/oilfund.htm

U.S. Environmental Protection Agency. (2012, March 6). The plain English guide to the Clean Air Act. Retrieved from http://www.epa.gov/air/peg/index.html

U.S. Environmental Protection Agency. (n.d.).Summary of the Clean Water Act. Retrieved from http://www.epa.gov/lawsregs/laws/cwa.html

U.S. Environmental Protection Agency. (n.d.). Summary of the Endangered Species Act. Retrieved from http://www.epa.gov/lawsregs/laws/esa.html

U.S. Environmental Protection Agency. (n.d.). Summary of the Resource Conservation and Recovery Act. Retrieved from http://www.epa.gov/lawsregs/laws/rcra.html

U.S. Environmental Protection Agency. (2012, June 27). Toxic Substances Control Act. Retrieved from http://www.epa.gov/agriculture/lsca.html#Summary%20of%20Toxics%20Substances%20Control%20Act%20(TSCA)

U.S. Fish and Wildlife Service. (n.d.). Arctic National Wildlife Refuge. Retrieved from http://arctic .fws.gov/November

U.S. Fish and Wildlife Service. (2009). Brown pelican: *Pelicanus occidentalis.* Retrieved from http://www.fws.gov/contaminants/pdf/brown_pelicanfactsheet09.pdf

U.S. Fish and Wildlife Service. (n.d.). Endangered Species Act of 1973. Retrieved from http://www .fws.gov/laws/lawsdigest/ESACT.HTML

U.S. Fish and Wildlife Service. (n.d.). Endangered Species Program. Retrieved from http://www.fws .gov/endangered/

U.S. Fish and Wildlife Service. (n.d.). Rivers and Harbors Appropriation Act of 1899. Retrieved from http://www.fws .gov/laws/lawsdigest/RIV1899.HTML

U.S. Fish and Wildlife Service. (2013, May 13). Species reports. Retrieved from http://ecos.fws.gov/tess_public/pub/listedAnimals.jsp

U.S. Food and Drug Administration. (n.d.). About FDA. Retrieved from http:// www.fda.gov

U.S. Forest Service. (n.d.). About the Forest Service. Retrieved from http://www.fs.fed.us/

U.S. Geological Survey World Energy Assessment Team. (2001). *World petroleum assessment 2000.* Retrieved from http://pubs.usgs.gov/dds/dds-060/

Walsh, B. (2011, November 14). On coal, jobs and regulations. *Time Magazine.* Retrieved from http://ecocentric.blogs.time.com/2011/11/14/on-coal-jobs-and-regulations/

Wayne, A. (2012, January 4). Health effects of hydraulic fracturing for natural gas needs study, says CDC scientist. *Bloomberg.com.* Retrieved from http://www.bloomberg.com/news/2012-01-04/health-effects-of-hydraulic fracturing -for-natural-gas-need-study-says-cdc-scientist.html

Whitney, G., Beherns, C., & Glover, C. (2010, November 30). U.S. fossil fuel resources: Terminology, reporting, and summary (Congressional Research Service Report No. 7-5700). Retrieved from http://epw.senate.gov/public/index.cfm?FuseAction=Files.View&FileStore_id=04212e22-c1b3-41f2-b0ba-0da5eaead952

Williams, T. (2004). For a week's worth of gas. *Mother Jones.* Retrieved from http://motherjones .com/politics/2004/09/weeks-worth-gas

Chapter 9

Allaby, A., & Allaby, M. (1999). A dictionary of earth sciences. New York, NY: Oxford University Press. Retrieved from http://www.encyclopedia.com/doc/1O13-gangue.html

Bian, Z., Inyang, H. I., Daniels, J. L., Otto, F., & Struthers, S. (2010). Environmental issues from coal mining and their solutions. *Mining Science and Technology (China), 20*(2), 215–223.

Biodiesel: A painless transition from fossil fuels. (2005, October 26). *Biodiesel Times.* Retrieved from http://biodiesel.rain-barrel.net/biodiesel/

ESA21: Environmental science activities for the 21st century: Fossil fuels, coal. (n.d.). Retrieved from http://esa21.kennesaw.edu/activities/coal/coalactivity.pdf

Etemadi, A., Emdadi, A., AsefAfshar, O., & Emami, Y. (2011). Electricity generation by the ocean thermal energy. *Energy Procedia, 12,* 936–943.

Fahey, J. (2011, September 28). Google wants to help homeowners add solar power panels. *BostonGlobe.com.* Retrieved from http://articles.boston.com/2011-09-28/

business/30213497_1_solarcity-green-business-operations-rick-needham

Geothermal energy facts. (2008, March 20). Retrieved from http://interestingenergyfacts.blogspot.com/2008/03/geothermal-energy-facts.html

International Atomic Energy Agency. (2008). Looking back to go forward: Proceedings of an international conference. Vienna, Austria, September 6–7, 2005 (Proceedings series, ISSN 0074–1884). Retrieved from http://www-pub.iaea.org/MTCD/publications/PDF/Pub1312_web.pdf

Kargbo, D. M., Wilhelm, R. G., Campbell, D. J., & Al-Abed, S.R. (2010). Natural gas plays in the Marcellus shale: Challenges and potential opportunities. *Environmental Science & Technology, 44*(15), 5679–5684.

King, R. S. (2011). The post-Fukushima world. *IEEE Spectrum, 48*(11), 44–45. doi: 10.1109/MSPEC.2011.6056622

Patel, P. (2011, October 31). Three Mile Island, Chernobyl, and Fukushima: A comparison of three nuclear reactor calamities reveals some key differences. *IEEE Spectrum, 48*(11). Retrieved from http://spectrum.ieee.org/energy/nuclear/three-mile-island-chernobyl-and-fukushima

Ragheb, M. (2012, May 28). *Fukushima earthquake and tsunami station blackout accident.* Retrieved from http://mragheb.com/NPRE%20402%20ME%20405%20Nuclear%20Power%20Engineering/Fukushima%20Earthquake%20and%20Tsunami%20Station%20Blackout%20Accident.pdf

Schmitt, G. J. (2006, April 13). Energy security, national security, and natural gas. *AEI Online.* Retrieved from http://www.aei.org/article/foreign-and-defense-policy/regional/europe/energy-security-national-security-and-natural-gas/

Si, H., Bi, H., Li, X., & Yang, C. (2010). Environmental evaluation for sustainable development of coal mining in Qijiang, Western China. *International Journal of Coal Geology, 81*(3), 163–168.

Singh, T. (2011, May 19). Wind power could be the best alternative energy source for Japan. Retrieved from http://inhabitat.com/wind-power-could-be-the-best-alternative-energy-source-for-japan/

Solar Energy Industries Association. (2010). The history of solar energy. Retrieved from http://www.seia.org/galleries/FactSheets/Factsheet_solar%20history.pdf

STM. (2003, May 27). BIOBUS project cuts Montreal CO2 emissions by roughly 1,300 tons [Press release]. Retrieved from http://www.stm.info/English/info/comm-03/a-co030527.htm

Strickland, E. (2011). 24 hours at Fukushima. *IEEE Spectrum, 48*(11), 35–42. doi: 10.1109/MSPEC.2011.6056620

Tabor, H., & Zeimer, H. (1962). Low-cost focussing collector for solar power units. *Solar Energy, 6*(2), 55–59. doi: 10.1016/0038-092X(62)90004-X

U.S. Department of the Interior, Bureau of Reclamation, Power Resources Office. (2005, July). Hydroelectric power: Reclamation – Managing water in the West. Retrieved from http://www.usbr.gov/power/edu/pamphlet.pdf

U.S. Department of the Interior, Bureau of Land Management. (2008, December 19). Wind Energy Development Programmatic environmental impact statement (Instructional Memorandum No. IM 2009-043). Retrieved from http://windeis.anl.gov/documents/docs/IM_2009-043_BLMWindEnergyDevelopmentPolicy.pdf

U.S. Geological Survey, the USGS Summer School. (2012). Hydroelectric power water use. Retrieved from http://ga.water.usgs.gov/edu/wuhy.html

Wind Energy Development Programmatic EIS. (n.d.). Wind energy development environmental concerns. Retrieved from http://windeis.anl.gov/guide/index.cfm

World Health Organization. (2012). *Preliminary dose estimation from the nuclear accident after the 2011 Great East Japan Earthquake and Tsunami.* Retrieved from http://whqlibdoc.who.int/publications/2012/9789241503662_eng.pdf

World Nuclear Association. (2013, April 2). Fukushima accident 2011. Retrieved from http://www.world-nuclear.org/info/fukushima_accident_inf129.html

World Nuclear News. (2011, September 28). WHO warns on urban air pollution. Retrieved from http://www.world-nuclear-news.org/EE-WHO_warns_on_urban_air_pollution-2809116.html

Yokayo Biofuels. (2006). Yokayo biofuels: Biodiesel. Retrieved from http://ybiofuels.org/bio_fuels/history_biofuels.html

Zekai, S. (2004). Solar energy in progress and future research trends. *Progress in Energy and Combustion Science, 30*(4), 367–416.

Chapter 10

American Farmland Trust. (2011). Sustainable agriculture. Retrieved from http://www.farmland.org/programs/environment/solutions/farming-practices.asp

Anderson, J. R., Harty, E. E., Roach, J. T., & Witmer, R. E. (1976). *A land use and land cover classification system for use with remote sensor data* (Geological Survey Professional Paper No. 964). Retrieved from http://landcover.usgs.gov/pdf/anderson.pdf

Barrionuevo, A. (2011, May 26). China's interest in farmland makes Brazil uneasy. *The New York Times.* Retrieved from http://www.nytimes.com/2011/05/27/world/americas/27brazil.html?pagewanted=all

Cederberg, C., Persson, U. M., Neovius, K., Molander, S., & Clift, R. (2011). Including carbon emissions from deforestation in the carbon footprint of Brazilian beef. *Environmental Science & Technology, 45*(5), 1773–1779. Retrieved from http://www.ibcperu.org/doc/isis/13743.pdf

City Population. (2011). Megacities. Retrieved from http://www.citypopulation.de/world/Agglomerations.html

Clean Water Action Council. (2009). Land use and urban sprawl. Retrieved from http://www.cwac.net/landuse/index.html

Cook, B., Miller, R., & Seager, R. (2011). *Did dust storms make the Dust Bowl drought worse?* Lamont-Doherty Earth Observatory. Retrieved from http://www.ldeo.columbia.edu/res/div/ocp/drought/dust_storms.shtml

Flaskerud, G. (2003, July). *Brazil's soybean production and impact.* Fargo, ND: North Dakota State University Extension Service. Retrieved from http://www.ag.ndsu.edu/pubs/agecon/market/eb79.pdf

Ikerd, J. (2002, November 27). Farm economy state of the union address: The logical consequences of industrial agriculture. Retrieved from http://newfarm.rodaleinstitute.org/features/1102/ikerd_address/index.shtml

Institute for Local Self-Reliance. (2001). The paradigm shift in NYC's solid waste management. Retrieved from http://www.ilsr.org/recycling/NYC/NYCmain.html

JBS-Friboi. (2011). JBS-Friboi sustainability practices. Retrieved from http://www.jbs.com.br/ir/

Kirkman, E. (2007). Architecture in the era of Napoleon III. Retrieved from http://www.arthistoryarchive.com/arthistory/architecture/Haussmanns-Architectural-Paris.html

Lilly, J. P. (1997). *Best management practices for agricultural nutrients.* North Carolina Cooperative Extension Service. Retrieved from http://www.soil.ncsu.edu/publications/Soilfacts/AG-439-20/

Lindsey, R. (2003, April 23). Escape from the Amazon. NASA Earth Observatory. Retrieved from http://earthobservatory.nasa.gov/Features/LBA_Escape/

Luninarium Encyclopedia Project. (2010). Great London Fire 1666. Retrieved from http://www.luminarium.org/encyclopedia/greatfire.htm

Mydans, S. (2006, May 21). Manila: Sifting for a living on trash mountain. *The New York Times.* Retrieved from http://www.nytimes.com/2006/05/21/world/asia/21iht-city7.1790859.html?pagewanted=all

New York City, Parks & Recreation. (n.d.). Freshkills Park. Retrieved from http://www.nycgovparks.org/park-features/freshkills-park

Pierzynski, G. M., Sims, J. T., & Vance, G. F. (2005). *Soils and environmental quality* (3rd ed.). Boca Raton, FL: Taylor & Francis Group.

Polopolus, L. C. (n.d.). Athens, Greece: A city-state that grew from optimaility in the golden era to excessive urbanization by the 21st century [Lecture transcript]. Retrieved from http://www.clas.ufl.edu/users/kapparis/AOC/ATHENS.htm

Smart Growth Network. (2010). Getting to smart growth: 100 policies for implementation. Retrieved from http://www.smartgrowth.org/pdf/gettosg.pdf

Smart Growth America. (2010). Measuring urban sprawl. Retrieved from http://www.smartgrowthamerica.org/sprawlindex/MeasuringSprawl.PDF

Tuan, F. C., Fang, C., & Cao, Z. (2004, October). *China's soybean imports expected to grow despite short-term disruptions* (USDA Report No. OCS-04J-01). Retrieved from http://www.ers.usda.gov/publications/OCS/Oct04/OCS04J01/ocs04j01.pdf

"Urban sprawl" responsible for collapse of ancient Cambodian city of Angkor. (2009, June 24). *Thaindian News.* Retrieved from http://www.thaindian.com/newsportal/health/urban-sprawl-responsible-for-collapse-of-ancient-cambodian-city-of-angkor_100208779.html

The urbanization of the world. (n.d.). Retrieved from http://www.faculty.fairfield.edu/faculty/hodgson/Courses/so11/population/urbanization.htm

U.S. Department of Agriculture, Economic Research Service. (2012, October 10). Soybeans and oil crops: Trade. Retrieved from http://www.ers.usda.gov/Briefing/Soybeansoilcrops/trade.htm

WATT Publishing. (2011, April 21). China increasing soybean imports due to record pig numbers. Retrieved from http://www.wattagnet.com/China_increasing_soybean_imports_due_to_record_pig_numbers.html

INDEX

A

Notes

Notes

Notes

Notes

Notes